Elementary Geometry for Teachers

Thomas H. Parker
Professor of Mathematics
Michigan State University

Scott Baldridge
Assistant Professor of Mathematics
Louisiana State University

SEFTON-ASH PUBLISHING
Okemos, Michigan

August, 2008

Published by Sefton-Ash Publishing.
Printed and bound by Quebecor World, MI.
Printed in the United States of America.

ISBN 978-0-9748140-5-6

To buy this textbook, please visit www.singaporemath.com or call (503) 557−8100.

Cover Artwork: Copyright © 1998 Mary Jean Reusch, *Moral Compass: Pencil and Silver Ball,* oil on canvas, dimensions: 24"× 14", Collection of Aquinas College.
Cover Design: Justin Reusch.

To our wives,

Judith Fleishman

and

Lisa Baldridge,

and our children Daniel and Gregory Parker and Autumn Baldridge.

Contents

About the Textbook

This is a mathematics textbook for teachers that focuses on the parts of the K-8 curriculum involving measurement and geometry; it also includes a chapter on data, probability and statistics. It is a sequel to our text *Elementary Mathematics for Teachers* (EMT), which focused on arithmetic. Like EMT, this text does not talk about teaching methods per se — that is left for teacher education courses. However, understanding mathematics from a teacher's perspective requires many things not discussed in most math courses. All teachers, of course, must have a solid knowledge of the material to be taught. But mathematics teachers need to know more, including: (i) how to present the material simply and clearly, (ii) the appropriate sequential order for developing mathematics skills, and (iii) where the difficulties lie and what errors students are likely to make. A teacher also needs a sense of how each topic advances the mathematical level of the students.

Obviously, such teaching knowledge can be mastered only after years in the classroom. But like EMT, this textbook is intended to get you started and provide a viewpoint on elementary geometry that will guide you as you teach.

This textbook presents topics in roughly the same order in which they are taught. Chapter 1 describes the measurements topics that students learn in grades K-4; these include measuring *and calculating with* lengths, weights, capacities and angles. Chapters 2, 3 and 4 tell the story of how deductive geometry is introduced in grades 2–8. The main theme in these chapters is the role of *unknown angle problems* in developing reasoning ability. Chapter 5 returns to measurement and traces the development of area in grades 2–5. Chapters 6 and 7 examine two fundamental mathematical ideas that are introduced in middle school: the Pythagorean Theorem and the concept of similarity. These are often seen as the starting point of trigonometry and other high school topics, but from our perspective they are the culmination of the geometry learned in grades K–8. Chapters 8 and 9 present the area and volume topics done in grades 5, 6 and 7. For completeness, there is a final chapter on data, probability and statistics.

Supplementary Texts

This textbook is designed to be used in conjunction with six elementary and middle school textbooks. Two of these were also used with EMT, namely

Primary Mathematics 4A Textbook (U.S. Edition)   ISBN- 981-01-8506-5
Primary Mathematics 5A Textbook (U.S. Edition)   981-01-8510-3

You are expected to have retained these. You will also need the following 4 textbooks:

Primary Mathematics 3B Textbook (U.S. Edition)   ISBN- 981-01-8503-0
Primary Mathematics 5B Textbook (U.S. Edition)   981-01-8511-1
Primary Mathematics 6B Textbook (U.S. Edition)   981-01-8515-4
New Elementary Mathematics Textbook 1   981-208-459-2

Primary Math 3B, 5B and 6B are second semester (semester B) sequels of the grades 3, 5, and 6 textbooks that were used with EMT. New Elementary Mathematics 1 (NEM1) is for the entire seventh grade year (in Asian countries, seventh grade is called secondary grade 1). You will be assigned homework problems directly from these books and will quickly become familiar with these elegant texts. As you study the texts and do problems from them, you will acquire a sense of the structure of the measurement and geometry curriculum for grades K-8.

The Primary Mathematics books (published by Marshall Cavendish International) and the New Elementary Mathematics books (published by Pan Pacific Publications) follow a curriculum developed by Singapore's Ministry of Education. These books were initially created for students in Singapore, but are now widely used in the U.S. and in many other countries. *They can be ordered, alone or together with this textbook, from www.singaporemath.com.*

The Role of the Primary Mathematics and New Elementary Mathematics Books

The aim of this course is to develop an understanding of elementary mathematics *at the level needed for teaching.* The best way to do that is to study actual school textbooks and to do many, many actual school mathematics problems. The Primary Mathematics and New Elementary Mathematics books were chosen for that purpose.

We will read and study these books with two goals in mind: understanding the mathematics and understanding the curriculum. The Primary Mathematics books give a very clear presentation of what elementary mathematics is and how it is organized and developed. They lay out the subject in depth, and they include a rich supply of exercises and word problems. The presentation is always clear, correct and child-friendly. These books provide better guidance than any other textbook series currently available.

It is not surprising, then, that the Primary Mathematics books are also successful with children. The Trends in International Mathematics and Science Study (TIMSS) rated Singapore's elementary students the best in the world in mathematics (it also found that the curriculum is highly coherent). Primary Mathematics books are a major factor in student success. (In fact, the treatment of geometry is strong in many East Asian curricula; textbooks from Japan, Korea and Hong Kong share the scope and coherence of the Singapore books.)

As you read and do problems from these books, notice the following:

1. The absence of clutter and distraction. The books contain mathematics and nothing but mathematics.

2. The coherent development. Each topic is introduced by a very simple example and is incrementally developed until, quite soon, difficult problems are being done. Topics are revisited for 'review' and the level is constantly ratcheted upward.

3. The short, precise definitions. The 'student helpers' pictured in the margins define key ideas in very few words. They often clearly convey an idea that might otherwise take an entire paragraph.

We measure angles in **degrees**.
90 degrees = 1 right angle.

4. The books serve as teacher guides. They clearly display the content of each lesson and help teachers by providing examples and suggesting classroom activities.

Point 1 should be stressed. Many textbooks obscure the mathematics with distracting sidebar messages, unnecessary drawings, showy photographs, long introductions and summaries, biographical stories, explorations, and discussions of non-mathematical topics. In contrast, the Primary Mathematics books are deliberately focused. They contain no distractions. Homework is relegated to workbooks, and group projects and explorations are put into separate teacher guides. The pictures convey ideas; they are not there for stylistic reasons. The judicious use of white space makes the books easy and enjoyable to read. The resulting short textbooks keep young students focused on learning mathematics.

The New Elementary Mathematics books incorporate many of the laudable features of the Primary Math books. These middle school books are written for more mature students who are taught by teachers who specialize in mathematics. Accordingly, the material is more densely packed. But the focus and coherence of the mathematics still shine through.

Study and enjoy these books — and keep them. When you become a teacher, these books will be a valuable resource, helping with explanations, providing extra problems, and giving guidance in how to present mathematics.

The Geometry Curriculum in School Mathematics

The school geometry curriculum is not structured like the arithmetic curriculum. As described in *Elementary Mathematics for Teachers*, the arithmetic curriculum begins in kindergarten and proceeds sequentially, with each topic building on the previous topics. The mathematics itself determines the teaching order. Consequently, most good curricula teach the same topics in the same order:

- Grades K-3: counting, place value, the four operations with whole numbers.
- Grades 4-5: fractions, decimals, percents.
- Grades 6-7: ratios, negative numbers, real numbers, linear equations.

After grade 7 *arithmetic is finished.*

The geometry curriculum is different: it has several stages and returns to the beginning of the subject in each stage with increasing sophistication. For example, parallelograms may be introduced in kindergarten, defined precisely in grade 4, studied in grade 7, and set in an axiomatic context in grade 10. This organization into stages is necessary. While geometry can be presented in rigorous logical order, children cannot appreciate a logical development until *after* they know the spirit of the subject and know many specific facts.

Chapter 3 of this book describes how students learn the spirit of geometry and some initial facts by doing *unknown angle problems* in grades 4–6. These fun puzzles quickly get students started on multi-step geometry problems. Unknown angle problems are a major theme of this book, just as "bar diagrams" were a theme of EMT.

Another distinct feature of the geometry curriculum is the fact that *nearly all of the important concepts are introduced in grades 5-8*, as shown in the diagram below. Elementary teachers are preparing students for these topics, and some are taught in grades 5 and 6. It is wrong to think of geometry as a high school subject.

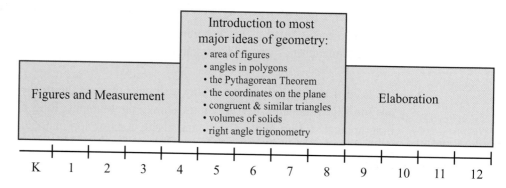

Similar comments apply to measurement. In science, middle school students use metric units and do calculations with speed, density, force, etc. These science topics are easily understood by students whose elementary teachers have given proper attention to developing measurement skills.

This view of the curriculum suggests that the geometry and measurement skills children learn in elementary school are more important to their later success than is commonly realized.

To the Student

This book focuses exclusively on K-8 mathematics — nothing is beyond the grade 8 level. Elementary teachers need to know this material because they will be teaching part of it and preparing students to learn all of it.

There will undoubtedly be times when the level or depth of this book seems beyond what you think you will need for your own teaching. When in doubt, remind yourself of these points:

- You cannot assume that you will be teaching a low grade or that you will not be teaching mathematics. There is a surplus of teachers for grades K-3 and a shortage of middle school mathematics and science teachers. As a beginning teacher, your principal and superintendent will determine which grade you teach, and you may be assigned to teach several different grades in the first few years of your career.

- Elementary teachers teach mathematics for an hour a day, every day. The better you know elementary mathematics, the more enjoyable the time will be for you and your students, and the more confident and effective you will be at teaching mathematics.

You have a head start because you learned K-8 mathematics years ago. The goal now is to upgrade that knowledge to a professional level. Much of this is a matter of perspective — learning to distinguish what is important and effective, to see the focus of a lesson, and to see how a lesson fits into curriculum. None of this is hard, but it takes practice.

To get you started, here are three principles that provide perspective on the elementary geometry curriculum. Keep these in mind as you read this book and as you teach.

1. *Measurement is a vital part of elementary mathematics and is a prerequisite for middle and high school science classes.*

2. *When teaching geometry, the focus should be on multi-step reasoning*, not on visualizing and naming shapes or memorizing geometric facts. The teaching goal and the educational value of school geometry is to have students *use* geometric facts by combining them and, after several clear, logical steps, arrive at a conclusion that was not initially obvious.

3. *Unknown angle problems are a powerful device for teaching geometry.* As explained in Chapter 3, unknown angle problems teach children how to organize their thoughts when solving multi-step problems.

The Homework Sets

The homework sets in this textbook ask you to do many actual grades 3-7 problems. These problems will show you the level and the sequence of topics of elementary school mathematics. Special problems labeled "*Study the textbook*" ask you to do the elementary problems and then answer "teacher-level" questions such as these:

- What do students learn from doing this problem?
- How would I present this problem to my own students?
- Which aspects of this problem might give students difficulty? What errors are likely?
- What prerequisite skills should students have before approaching this problem?
- How does this problem fit into the overall curriculum?

Teacher's explanations are often crucial for student understanding. In mathematics, the clearest explanations are often the shortest and simplest. Consequently, whenever a homework problem asks for an explanation, be sure to:

Make your written explanations simple, clear, concise and grade-appropriate.

The meaning "grade-appropriate" is determined by the source of the problem. If a problem comes from the grade 4 Primary Math book, imagine yourself as a 4th grade teacher making an answer key to be handed out to your class.

Of course, learning to write clear concise solutions takes special knowledge and practice. To help you in that effort, the text describes some efficient abbreviations and some specific formats, including a method for writing step-by-step explanations for constructions (Section 2.5), "Teacher's Solutions" to unknown angle problems (Section 3.1), and the "Elementary Proof" format (Section 4.1). These ways of presenting specific geometry content to elementary and middle school students are standard in some of the world's most highly regarded curricula.

A few problems are marked with a star ✳. Starred problems are challenging middle school problems that require extra time and thought.

As you do homework, you will undoubtedly be impressed, as we are, by the level of sophistication that children are able to achieve in a well-designed curriculum. Reset your expectations and do not underestimate your future students!

To the Instructor

This book is designed to be used for a second-semester course for prospective elementary teachers taught by a mathematics department. It can also be used for a geometry course for prospective middle school teachers and for teacher professional development workshops. It expects that students have taken a course in elementary mathematics either using the authors' book, *Elementary Mathematics for Teachers,* or a similar textbook that covers arithmetic through fractions, ratios and real numbers. The last chapter is included for the benefit of university instructors whose course syllabus includes elementary probability and statistics.

This is not a high school geometry book. Our guiding principle is that the preparation of teachers should focus exclusively on the mathematics that they will teach. Consequently, everything in this book is at the K-8 level. Elementary teachers should know all of this material well, because it is needed for teaching, for background, for understanding the organization of the curriculum, and for understanding the spirit of the subject. We have found that most prospective elementary teachers enjoy learning the story line of the K-8 geometry curriculum.

Some students will ask: "Why the Primary Math books?" Many textbook series are currently used in elementary schools. The Primary Mathematics books were chosen because of their clarity, organization, low cost, and their exceptional fidelity to mathematics. Understanding these books prepares teachers for teaching from *any* elementary school materials. All elementary education majors wish to be good teachers. Working with actual elementary school books reminds prospective teachers that they will soon be standing in front of a class teaching mathematics. This thought sharpens their wits and motivates them to learn this material.

The text is written to be covered at a rate of one section per (50 minute) class with every homework problem assigned. Three sections per week can also be successfully covered in two 75 minute sessions, with $1\frac{1}{2}$ homework sets assigned after each session. Each section is only 4-5 pages, making it is realistic to expect students to read the entire section. We find it productive to devote part of nearly every class to looking at the Primary Math textbooks, discussing the presentation, and calling on students to do problems verbally. Instructors can also summarize pages from this book and discuss the exercises embedded in the text. Finally, prospective teachers benefit from presenting solutions at the blackboard with feedback from their peers. The "Teacher Solution" and "Elementary Proof" formats (pages 59 and 79) give them formats for their presentations.

It may not be feasible to cover all of the 40 sections in this book. Instructors may choose to skip Sections 4.5, 7.4 and 8.4, or ask students to read those sections on their own. Sections 3.1, 4.1 and 8.1 contain review material and therefore require less class time than other sections. In our experience, Sections 10.1 and 10.2 require little time because the topics are very familiar to prospective elementary teachers — much more familiar than any geometry topic.

Acknowledgements

We wish to express our appreciation to the many mathematicians, educators, and teachers who have contributed to this book. Particular thanks are due to Richard Askey, Anna Bargagliotti, Madge Goldman, Betty Harmsen, Steffen Lempp, James Madden, Daniel Maki, Ralph Raimi, Fred Reusch, Pavel Sikorskii, and Patsy Wang-Iverson. We also benefited from engaging discussions and correspondences with Richard Bisk, Tom Fortmann, Barry Garelick, Herb Gross, Richard Hill, Roger Howe, David Kirshner, Frank Lester, Liping Ma, Frank Neubrander, Robert Perlis, Sharon Senk, Alla Sikorskii, Akihiko Takahashi, Patrick Thompson and Hung-Hsi Wu.

We received valuable feedback from the professors and instructors who taught from preliminary versions of this book:

Onur Agirseven, Michigan State University
Leah Childers, Louisiana State University
Charles N. Delzell, Louisiana State University
David Klein, California State University, Northridge
Steffen Lempp, University of Wisconsin, Madison
Cathy Liebars, The College of New Jersey
Karen E. Smith, University of Michigan, Ann Arbor
Alejandro Uribe, University of Michigan, Ann Arbor

Particular thanks goes to Onur Agirseven and Charles Delzell, who gave us lesson-by-lesson feedback on earlier drafts of this book, and to Patsy Wang-Iverson for her late-night edits of the final draft.

We are especially grateful to Madge Goldman of the Gabriella & Paul Rosenbaum Foundation for her detailed comments and her vigorous and unflagging encouragement of our efforts. Production was smoothly handled by Misty Wright at Quebecor World and the tireless work of Dawn and Jeffery Thomas at our distributor SingaporeMath.com. Finally, we thank Mary J. Reusch for the use of her painting for the cover, and Justin Reusch and Virginia Jones for their splendid work creating diagrams and illustrations.

CHAPTER 1

Learning to Measure

Learning to measure and calculate measurements is an essential first step toward both geometry and science. Geometry is the study of relationships among the measurements — lengths, angles, areas and volumes – of figures. Before children can comfortably work with measurements, they need practice using measuring tools and solving arithmetic and word problems involving lengths and other measurements. Skill at measurement is also needed for school science, where students routinely read about and discuss distances (large and small), weights and volumes. Children who acquire these skills early will be one step ahead in both mathematics and science, all the way through school. Elementary school teachers play a crucial role in this learning.

This chapter examines how the Primary Mathematics curriculum develops facility at measuring and calculating lengths, weight, capacity, and angles. The diagram below shows the approximate timetable for these four measurement topics; it also shows that they are the foundation for later measurement topics. Area and volume are more abstract than the measurements discussed in this chapter, and consequently begin later and extend across a much longer period. We will discuss area in Chapters 5 and 8, and volume in Chapter 9.

Measurement topics build on one another.

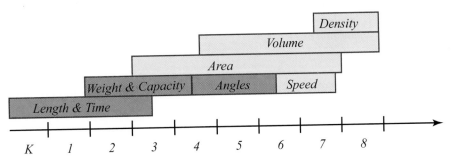

1.1 Measurement Problems

Children learn elementary mathematics by *solving problems*—hundreds of short directed problems each year. As they solve problems, they learn new concepts, they learn how to organize calculations and they learn the power of mathematics.

Teachers guide this process. As you learned in *Elementary Mathematics for Teachers* (EMT), "bar diagrams" are one of the most effective tools available to teachers to guide students' work on problem-solving. This section begins with a review of bar diagrams, which we now apply to problems involving measurements of all kinds. It continues with a review of the very beginnings of geometry — just enough to set the stage for the next section.

Bar diagrams are pictures designed to display the reasoning used to solve word problems. Students can use bar diagrams to help figure out a strategy for solving problems. Teachers can use bar diagrams in classroom explanations, and to assist and guide students. Bar diagrams are often far clearer than verbal explanations. The power of this approach is evident as one studies the Primary Mathematics books.

In this book, as in EMT, you will be asked to solve problems using bar diagrams and to present your solutions with the clarity required of a teacher. As you work toward that goal use the following example as a model. It displays the features that make a bar diagram solution useful for teaching. As in EMT, we will refer to solutions with these features as *Teacher's Solutions*. In this section, the term "Teacher's Solution" will always mean a solution with bar diagram and units included.

EXAMPLE 1.1. *A bookcase contains two rows of identical textbooks. One row is 18 inches long, the other is 24 inches long. The longer row contains 4 more textbooks than the shorter row. How thick is each textbook?*

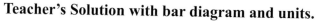

Teacher's Solution with bar diagram and units.

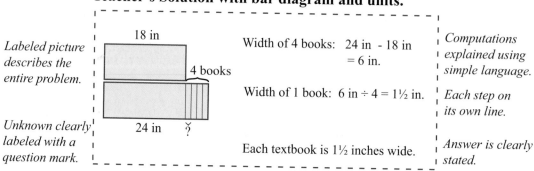

Labeled picture describes the entire problem.

18 in

4 books

24 in   ?

Unknown clearly labeled with a question mark.

Width of 4 books: 24 in - 18 in
                          = 6 in.

Width of 1 book: 6 in ÷ 4 = 1½ in.

Each textbook is 1½ inches wide.

Computations explained using simple language.

Each step on its own line.

Answer is clearly stated.

Notice the features of a "Teacher's Solution": the problem is clear from the picture alone, a clear, complete solution is shown next to the picture, and the answer is clearly stated as a complete sentence on the final line. Here is another example:

EXAMPLE 1.2. *Katie bought 2.4 m of ribbon. She used $\frac{1}{3}$ of it to wrap a present and $\frac{1}{4}$ of the remainder to make a bow. How many meters of ribbon were left?*

Teacher's Solution with bar diagram and units:

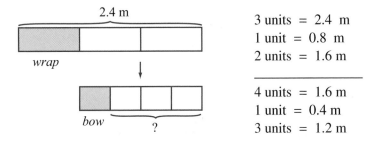

2.4 m

wrap

bow

?

3 units = 2.4 m
1 unit = 0.8 m
2 units = 1.6 m
_____
4 units = 1.6 m
1 unit = 0.4 m
3 units = 1.2 m

Katie had 1.2 m of ribbon left.

Both of these examples involve length measurements. Although the bar diagrams show rectangles, length is actually a way of expressing the size of one-dimensional objects: line segments. The entire next section is devoted to length measurement. In preparation, we pause to introduce lines and segments.

Points, Lines and Segments

point
line
plane

The basic objects of geometry are easily explained to children. A *plane* is a flat surface that extends without edges; it can be envisioned as an extended desktop or large sheet of paper. A *line* can be envisioned as a thin straight pencil mark, or a tightly-stretched thread; lines extend without end in both directions. A *point* is a location, envisioned as a dot of negligible breadth.

The ideas of "infinitely long" and "infinitely thin" are not issues to dwell on. They are actually assumptions that make geometry *simpler* by telling us never to worry about the shape of a point, the thickness of a line, or what happens at the ends of a line.

Geometry starts with two basic principles:

(1) Through any two different points there is one and only one line.

(2) If two different lines intersect, their intersection is a single point.

Because of (1), a line can be specified by naming any two points on it. Points are often drawn as small dots labeled by capital letters. We write the line through points *A* and *B* as $\overleftrightarrow{AB}$. A **segment** is the part of a line between two points on the line. A **ray** is part of a line on one side of a point on the line. Two points *A* and *B* determine a line, a segment and *two* rays:

notation for
segments, rays,
and lines

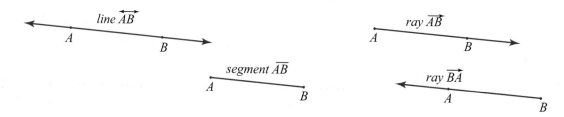

We will use the notation in the pictures above to label lines, rays, and segments.

Three or more points are **collinear** if there is a line containing all of them; otherwise the points are **non-collinear**. Three non-collinear points determine three line segments which together form a triangle.

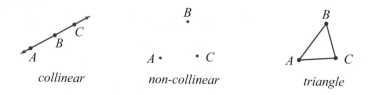

Drawing Lines

Kindergarten and first grade students learn simple ideas about points and lines as they do connect-the-dot puzzles and other drawing activities (these also help develop dexterity needed for learning to write). Young children have difficulty drawing perfectly straight lines. They appreciate being taught how to use a tool that makes their lines come out straight.

Geometry students typically use five tools: straightedge, compass, set square, ruler, and protractor. A **straightedge** is any straight object that can be used for drawing a straight line through two given points. One can use the edge of a book or piece of cardboard, but one usually uses the edge of a ruler. A ruler can also be used to measure lengths, but that should be ignored when using a ruler as straightedge. In this sense a straightedge is a "ruler without markings".

There is one line through A and B.
We can draw it using a straightedge.

Drawing lines with a straightedge seems like an easy task until you watch a child's first attempt at it. Children have trouble keeping the straightedge from slipping, and they neglect to press their pencils against the straightedge. They also discover that they must offset the straightedge to compensate for the width of the pencil point.

EXERCISE 1.3. *What other difficulties might children have? What suggestions could a teacher make to help?*

Length in Geometry

notation for
the length of
a segment

In geometry one also has a notion of length and distance. The distance between two points A and B is the length of the segment $\overline{AB}$; *in this book we will denote this length by AB* (some textbooks use a different notation for length). Note that AB is a number whereas $\overline{AB}$ is a segment. Two segments are called **congruent** if they have the same length. In pictures, it is often convenient to denote the length of a segment by a number or letter placed near the middle of the segment, as is done in the following chart.

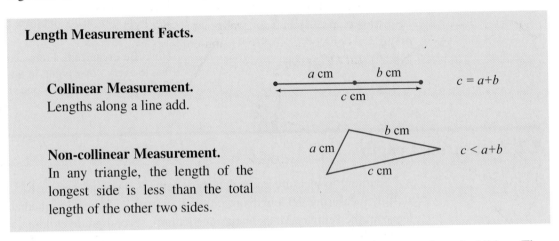

Length Measurement Facts.

Collinear Measurement.
Lengths along a line add.

a cm b cm $c = a+b$
c cm

Non-collinear Measurement.
In any triangle, the length of the longest side is less than the total length of the other two sides.

a cm b cm $c < a+b$
c cm

Both facts are intuitive. The first is the measurement model interpretation of addition. The second is the fact that the shortest path-of-travel is a straight segment. Imagine one person walking along segment c and another walking along segments a and b; who walks the shortest distance?

The facts in the blue box are often presented as a single fact called the *triangle inequality*. Textbooks usually state the triangle inequality in this less transparent form: for any three points A, B and C, the distances between them satisfy

triangle
inequality

$$AC \le AB + BC,$$

and the $=$ sign occurs if and only if the points are collinear with B between A and C. Some curricula and state standards require elementary students to know the Triangle Inequality. This simply means understanding the intuitive facts in the blue box above.

Homework Set 1

1. Using your ruler, draw a segment 4 cm long, one of 10 cm long, and one 20 cm long.

2. Measure your 10 cm segment in inches. It is roughly _____ inches long. Therefore, one inch is approximately _____ cm long.

3. Mark 5 points on your paper, making sure that no three of them are collinear. Label the points using letters A to E.

    a) Draw $\overline{CE}$.

    b) Draw $\overrightarrow{BA}$.

    c) Draw $\overleftrightarrow{BD}$.

    d) Name the intersection of $\overrightarrow{BA}$ and $\overrightarrow{AB}$.

4. Give "Teacher's Solutions with bar diagram and units" to Problems 6 and 8 on page 51 of Primary Math 4A. (Use the bar diagrams on the preceding pages as guides.)

5. Similarly, give a Teacher's Solution to Problem 21 on

page 69 of Primary Math 4A.

6. Give Teacher's Solutions with bar diagram and units to Problems 8, 9, and 11 on page 10 of Primary Math 6B. Read pages 16–19 to get ideas on how to create bar diagrams for these problems.

7. Give a Teacher's Solution to the following problem.

Segment $\overline{AB}$ is 4 times as long as segment $\overline{CD}$. Segment $\overline{EF}$ is 3 cm longer than $\overline{CD}$. If $\overline{EF}$ is 8 cm long, how long is $\overline{AB}$?

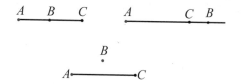

8. Examine the pictures above. Write a precise definition of the term "midpoint" by completing this sentence: "B is the **midpoint** of segment $\overline{AC}$ if ...."

9. How many lines can be drawn through distinct points P, Q, R, and S if

   a) P, Q, and R are collinear?

   b) no three of the points are collinear?

10. If you are given 5 points in a plane, no three of which are collinear, how many lines can be drawn through pairs of those points?

    Hint: Be organized! From each of the 5 points, draw a line to every *other* point; in the end you will have drawn each possible line *twice* – once from each of its endpoints.

1.2 Measuring Length

Learning to measure and calculate lengths is a crucial part of K-3 mathematics. Children start by measuring the lengths of physical objects and almost immediately begin solving problems. In the Primary Mathematics curriculum, second grade children add and subtract lengths in centimeters and meters, and in inches and feet. They are also find lengths from information provided in pictures and simple word problems.

Children's work with length enhances their understanding of arithmetic. Activities with rulers make the number line a familiar mental image. Calculations with length develop arithmetic skills and show the uses of the "measurement model" of addition, subtraction, multiplication and division. Problem-solving shows the practical value of mathematics. Work with length also sets a stage for other parts of the curriculum. Rulers with half-inch and quarter-inch marks can motivate fractions, and metric rulers help introduce decimals. Less obviously, measurement topics lay the conceptual foundation for geometry, a point we will return to in Chapter 2.

We begin this section with a general discussion of length measurement, emphasizing the fundamental role of "unit lengths". The story includes the rationale for the specific units commonly used in grades K-3: centimeters, meters, inches and feet.

Lengths are not numbers because any measurement of length involves a two-step process:

- Choose a unit length.

  1 unit

- Express other lengths as multiples of that unit.

  The bar is 4 units long.

quantity

The resulting length measurement is then a *quantity*: a number times a unit.

48 inches

number unit

Units of Length

When measuring, we may declare any length to be a unit of length. The choice of unit is an important aspect of any discussion of measurement, even for first-grade students (especially for first-graders!). What is the best choice?

One can imagine a caveman carrying around a stick and saying that the bison he killed was "5 sticks long". Of course, different sticks have different lengths. It is therefore advantageous to have *standard units* — lengths that have been agreed on, named, and made available to everyone in the world. In fact, it is useful to have several different units: one for measuring small lengths, one for medium lengths, and one for large lengths. One familiar set of standard units is

$$\begin{cases} 1 \text{ inch} \\ 1 \text{ foot} = 12 \text{ inches} \\ 1 \text{ mile} = 5280 \text{ feet.} \end{cases}$$

Three units are enough for most purposes; one can measure the thickness of a book in inches, the height of a person in feet and inches, and the distance to a nearby city in miles.

When there are several different standard units, one sometimes wants to rewrite a measurement in one unit in terms of another unit. Such conversions are done using multiplication.

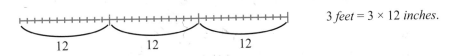

$$3 \text{ feet} = 3 \times 12 \text{ inches.}$$

Such multiplications can be challenging to do mentally, even in relatively simple cases.

EXAMPLE 2.1. *How many inches are in 17 feet? How many feet are in 5 miles?*

$$17 \text{ feet} = 17 \cdot \underbrace{12 \text{ inches}}_{1 \text{ foot}} = 204 \text{ inches.} \qquad 5 \text{ miles} = 5 \cdot 5280 \text{ feet} = 26,400 \text{ ft.}$$

In the metric system, the basic unit is the *meter*. All elementary classrooms should have several meter sticks available for student use. A meter is a bit more than 3 feet. A convenient large unit is 1000 meters, called a *kilometer* (abbreviated km). Small units of length are obtained by dividing the meter into 100 equal parts, each called a *centimeter* (cm), and then dividing the centimeter into 10 equal parts is called a *millimeter* (mm).

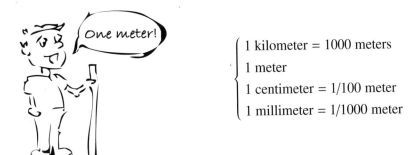

$$\begin{cases} 1 \text{ kilometer} = 1000 \text{ meters} \\ 1 \text{ meter} \\ 1 \text{ centimeter} = 1/100 \text{ meter} \\ 1 \text{ millimeter} = 1/1000 \text{ meter} \end{cases}$$

A centimeter is roughly the diameter of a dime and a millimeter is about the thickness of a dime. One can measure the thickness of a book in millimeters or centimeters, the height of a person in meters and centimeters, and the distance to a nearby city in kilometers.

The names of metric units describe their relation to the meter. Units larger than the meter use the Greek prefixes *deca-* for 10, *hecto-* for 100, and *kilo-* for 1000. Units smaller than the meter use the Latin prefixes *deci-*, *centi-*, and *milli-* to mean tenth, hundredth, and thousandth.

milli-	*centi-*	*deci-*	METER	*deca-*	*hecto-*	*kilo-*
$\frac{1}{1000}$	$\frac{1}{100}$	$\frac{1}{10}$	1	10	100	1000

Most of these prefixes appear in familiar words:

- A *decade* is 10 years, and the *decimal system* uses powers of 10.

- A *century* is 100 years and 100 *cents* make a dollar.

- A *millennium* is 1000 years and a *millipede* has 1000 legs (supposedly).

- Someone whose "salary is 50K" earns $50,000 a year, and a 35KB computer file contains 35 *kilobytes* (35,000 bytes) of data; in both cases K stands for kilo, meaning "thousand".

Of course, children have no trouble learning new words, and learning these six prefaces makes the names of metric units clear, even obvious.

Because metric units are related by powers of 10, conversions are extremely easy. *All metric conversions involve simply shifting the decimal point* by an amount specified by the prefixes.

EXAMPLE 2.2. *How many centimeters in 17 meters? How many meters in 5.8 km?*

$$17 \text{ m} = 17 \cdot \underbrace{100 \text{ cm}}_{1 \text{ meter}} = 1700 \text{ cm} \qquad 5.8 \text{ km} = 5.8 \cdot 1000 \text{ m} = 5800 \text{ m}$$

Two Systems

In medieval Europe, the units of measurement were not standardized. Units varied from region to region and from one context to another. For example, goldsmiths and blacksmiths measured weight using different units. As time passed and trade increased, governments made efforts to create uniform measurements and reduce the number of different units in use. But standard units, once established, are not easily changed or eliminated.

In 1795, soon after the French revolution, the new French government ordered the adoption of a newly-designed system of measurement — the metric system. The advantages of the metric system ultimately led to its use in every country in the world, including the United States. While the U.S. has never officially adopted the metric system, it is used routinely in many contexts. In fact, there are two systems in common use:

metric
system

(1) The metric system is used whenever accuracy and precision are important. Almost all technical measurements used in hospitals, industry, and science in the U.S. use the metric

system. The medicines you take and the vitamins in your cereal are measured in metric units. The U.S. Army uses the metric system exclusively.

customary
system

(2) In many contexts, the U.S. continues to use units descended from old British units. This includes familiar units such as inches and feet, ounces and pounds, cups, quarts, and gallons. It also includes many units that are used for special purposes. Racetracks are measured in furlongs, corn is measured in bushels, the thickness of wire is measured by gauge, wood is measured in cords, etc. We will call this eclectic mix the *Customary System*, although it is really not a system because many of the units are completely unrelated.

Teaching Standard Units.

Lessons on measurement usually begin with students using concrete "non-standard units" to measure the objects in the classroom, then recording and comparing their results. Paper clips, for example, are often used as non-standard units of length. This work with non-standard units is brief and transitory. The goal is to have students appreciate three aspects of measurement:

(i) There are two steps: choose a unit, then measure in terms of that unit.

(ii) One is free to choose a unit of any size.

(iii) To communicate measurements, it is very helpful to pick a standard unit.

Children's first experiences with standard units should be physical. They need time and practice handling and using rulers, metersticks and tape measures, lifting standard weights and using scales, and pouring water into measuring cups. Children who acquire a good sense of the size of the standard metric units in the early grades will better understand discussions of measurement from that point on — all the way through college.

Rulers.   Measuring lengths with a ruler is easy and natural for adults. But it is a learned skill that requires instruction from a teacher. Children encounter several difficulties.

1. The scale on most rulers does not begin at the end of the ruler. Instruction is needed on how to align the object being measured with the zero mark, not with the end of the ruler.

2. The length of most objects is not a whole number of units. To avoid confusion, the exercises in the grade 1 and 2 Primary Math books all involve objects (pictured or described) with whole-number lengths.

3. When children do begin measuring fractions of an inch, they must learn to count and interpret the unmarked tick marks on the ruler.

Rulers differ in the way they subdivide units. Inches are subdivided into halves, quarters, and eighths; centimeters are subdivided into tenths (millimeters). Measuring lengths to the nearest quarter-inch helps motivate fractions, and measuring to the nearest tenth-centimeter helps motivate decimals. Consequently, children should learn to measure in both centimeters and in inches.

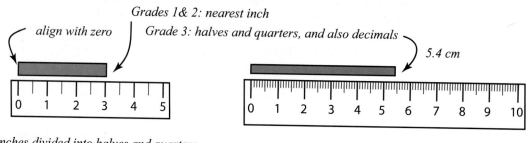

Grades 1& 2: nearest inch

align with zero | Grade 3: halves and quarters, and also decimals

5.4 cm

0 1 2 3 4 5

0 1 2 3 4 5 6 7 8 9 10

inches divided into halves and quarters
(introduces fractions)

centimeters divided into tenths
(introduces decimals)

Practice with rulers is vital for other reasons. It builds intuition about the number line and the measurement model for arithmetic (which is used to interpret addition, subtraction, multiplication and division). It makes metric units familiar and provides needed background for geometry. It is too important to skip over.

Every grade K– 4 teacher should assign exercises measuring lengths in centimeters and meters, inches and feet.

adult
tools

Rulers, carpenter's tape measures and sewing tape measures are all highly effective "manipulatives". These are the tools adults use to measure. Children enjoy learning to use genuine adult tools and are very open to instruction about them.

Homework Set 2

1. Make a 1-meter "tape measure" as follows:

   a) Cut an (unlined) sheet of paper into strips about an inch wide and tape the strips together end-to-end.

   b) If necessary, cut lengthwise again to give your long strip one straight side.

   c) Using your ruler, draw marks at 1 cm intervals along the straight edge up to the 1-meter mark. Make every tenth mark longer to indicate decimeters, and label these 10, 20, 30 · · ·

   d) Color your tape measures (e.g. using a highlighter) in two alternating colors in 1-decimeter strips as pictured below.

2. (*Study the Textbook!*) Read Primary Math 3B pages 14-17, doing the problems in your text as you go and writing answers to the following questions on your HW paper.

   a) Problem 8 on page 16 asks students to order lengths. Write down (in one sentence) a 2-step process for determining such orderings.

   b) On page 17, the thought bubbles of the "student helpers" show the mental math method "first add (or subtract) _____, then add (or subtract) _____".

   c) On page 18, answer parts (a), (d) and (f) of Problems 1–4, writing your answers as a list without the labels (a), (d) and (f). Then answer Problems 5 and 6.

3. (*Study the Textbook!*) Continue in Primary Math 3B, reading pages 19-22 and doing the problems in your text as you go. Then on page 23, list the answers to parts (a), (d) and (f) of Problems 1–4 and answer Problem 5.

4. (*Study the Textbook!*) Continue, reading and doing the problems on pages 24-27. Then on page 28 answer: Part (b) only for Problems 1-4, parts (a), (d) and (f) for Problems 5-7.

5. (*Study the Textbook!*) On page 26, Problem 8b uses which interpretation of subtraction: take-away, whole-part, or comparison?

6. Write a Teacher's Solution (with a bar diagram and units) for Problems 6 and 8 on page 54 of Primary Math 5B.

7. Conversions between metric units are done simply by shifting the decimal point. Make the following conversions.

   a) 867 cm = _____ m

   b) 532 mm = _____ cm

   c) 63.2 m = _____ mm

   d) 2.35 km = _____ m

8. How tall are you in meters and centimeters? (Make a mark on the wall and use your homemade tape measure.)

9. It takes about 10 minutes to walk 1 kilometer. A car on the highway goes about 100 kilometers in an hour. Roughly,

   a) how many kilometers is it across campus?

   b) how many kilometers to your dorm or apartment?

   c) how many kilometers is it to another city? (Pick a particular city and name it in your answer.)

10. If one side of a triangle is 6 cm and another is 10 cm long, the third side must be shorter than _____ cm and longer than _____ cm. (Hint: Draw several possible triangles before answering.)

11. A point B is said to be *between* points A and C if B is on the segment $\overline{AC}$.

If B is between A and C, what equality involving the distances AB, BC, and AC must be true? Draw a sketch.

12. A point B is called a **midpoint** of a segment $\overline{AC}$ if B is between A and C and $AB = BC$.

   a) Draw a segment $\overline{AC}$ and mark the midpoint.

   b) Does it make sense to speak of a "midpoint of a line $\overleftrightarrow{AC}$"? Why or why not?

13. A line that intersects a segment at its midpoint is called a **bisector of the segment**.

   a) Draw a segment $\overline{AB}$ and two different bisectors.

   b) Does it make sense to speak of a "bisector of a line $\overleftrightarrow{AB}$"? Why or why not?

A *counterexample* to a mathematical statement is an example where the statement is false. To prove that a statement is true, one must prove it true in *all cases*, but to show that it is false requires *only one* counterexample. Counterexamples are useful for teaching. Use this idea of *instructional counterexamples* to answer the following question.

14. Kevin thinks that the definition of midpoint can be shortened to this:

   A point Q in the plane is the midpoint of a segment $\overline{PR}$ if $PQ = QR$.

Show that Kevin's definition is incomplete by drawing a counterexample.

1.3 Measuring Weight and Capacity

The elementary school curriculum includes seven different types of measurement: length, weight, capacity, angles, area, volume and time. Each is developed over several years. For each, students first understand what is being measured and learn the units of measurement. They practice using measuring tools and reading ruled scales. But they quickly move on to solving problems that require adding, subtracting, multiplying and dividing measurements, and re-expressing measurements in different units.

Measurement skills have enormous practical value. They are used for cooking, doing household repairs, comparison shopping, and for innumerable activities in the workplace. Many well-paying professions (medical doctor, engineer, scientist, nurse, lab technician, etc.) require frequent work with measurements. For students, the ability to work with measurements, especially metric measurements, is essential for middle school science classes.

The first page of the section describes an instructional program that is repeatedly used to introduce measurement topics. As we proceed, we will track how this "Teaching Sequence for Measurement" is implemented for each measurement topic. To start, this section examines how the Primary Mathematics curriculum follows the sequence to teach grade 2 and 3 children about weight and capacity.

Teaching Measurement — the Common Themes

The seven measurement topics in elementary mathematics are conceptually similar. All are applications of the same 2-step procedure:

The measurement procedure and measurement systems

Lengths, weights, capacities, angles, areas, volumes and times are measured by the same simple *measurement procedure*:

a) Choose a standard unit.

b) Express measurements as multiples of that unit.

A *measurement system* consists of several standard units related by whole-number ratios.

In the metric system, the ratios between units are always powers of 10. All convenient systems involve three or more units that together allow one to express any small, medium, or large measurements as a number times a unit, with the number usually between 1 and 1000. The metric length units centimeter/meter/kilometer form one such system. Two others are discussed in this section.

measurement model

Work with measurement helps children understand two key concepts: the measurement model for arithmetic and the idea of "forming a unit". Recall that the term *measurement model* refers to any use of the number line to visualize arithmetic; this includes everything that can be depicted by a bar diagram. There are measurement model interpretations of addition, subtraction, multiplication and division, and measurement models give simple ways to think about fractions and decimals. But the success of these visual models depends on children's ongoing experiences reading rulers and scales.

As in the box above, the first step in measuring length is to *choose a unit*. The realization that one can choose units — of any convenient size — gives concise ways to think about multiplication, division, fractions and ratios. For example, the division $42 \div 7$ can be interpreted in terms of units: 42 cm is how many units of length 7 cm? As you learned in EMT, fraction and ratio problems can often be solved by choosing an appropriate unit and drawing a bar diagram. Again, these ideas implicitly draw on children's practice with measurement tools.

Elementary curricula develop measurement topics using a specific teaching sequence. This sequence is repeated for each of the seven measurement topics. In each case, instruction begins with hands-on activities and moves quickly to arithmetic problems.

Teaching Sequence for Measurement

1. a) Students directly compare objects according to their length, weight, etc.
   b) A simple non-standard unit is used to measure objects.
   c) A standard unit is introduced and students learn to read measurements along a scale.

2. Bigger and smaller standard units are introduced and students learn to convert between measurements expressed in different units.

3. In each step, *students solve problems* — both calculational problems and word problems. The problems are initially simple, and build to multi-step problems.

Steps 1–3 require different levels of classroom time. Very roughly, Step 1 requires a few days of class time and Step 2 requires 1–2 weeks. Step 3 requires several weeks, ideally with students continuing to do problems of this type regularly throughout the school year.

This teaching sequence is modified slightly for three topics. Elementary students are taught both to *tell time* and to find *elapsed time*, but only standard units are discussed (months, weeks, days, hours, minutes and seconds), so Steps 1a and 1b are skipped. When teaching area and volume, Step 1c must be skipped because *there is no simple device for measuring areas or volumes along a scale.* As a result, measuring area and volume is more difficult and abstract, and therefore begins later in the curriculum. These issues are addressed in Chapter 5.

The remainder of this section describes how this teaching sequence is carried out for weight and capacity in the Primary Mathematics textbooks.

Weight

The Primary Mathematics texts introduce weight in grades 1–3 following the above teaching sequence. At the beginning, textbook pictures suggest several hands-on classroom activities. These are important for an obvious reason:

To learn about weight, hands-on activities are necessary because students cannot see how much an object weighs by looking at it!

In particular, objects of the same size can have different weights, and objects of different sizes can have the same weight.

Grade 1: Non-standard units. Students are introduced to weight in the first grade. To start, they pick up two objects, try to judge which is heavier, and check their judgement using a balance scale. This shows that the phrases "heavier than", "lighter than" and "equal weight" have precise meaning (unlike subjective judgments like "happier than" or "hungrier than").

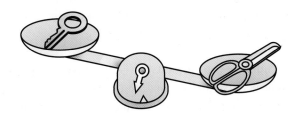

Next, a unit is introduced: the weight of a marble. Students use the balance to express weights as multiples of this unit and to compare the weights of different objects. For example, a pair of scissors that weighs 8 marbles is heavier than a box that weighs 6 marbles. This lesson shows the advantages of establishing a unit and expressing weight as a multiple of that unit.

The ruler weighs 8 units.

Grade 2—Standard Units and Spring Scales. Second-graders learn four standard units: first kilograms and grams, and later pounds and ounces. They begin by picking up a 1 kilogram object to get a sense of its weight. A 1 liter bottle filled with water, which weighs 1 kilogram, can be used for this purpose (similarly, a 1 pint bottle of water weighs 1 pound). Students then use balance scales to weigh objects in kilograms.

spring
scale

For weight, Step 2 of the teaching sequence is complicated by the need to change measurement devices, switching from balance scales to spring scales. Children can see how a balance scale works, but the workings of a spring scale are not evident — the spring is hidden and the mechanism (which turns a downward force into the rotation of a needle) is not intuitive. Textbook pictures like the one below are hints to teachers to have students weigh objects with both devices to see that they measure the same quantity and that spring scales are easier and quicker to use. From that point on, spring scales are used to illustrate weight.

Make a bag of beans which weighs 1 kg.

Then comes the crucial third step: the Grade 2 Primary Math lessons on weight culminate with word problems. (Yes, first and second grade students can do word problems!) In these problems students practice arithmetic skills with all four operations as they learn about weight. The best are multi-step problems.

Grade 3—Conversions. Third graders learn to convert between grams and kilograms, and later between ounces and pounds. In your homework you will examine how this is done in the Primary Math books. Right now, leaf through Primary Math 3B and answer this question:

EXERCISE 3.1. *Look through pages 29–41 of Primary Math 3B. How many grams are in one kilogram? How many ounces are in one pound?*

A gram is a small unit used for light objects (a paper clip weighs about 7 grams). A kilogram (1000 grams) is used for the weight of medium-to-heavy objects, such as people. For very heavy objects, such as a train car or a trailer truck, the *metric ton* (1000 kg) is used. A kilogram is approximately 2.2 pounds, and therefore a metric ton is roughly the same as a U.S. ton (2000 pounds).

Metric System	Customary System
1 gram	1 ounce
1 kilogram = 1000 grams	1 pound = 16 ounces
1 metric ton = 1000 kilograms	1 U.S. ton = 2000 pounds

Notice that children learn metric and customary units as separate systems and only convert *within each system*. There is never a need or an occasion to convert between systems; kilograms are never translated into pounds or liters into quarts. Such conversions are not grade-appropriate.

Capacity

The **capacity** of a container is the amount of liquid it can hold. Capacity is not the same as weight: for example, a 1 gallon jug of water and a 1 gallon jug of honey have the same capacity but different weights. But like weight, the capacity of containers can be directly compared and measured with simple tools — measuring cups. Like all measurements, capacity is always expressed as a number times a unit. The metric units of capacity are liters and milliliters and the customary units are cups, pints, quarts and gallons.

The Primary Mathematics books introduce capacity at the end of grade 2 with activities and teacher demonstrations. As shown in the chart on page 1, work with capacity initiates a long curriculum sequence that ultimately ties together weight, capacity, volume and density by the end of middle school. The entire sequence is preparation for high school science classes.

Grade 2 — Measurement units. Students are introduced to liquid measurements in three steps. First, students compare the capacities of two containers by pouring water from one container to another (larger to smaller, then smaller to larger).

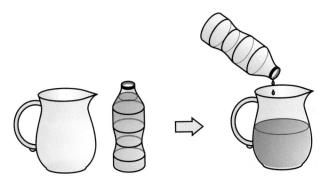

The pitcher has greater capacity than the bottle.

Next, students measure capacity using a non-standard unit (a water glass).

This container holds 3 units of water.

Then a standard unit (1 liter) is introduced and students measure capacity in liters. This step — only this step – is repeated using cups, quarts, and gallons.

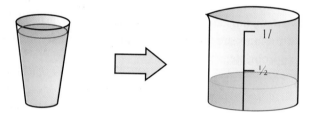

Grade 3— Conversions. In your homework, you will study how third graders learn to convert between milliliters and liters. For now, look at pages 45-48 in Primary Math 3B and see how the textbook answers the following questions.

EXERCISE 3.2. *How many milliliters are in 1 liter? What is the "capacity" of a container? What units are used to measure capacity?*

Because 1 liter is 1000 mℓ, conversions between liters and milliliters are done by multiplying or dividing by 1000. In decimal notation, the conversion is simply a shift in place value of each digit 3 places; for example, 1280 mℓ = 1.280 ℓ. However, decimal numbers do not appear in the curriculum for another year; they are introduced in grade 4. Thus, metric conversions help prepare students for decimals, rather than the other way around.

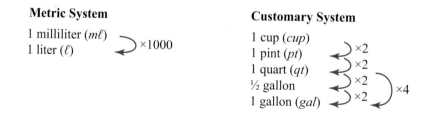

Metric System

1 milliliter (*mℓ*)
1 liter (*ℓ*) ×1000

Customary System

1 cup (*cup*)
1 pint (*pt*) ×2
1 quart (*qt*) ×2
½ gallon ×2   ×4
1 gallon (*gal*) ×2

Homework Set 3

1. (*Study the Textbook!*) Read Primary Math 3B pages 29 - 32, doing the problems in your text as you go.

   a) In Problem 1 on page 30, the scale changes from a 4 kg scale in parts (a) and (b) to a 2 kg scale in parts (c) and (d). Why did the textbook do that?

   b) On page 30, students begin doing what in Problem 2? Then, in Problems 3, 4, 6, 7, students begin doing what?

   c) On pages 29 - 32, which problem(s) ask students to order or compare weights?

   d) Problem (b) on page 32 can be solved by "counting down" (see [EMT] page 21). Illustrate this using a "jumps on a number line" picture.

2. In Practice 3A on page 33 of Primary Math 3B, answer Problems 1c, 2c, 3acf, 4e and 4f, and 5.

3. (*Study the Textbook!*) Primary Math 3B continues developing arithmetic with weight units by giving word problems on pages 34 - 38.

   a) Read pages 34 - 37 and write the answers to Problems 3, 4, 5, 9, 10 on your homework sheet.

   b) On page 38, give Teacher's Solution (with bar diagrams similar to those on pages 35 - 37) for Problems 5 - 7.

4. Continue, reading pages 39-42. On page 42, answer Problems 1b, 2b, 3b, and give Teacher's Solutions to problems 5–7.

5. Give a Teacher's Solution to Problem 33 on page 50 of Primary Math 6B.

6. (*Study the Textbook!*) Return to Primary Math 3B and read pages 45-50, doing the problems in your text as you go. This is the grade 3 introduction to capacity.

   a) What skill is required to answer the questions on page 45?

   b) Pages 46 and 47 give activities and exercises that show students that odd-shaped containers have definite capacities which can be measured by . . . by doing what?

   c) On page 48, students begin doing what in Problem 6? Then, in Problems 7-9, students begin doing what? Notice how quickly this lesson moves into arithmetic with units; that is possible because students have done similar exercises with length and weight.

   d) On pages 45-50, which problem(s) ask students to order or compare capacity?

   e) Problem (b) on page 50 can be solved by "counting up" (again, see [EMT] page 21). Illustrate this as "jumps on a number line".

7. In Practice 4A on page 51 of Primary Math 3B, answer Problems 1c and 1f, 2c, 3abc, 4e and 4f, and 5b.

8. (*Study the Textbook!*) Primary Math 3B continues developing arithmetic with units by giving word problems on page 52 (Practice 4B). On that page:

   a) Answer Problems 2-5.

   b) Give a Teacher's Solution to Problem 6.

   c) Answer Problem 7.

   d) Which of the following operations with metric units is NOT done in the exercises in Practice 4B: a) addition b) subtraction c) multiplication d) division e) ordering f) multistep.

9. Continue, reading pages 53-56. On page 56, answer Problems 1b, 2b, 3b, 4a, and 6, 7, and 8.

10. In Primary Math 5B, give a Teacher's Solution to Problem 17 on page 23.

11. In Primary Math 6B, give a Teacher's Solution to Problem 19 on page 69.

12. Complete the following expressions.

    a) 3.42 metric tons = _____ kg = _____ g.

    b) 1978 g = __ kg = _____ metric tons.

    c) 758 $m\ell$ = _____ ℓ.

    d) 70 kg = _____ metric tons.

    e) ※ In Primary Math 6B, give a Teacher's Solution to Problem 6 on page 98.

1.4 Measuring Angles

Angles are measured using the same procedure used for length, weight and capacity: first choose a unit, then express the measure of angles as multiples of that unit. For angles, there are two common units: full turns and degrees. This section traces how the Primary Mathematics textbooks introduce angle units and the tools for measuring angles.

Angles

Two rays with the same endpoint separate the plane into two infinite regions (the shaded and un-shaded regions in the example shown). In elementary school an **angle** is two rays with the same endpoint together with a choice of one of these two regions. The rays are called the *sides* of the angle, the endpoint is called its *vertex*, and the chosen region is indicated by a small arc.

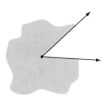

The symbol for angle is ∠. Angles are named by drawing an arc and using one of four notations (the notation $P\hat{Q}R$ is uncommon, but is used in the New Elementary Mathematics book that you will be reading).

By naming the arc
∠x.

By naming the vertex
∠E.

By naming three points
∠PQR or $P\hat{Q}R$.

Within figures, angles usually refer to interior angles, i.e., angles whose arc is in the interior of the figure. In that case the arc is sometimes not drawn.

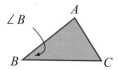

Teaching comment. The term "angle" is reintroduced twice in high school with definitions modified for the context. In high school geometry an angle is defined to be two non-collinear rays with the same endpoint; the corresponding arc is the one that is less than 180°. In trigonometry, students learn to associate an angle with each real number, both positive and negative. These alternative notions of "angle" are not taught or used in elementary school.

The Primary Math textbooks introduce angles in grades 3 and 4 in the following manner.

Grade 3—Right angles. Third grade students learn to construct a right angle by folding a piece of paper twice.

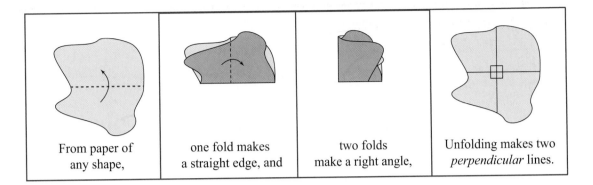

| From paper of any shape, | one fold makes a straight edge, and | two folds make a right angle, | Unfolding makes two *perpendicular* lines. |

With this homemade right angle, students are asked to go around the room and determine whether other angles, in pictures and parts of objects, are equal to, greater than, or less than a right angle (see page 94 of Primary Math 3B). The same tool is used to check angles in triangles and quadrilaterals (page 95). Along the way, students learn to align the vertex and one side of the measuring tool with the vertex and one side of the angle. These cleverly designed activities are an initial step toward measuring with protractors.

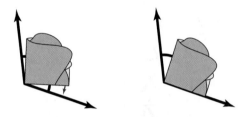

In elementary school angles are brought to life through the idea of "turning". Two rays with the same vertex can be thought of as the hands of a clock. One can imagine fixing one hand and rotating the other *along the arc* until the two hands are on top of one another. Intuitively, the size of the angle is the amount of turning required to do this.

Grades 4 and 5—Protractors and degrees. Students now learn to measure the size of angles. As with the previous types of measurement, this involves (i) choosing a unit angle, and (ii) expressing other angles in term of that unit angle. In elementary mathematics, students use two different units to measure angles.

(1) One can take the entire circle as the unit of angular measure. An angle is then expressed as a fraction of a "complete turn", as in the picture below.

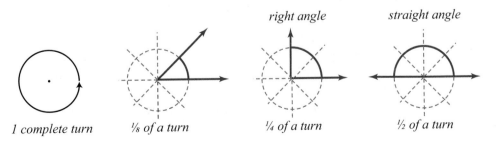

| *1 complete turn* | *⅛ of a turn* | *¼ of a turn* | *½ of a turn* |

With this unit, a right angle is $\frac{1}{4}$ turn. Two adjacent right angles form $\frac{1}{2}$ turn; this is called a **straight angle**. Adding angle measurements is then an exercise in adding fractions: $\frac{2}{3}$ complete turn plus $\frac{1}{2}$ turn is $\frac{2}{3} + \frac{1}{2} = \frac{5}{6}$ turn. Notice that such additions are not easy!

(2) More commonly, one uses a small unit called a **degree**. For this, we divide the circle into 360 equal arcs; the angle corresponding to each small arc is 1 degree.

> One complete turn is 360 degrees (denoted 360°).

Consequently,

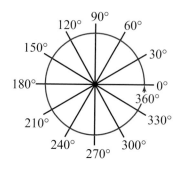

- A straight angle is half of a complete turn, so is 180°.

- A right angle is a quarter of a complete turn, so is 90°.

Notice that the word "of" in these sentences is one of the interpretations of fraction multiplication. Consequently, students often learn to convert fractions of a circle into degrees in the same grade that they learn to multiply fractions.

EXAMPLE 4.1. *How many degrees are in $\frac{1}{3}$ of a complete turn? In $\frac{1}{5}$ of a complete turn? How many degrees are in $\frac{1}{6}$ of a right angle?*

Solution:

$$\left.\begin{aligned}
\tfrac{1}{3}\text{ turn} &= \tfrac{1}{3} \times 360° = \left(\tfrac{1}{3} \times 36\right) \times 10° = 120° \\
\tfrac{1}{5}\text{ turn} &= \tfrac{1}{5} \times 360° = \left(\tfrac{1}{10} \times 360°\right) \times 2 = 72° \\
\tfrac{1}{6}\text{ right angle} &= \tfrac{1}{6} \times 90° = 15°.
\end{aligned}\right\} \quad \text{by mental math!}$$

One degree is small enough that all angles are closely approximated by a whole number of degrees. Consequently, fractions are unnecessary for most purposes — all angle measurements and calculations involve only whole numbers.

But why use the number 360? The unit 'degree' originated with the Mesopotamians (circa 4000 B.C.), who based their entire number system on the number 60. Some modern measurements retain vestiges of the Mesopotamian system: an hour is 60 minutes, a minute is 60 seconds, and a circle has $6 \times 60 = 360$ degrees. The use of 60 is a way of avoiding fractions: when a unit is made of 60 equal parts, many fractional units can be expressed as whole numbers. For example, $\frac{1}{3}$ of 60 is 20, $\frac{1}{4}$ of 60 is 15, $\frac{1}{5}$ of 60 is 12, and $\frac{1}{6}$ is 10.

Why 360°?

In particular, dividing a circle into 360 equal parts ensures that common angles are expressed in degrees as whole numbers, including the angles in Example 4.1. Calculations with common angles become much easier. For example, it is much easier to add $30° + 45°$ than to add $\frac{1}{12}$ turn $+ \frac{1}{8}$ turn. It also makes angles much easier to *teach* because children can learn to measure and calculate with angles in degrees before they have mastered fractions.

Learning To Use a Protractor

Degrees are introduced in Primary Math 4A. At that point, students learn to use a protractor to measure angles and to draw angles of specified sizes.

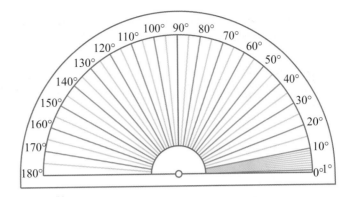

Looking at a protractor, one can see how its construction relates to the definition of a degree. One can envision starting with a blank semicircle of cardboard or plastic, wrapping a flexible tape measure along its outer edge, and drawing 180 equally-spaced marks. The angle formed by rays from the center point through two consecutive marks is 1°.

This angle is 1 degree.

1 degree is a surprisingly small angle! It is roughly the width of a pencil held at arm's length from your eye. Consequently, *one can describe the size of an angle very accurately by measuring it to the nearest degree.*

Measuring angles with a protractor is very much like checking for right angles, which students learned to do in grade 3. There are three steps:

1. Align the center hole on the vertex of the angle.

2. Align 0° with one side of the angle.

3. Read the measure of the angle on the appropriate scale (most protractors have two scales).

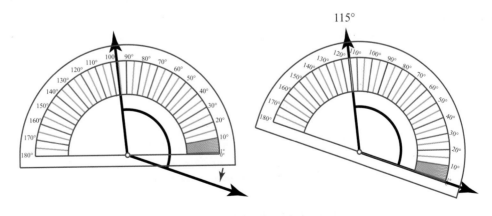

Careful instruction is required here! It is common for students to make errors on all three of these steps. You will learn about these errors in Homework Problem 10.

It is also important for students to learn to measure angles greater than 180°. This can be done either by measuring how much an angle exceeds a straight angle (then add to 180°), or by measuring how much the angle falls short of being a complete turn (then subtract from 360°).

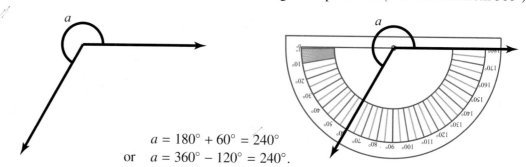

$$a = 180° + 60° = 240°$$
$$\text{or} \quad a = 360° - 120° = 240°.$$

Teaching Comment. Every student should have a protractor and should be given ample opportunities to use it! Learning to use a protractor correctly requires instruction and considerable practice. For this, there is no substitute for hands-on experience — a protractor is one of the most important "manipulatives" used in elementary mathematics. This experience should include exercises *drawing angles* of specified size. Practice with protractors is usually part of the curriculum for grades 4 or 5, but teachers of higher grades should provide further practice and not automatically assume that students know how use a protractor.

EXAMPLE 4.2. *a) How many degrees does the hour hand move per hour?*
 b) What is the angle between the hands on a clock at 4:00? 6:15?

Solution. a) Each hour the hour hand moves $\frac{1}{12}$ of a complete turn, which is $\frac{360°}{12} = 30°$.

  b) **Teacher's Solutions:**

$$90° + 30° = 120°$$
$$\text{or}$$
$$4 \times 30° = 120°.$$

At 6:15, the hour hand is a ¼ of the way between the 6 o'clock and 7 o'clock positions:

$$\frac{1}{4} \text{ of } 30° = 7.5°,$$

$$90° + 7.5° = 97.5°.$$

EXAMPLE 4.3. *The moon travels around the earth in 28 days. Through what angle does the moon appear to move per day?*

Solution. $\dfrac{360 \text{ degrees}}{28 \text{ days}} \approx 13°$ per day.

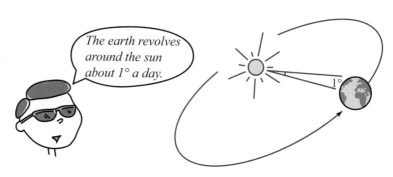

The earth revolves around the sun about 1° a day.

As students measure and draw angles, they learn the following terms. Note that, in contrast to phrases like "small angle" or "big angle", each of these terms has a precise definition that can be checked with a protractor. Routine use of these terms aids classroom communication.

acute angle	right angle	obtuse angle	straight angle	reflex angle	full rotation
less than 90°	90°	between 90° and 180°	180°	between 180° and 360°	360°

Adjacent angles are two angles with the same vertex that share a side. In the left-hand picture below, angles a and b are adjacent angles with common side $\overrightarrow{OC}$. For students with experience measuring angles, it is obvious that the measures of adjacent angles add: $a + b = c$.

Two angles are **congruent** if they have the equal measure. A **bisector** of an angle is a ray that separates the angle into two adjacent angles with equal measure. In the right-hand picture below, $\overrightarrow{OC}$ is a bisector of $\angle AOB$ because $c = 2a$.

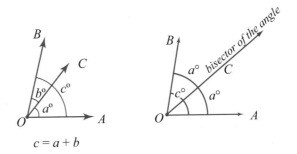

$$c = a + b$$

Two angles are called **supplementary** if the sum of their measures is 180°. Two angles are called **complementary** if the sum of their measures is 90°. Notice that these terms refer only to the measures of the angles; angles can be supplementary or complementary without having a common side or even being close to one another.

A pair of supplementary angles

Angles Properties

Experience measuring angles is a prerequisite for nearly all subsequent work in geometry. Obviously, practice helps students develop a sense of how the visual size of angles relates to their measure in degrees. Through experience, students also learn the properties listed in the chart below. These are used as intuitive principles in elementary school, then made explicit and precise in middle school.

Angle Measurement Facts. Every angle has an associated real number, called its **measure** in degrees, such that

1. Straight angles measure 180°.
   Right angles measure 90°.

2. The measures of adjacent angles add.
   (Abbreviation: ∠s **add**)

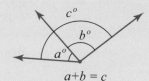

$$a+b = c$$

3. There is an angle with any specified measure:
   Given a ray $\overrightarrow{OP}$ and a number between 0 and 360, one can find a point Q such that the measure of $\angle POQ$ is the given number.

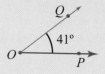

From a teaching perspective, these three facts are not on an equal footing. The first is actually the definition of our unit: it states two alternative ways of saying that 1 degree is 1/360th of a full circle. The second and third facts, however, are basic properties about angles that students learn from measuring angles and solving problems involving angles.

Homework Set 4

1. For the times shown, find the indicated *reflex* angle between the clock hands in degrees (without using a protractor).

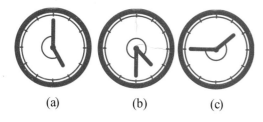

(a)   (b)   (c)

2. Through how many degrees does the earth revolve on its axis each hour? Each minute?

3. The distance from the equator to the north pole is almost exactly 10,000 km. Roughly, how many kilometers is:

   a) the distance around the earth at the equator?

   b) 1 degree of longitude?

4. (*Study the Textbook!*) An introduction to angles for third graders is given in Primary Math 3B, pages 92-95. Read these pages, doing the problems in your textbook as you

read (not to be handed in) and answer the following questions.

    a) On these pages, students do which of the following?

      (i) compare angles (larger, smaller).

      (ii) count the number of angles in a figure.

      (iii) measure angles in degrees.

      (iv) identify right angles.

      (v) learn that right angles measure 90°.

    b) One must measure carefully to determine whether an angle is a right angle; it is not enough for it to *look* like a right angle. Which of the angles (a)– (f) on page 94 leads students to realize that?

5. *(Study the textbook!)* Read Primary Math 4A pages 74-77.

    a) Does the Primary Math curriculum immediately define a right angle as 90°? In the 3B book, how do student check whether an angle is a right angle?

    b) In Primary Math 4A, the very first picture on page 74 gives the definition of a degree in a subtle way. How is it defined?

    c) On page 94 of Primary Math 3B and on page 77 of Primary Math 4A (Problem 7), the angles open in many different directions. Why did the writers of the textbook do this?

6. *(Study the textbook!)* Now do all problems on pages 74-77 of Primary Math 4A as you read (do not record your answers in your HW) and answer the following questions.

    a) An angle can be thought of either as an amount of rotation or as a geometric figure formed by two rays and a small arc. For each of the problems 1–5 on pages 75 and 76 indicate which interpretation is being used (write "rotation" or "figure" for each).

    b) What issue is addressed in Problem 5 (bottom of page 76) that did not occur in the previous problems?

    c) Examine Problem 6 carefully; it explains a method for measuring $\angle p$. Write a one or two sentence explanation of that method.

    d) Which problem on these pages introduces the idea of complementary angles?

    e) The textbook does not *tell* students that complementary angles add to 90°. What is done instead?

7. *(Study the textbook!)* Primary Mathematics curriculum uses letters (like $\angle a$) to represent numbers (prealgebra) for the first time in the curriculum in Primary Math 4A. They do so here because there is a visual link between the angle (Angle a) and its measure $\angle a$. How many different letters are used on pages 74–77 of Primary Math 4A?

8. Using a straightedge (e.g. your ruler) and a protractor, draw angles of 47°, 135° and 291°.

9. *(Study the textbook!)* Read Section 9.1 in NEM I (pages 231-237). Answer the following questions as you read

    a) Does this section assume that the students already are experienced at measuring angles in degrees, or is that taught here?

    b) This section introduces two ways of writing angles: angles $\angle ABC$ and $\angle p$ can also be written how?

    c) Write down the definition of *reflex angle* given in this section.

    d) In this text, the sides of an angle are also called the _____.

    e) Protractors usually have two scales. The text describes the appropriate scale to use in a very clear 10-word phrase. Write down that phrase.

10. *(Study the textbook!)* In NEM1 at the bottom of page 235 shows students (and teachers!) four common mistakes (the last of these uses the word "produced" in the British sense, meaning "extended"). For each error, give a one sentence description and draw a sketch. Make your sketch different than the pictures in the book.

11. Continuing in NEM1, in Problem 4 at the top of page 237, do Parts (a) – (e) and the version of part (f) below. Here is some guidance, of the sort that teachers are expected to provide, for each part:

    (a) Use a protractor.

    (b) and (c) Use protractor and straightedge.

    (d) This is asking you to extend the *ray RQ* past Q to some point that you name T.

    (e) Use protractor and straightedge as before.

    (f) What is the measure of $\angle SQU$? Can you explain this?

CHAPTER 2

Geometric Figures

This chapter describes how elementary students are introduced to the world of geometry. We have seen how children learn to measure lengths and angles and to solve arithmetic problems with measurements.. At the same time, in a separate part of the curriculum, geometry begins as a subject in its own right.

Geometry is the study of relationships among the measurements – lengths, angles, areas and volumes – of figures. Already by grade 2, geometry moves beyond naming figures: the activities direct attention to lengths and angles. In grades 2–4, children learn about parallel and perpendicular lines and solve problems involving supplementary and vertical angles. They also learn to draw figures using a rulers, protractor, compass and set square. In grades 5 and 6 the pieces come together and they begin solving problems involving lengths and angles within triangles and quadrilaterals.

The elementary geometry curriculum focuses on clear reasoning and simple geometric facts. There are no proofs; instead, facts are introduced using paper-folding or symmetry arguments. Reasoning skills are developed through daily problem sets, problem sets that can be great fun for both children and teachers.

2.1 Fundamental Geometric Ideas

As children learn to measure in grades K-3 they acquire intuition about segments, angles and other objects of geometry. Sometime near the end of elementary school, intuition is replaced by precise definitions. This section describes how angles, perpendicular and parallel lines, and figures are presented intuitively, and then in the precise but child-friendly form of a "school definition".

Angles

The "angle measurement facts" listed on page 24 have three especially useful consequences:

1. The total measure of adjacent angles around a point is 360°. (Abbreviation: ∠s **at a pt.**)

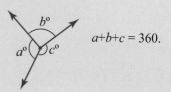

$a+b+c = 360.$

2. The total measure of adjacent angles forming a straight line is 180°.
(Abbreviation: ∠s **on a line**.)

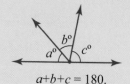

$a+b+c = 180.$

3. The sum of adjacent angles in a right angle is 90°.
(Abbreviation: ∠s **in rt.** ∠.)

$a+b = 90.$

As you will see, these facts will be used repeatedly; they are the springboard that launches deductive geometry in grades 5 and 6. We have given each an abbreviation. Learning geometry is easier in classrooms where everyone consistently uses the same short, clear abbreviations.

When two lines intersect, they form four angles around the point of intersection. If we know the measure of any one of these, we can determine the measures of all four by recognizing pairs of supplementary angles.

EXAMPLE 1.1. *In the figure, find the measures of angles b, c and d.*

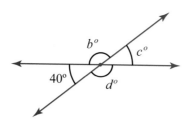

Solution: Moving around the vertex clockwise, we see successive pairs of supplementary angles:

$40 + b = 180,$ so $b = 140.$
$b + c = 140 + c = 180,$ so $c = 40.$
$c + d = 40 + d = 180,$ so $d = 140.$

vertical
angles

In the figure below, angles *a* and *c* are a pair of *vertically opposite angles* because they are opposite each other through the vertex. For short, one says that *a* and *c* are *vertical angles*. Teachers should avoid the phrase "opposite angles" because pairs of angles that might be called "opposite" occur in other, different contexts (see page 48).

The figure contains two pairs of supplementary angles. Angles *a* and *b* are angles on a line, so *a* is $180 - b$. Similarly, *c* is also $180 - b$. Therefore $a = c$, so the two vertical angles have equal measure.

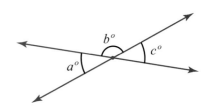

Vertical angles have equal measure.
(Abbreviation: **vert. ∠s.**)

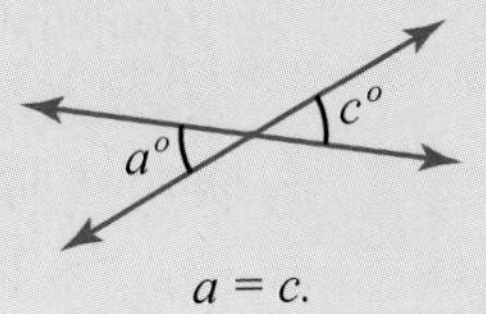

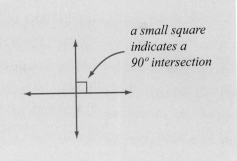

$a = c.$

EXERCISE 1.2. *Read pages 85–88 in Primary Math 5A. Which angle facts are introduced on these pages?*

Perpendicular and Parallel Lines

As we saw in Section 1.4, students are introduced to right angles in Primary Math 3B. Then in Primary Math 4A, they learn that a right angle measures $90°$ and, a few pages later, they learn the term "perpendicular".

DEFINITION 1.3. *Two segments, rays, or lines are perpendicular if the lines containing them intersect to form a $90°$ angle.*

If $\overleftrightarrow{AB}$ is perpendicular to $\overleftrightarrow{CD}$, we write $\overleftrightarrow{AB} \perp \overleftrightarrow{CD}$.

a small square indicates a $90°$ intersection

Two intersecting lines form four angles. If one of those angles is $90°$, then by symmetry each of the other angles must be $90°$.

Drawing perpendicular lines is harder than recognizing them because it requires motor skills. Hands-on activities drawing perpendicular lines deepen students' understanding and develops skills that will be useful later. In classrooms, right angles are usually drawn with the aid of a *set square* (or *plastic triangle*), although any object with a right angle such as a piece of cardboard can be used.

set square

EXAMPLE 1.4. *Use a set square to draw a perpendicular to the line $\overleftrightarrow{AB}$ through the point C.*

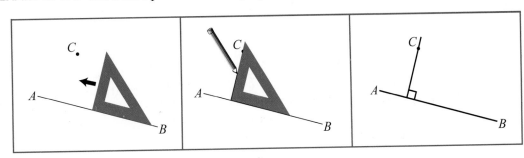

parallel lines

Two lines are *parallel* if they lie in the same plane and do not intersect. In addition, in K-8 geometry — but not always in high school geometry — a single line is considered parallel to itself. When lines $\overleftrightarrow{AB}$ and $\overleftrightarrow{CD}$ are parallel, we write $\overleftrightarrow{AB} \parallel \overleftrightarrow{CD}$. In pictures, pairs of matching arrows are used to indicate that two lines are parallel.

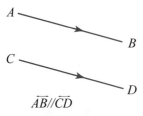 

$\overrightarrow{AB}/\!/\overrightarrow{CD}$

parallel segments

Two segments are parallel if they are part of parallel lines.

As always, the word "line" means a straight line that extends indefinitely in both directions. Consequently, to make sense of the phrase "do not intersect" children must envision extending the segments on their paper indefinitely into space, past distant galaxies — something that is not very concrete. Furthermore, the condition that two lines do not intersect does not suggest a way of drawing parallel lines, or a way to determine when two segments are parallel. Consequently, a different definition of parallel lines is used in elementary school.

DEFINITION 1.5 (School Definition). *Two lines, segments, or rays are **parallel** if they lie in the same plane and are both perpendicular to a third line.*

This school definition gives a mental picture that is concrete and easily explained. Examples of segments that have a common perpendicular are all around us, while there are few examples of non-intersecting lines extending indefinitely into space past distant galaxies.

Railroad tracks and lined paper have many parallel lines.

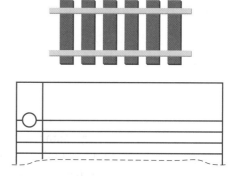

After describing parallel lines, the Primary Mathematics curriculum focuses on two activities to help students develop intuition about parallel lines: a method for determining whether two lines are parallel and a method for constructing parallel lines using a set square. The first method calls children's attention to a fact that is treated as common knowledge in elementary mathematics: if two lines are both parallel to a third line, then they are parallel to each other.

EXAMPLE 1.6. *Use a set square to determine whether two lines are parallel.*

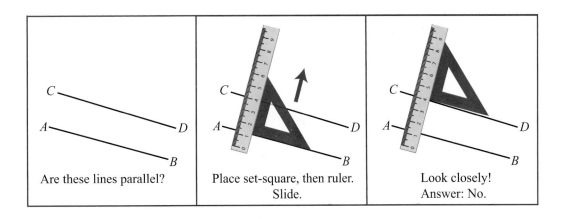

| Are these lines parallel? | Place set-square, then ruler. Slide. | Look closely! Answer: No. |

EXAMPLE 1.7. *Use a set square and a ruler to draw a line parallel to $\overleftrightarrow{AB}$ through the point C.*

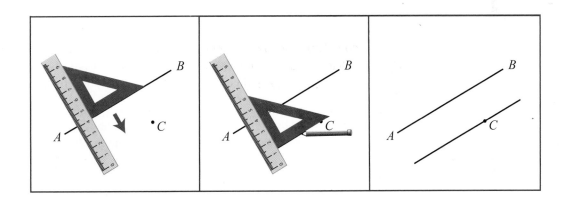

The Primary Math books include a marvelous set of problems involving parallel lines within parallelograms and other figures (see Section 2.4). Then in seventh grade, students study perpendicular and parallel lines more abstractly.

Circles

Children learn to recognize and name circles in kindergarten and first grade, but it is usually not until third or fourth grade that they encounter the precise definition of a circle. At this time they learn the terms "radius" and "diameter", and learn to draw circles with compasses. Here is a three-step teaching sequence for introducing circles:

Step 1 — Definition. Circles are defined in terms of distance, not visual shape. The following activity helps children understand the key idea.

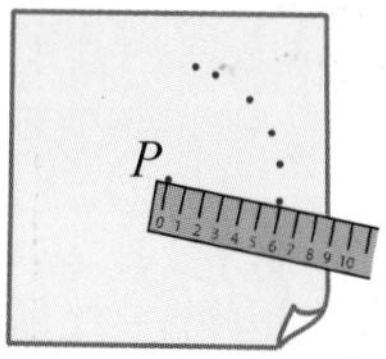 Mark point *P* on a transparency. Then mark as many points as you can that are 6 cm from point *P*.	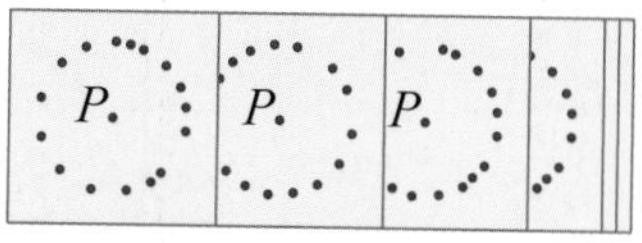 Put your transparency on top of your classmates' papers.	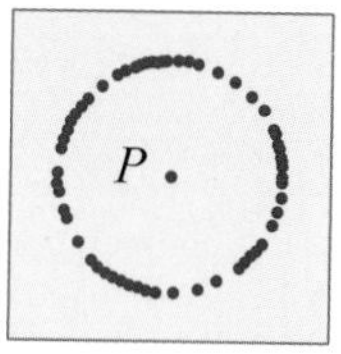 What do you notice?

This activity shows that (i) a circle is a collection of points, and (ii) a circle is completely determined by its center and its radius. With these two realizations, children understand the essence of the mathematical definition

circle
center
radius

DEFINITION 1.8. *Choose a point P in the plane and a distance R. The **circle** with center P and radius R is the set of all points in the plane that are distance R from the point P.*

The word "radius" has two meanings. *The radius* of a circle is a distance, as in Definition 1.8, while *a radius* is any segment with one endpoint on the center and the other endpoint on the circle. (The plural of this word is " radii", pronounced "ray-de-eye".) Because double meanings engender confusion, alert teachers always clarify whether "radius" refers to a distance or a segment.

radius

In a circle *all radii have the same length*. Teachers can reinforce this aspect of the definition by having students use rulers to check that all radii have the same length.

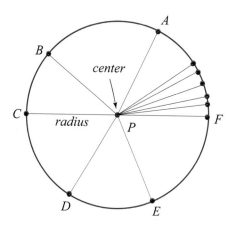

compass

Step 2 — Drawing Circles. A *compass* is a tool for drawing circles. Learning to use a compass is a prerequisite for later geometry.

EXERCISE 1.9. *Mark a point P on your paper. Draw a circle with center P and radius 5 cm.*

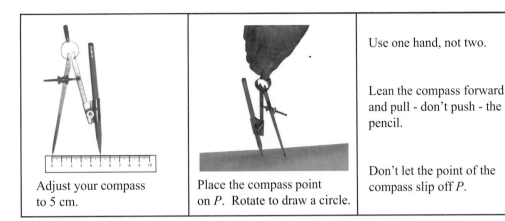

Adjust your compass to 5 cm.	Place the compass point on *P*. Rotate to draw a circle.	Use one hand, not two. Lean the compass forward and pull - don't push - the pencil. Don't let the point of the compass slip off *P*.

As in Definition 1.8, a circle is determined by choosing a center point and choosing a radius. These are exactly the choices students make when they use a compass to draw circles. Other methods for drawing circles, such as tracing around a tin can, hide those choices. The simplicity of the definition gets lost!

Using a compass to draw circles is easy, but requires some practice. The quality of the compass is a factor here. Compasses with screw adjustments work well, but the arms of low-quality compasses tend to slip, making it frustratingly difficult to maintain a constant radius while drawing circles.

Step 3 — Properties of Circles. A line and a circle can intersect in zero, one, or two points.

disjoint   *one intersection point*   *two intersection points*
tangent circle

Likewise, two different circles intersect in zero, one, or two points.

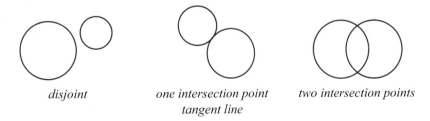

disjoint   *one intersection point*   *two intersection points*
tangent line

EXERCISE 1.10. *Use a compass and a straightedge to draw two circles that are tangent. (Hint: Draw a circle with center P and a ray with endpoint P. How can you choose a center point and a radius for a second, tangent circle?)*

EXERCISE 1.11. *The following third grade problem describes circles that intersect in two points, but the problem has only one solution. Why?*

Gold is buried 4 cm from point B and 2 cm from point C. Use your compass to find the treasure.

The teaching sequence continues in Primary Mathematics textbooks in sixth grade with definitions and applications of terms like diameter, circumference, and semicircle (see pages 26–29 of Primary Math 6B). We will examine this phase of the curriculum in Chapter 8.

Homework Set 5

1. For each of the following times of day, sketch a clock face showing that time and find the measure (in degrees) of the angle formed by the hour hand and the minute hand. (Remember that the hour hand moves 30° per hour.)

    a) 3:00   b) 3:30   c) 10:30   d) 2:45.

2. In the figure, $a = 38°$. Find b, c, and d.

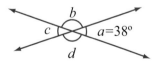

3. On page 238 of NEM1, do Problem 1 of Class Activity 2.

4. *(Study the textbook!)*   Read the rest of Class Activity 2. These exercises have students accept three basic facts after checking them in one example. These are not proofs; the purpose of the activity is to make clear *what the facts*

mean and help make them evident to the students (rather than being teacher-announced truths).

   a) Copy down the three facts with their abbreviations. We will shorten the first two abbreviations to "∠s on a line" and "vert. ∠s".

   b) Are these the same three facts introduced on pages 85-86 of Primary Math 5A?

5. In Exercise 9.2 on pages 240-241 of NEM1, do problems 1b and parts b), f), h) and j) of Problem 2. Write your solutions in the manner of Worked Examples 1 and 2 on pages 239 and 240 on NEM 1. Be sure to include reasons in parentheses.

6. *(Study the textbook!)*

   a) Read pages 78–83 of Primary Math 4A. Does the book define the terms perpendicular and parallel, or does it just show examples?

   b) Now read pages 242–243 of NEM1. Does NEM1 define the terms perpendicular and parallel?

c) Give a one or two sentence explanation of how Problem 2 on page 80 of Primary Math 4A helps students make sense of the seventh grade definition of perpendicular.

d) Give a similar explanation of how Problem 2 on page 83 helps students make sense of the seventh grade definition of parallel lines.

7. On page 243 of NEM1, do Problem 1 of Class Activity 3 using a ruler and a set square. Then write a precise definition for the term *perpendicular bisector*.

8. *(Common Student Error)* When asked to find x in the figure below, Mary writes "$x = 50$" and explains "because vertical angles are equal". What is x actually? What erroneous assumption did Mary make?

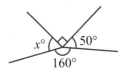

9. *(Common Student Error)* In the figure, Jerry claims that "$a + b = 180$" stating as the reason, "∠s on a line."

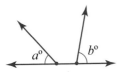

There may be several reasons why Jerry is making this error. He may not understand angle measurements or how to add angle measurements, he may not understand that to apply this fact the angles must be _____, or he may not understand that there are _____ degrees on a straight angle.

10. Draw a line L and a point P not on L. Using a ruler and set square, follow the procedure of Example 1.7 in this section to draw a line through P parallel to L.

11. A teacher asks her students for a precise definition of the term *circle*.

a) Sarah says "A circle is a round segment with no endpoints". Name at least two things wrong with Sarah's definition.

b) Michael says "A circle is 360°". What two notions is Michael confusing?

c) Write down a precise definition of the term *circle*.

12. Practice drawing circles with a compass until you can draw complete circles without stopping. Then on your homework paper draw circles of radius 2 cm, 6 cm and 10 cm, using your ruler to set the compass width.

13. Use your compass to draw a circle; label your circle C and its center O. Choose any point on the circle and label it P. Draw another circle of radius OP with center P.

14. Use your compass to draw circle B; label its center 0. Choose any point on the circle and label it Q. Draw two more circles of different radii such that both circles intersect circle B only at point Q. (Hint: Draw line $\overleftrightarrow{OQ}$ first.)

2.2 Triangles

This section explains how an elementary school teacher might introduce one of the most important ideas in geometry: the fact that the sum of measures of the interior angles in any triangle equals 180°. To set the stage, we briefly discuss how children are introduced to shapes and figures in grades K-2.

Geometric Figures in the Early Grades

Pre-school, kindergarten, and first grade children learn to name, identify and draw 10 – 15 types of figures in the plane. There are two distinct levels to this learning. At the lower level, students identify shapes by sight-recognition: a square is a shape that *looks* like a square. Shape-naming is easy because young children have an innate ability to recognize and match shapes and are dazzlingly quick at learning new vocabulary words. At the higher level, students learn a precise definition and learn to check that the figures satisfy the required conditions. A "hexagon", for example, is not simply something that looks like a hexagon. Rather, a hexagon is a figure with six straight sides — count 'em to be sure! The teacher's role is to move students from the first level to the second.

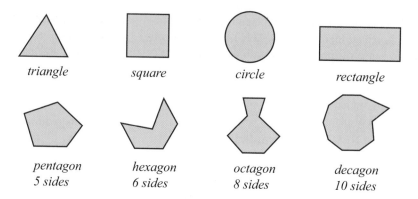

triangle   *square*   *circle*   *rectangle*

pentagon   *hexagon*   *octagon*   *decagon*
5 sides   *6 sides*   *8 sides*   *10 sides*

Learning to apply precise definitions is not automatic or easy. Children do not naturally think in precise terms, so they need guidance from their teacher. School textbooks facilitate learning by presenting **school definitions**: definitions that are precise and understandable to young children, but may not be the complete mathematical definition. In the previous section we saw how a school definition is used to introduce parallel lines. Here are two other common school definitions:

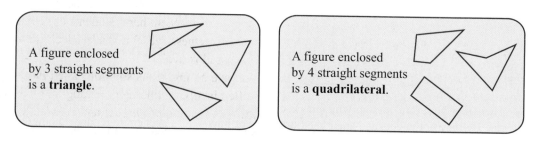

A figure enclosed by 3 straight segments is a **triangle**.

A figure enclosed by 4 straight segments is a **quadrilateral**.

Grade 2 School Definitions

School definitions evolve and the wording becomes more sophisticated in later grades. But at the start, school definitions like those above help focus children's attention on the *parts* of the figure. The parts are given names: vertices, sides and angles. The region enclosed is called the *interior* of the figure; the interior does *not* include the sides or the vertices.

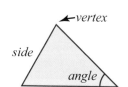

Figures are classified by their parts, not their appearance. For example, to distinguish an octagon ("a figure enclosed by 8 segments") from a decagon ("... 10 segments") one must *know the definition* and one must *count the number of sides*. Visual recognition is not enough. With practice, young children quickly become proficient at this.

The mathematical definition of triangle, typically given sometime in grades 4-7, is not just more sophisticated than the second grade definition, it is actually different.

DEFINITION 2.1. *A* **triangle** *consists of three non-collinear points and the line segments joining them. (The points are called the* vertices, *and the segments are called the* sides *of the triangle.)*

Notice what has changed: in grades K-2, a triangle included the vertices, sides, *and the interior.* Definition 2.1 switches children's thinking to the more abstract "adult" meaning, in which a triangle consists of vertices and sides, but not the interior.

A triangle with vertices *A*, *B* and *C* is denoted △*ABC*. Because vertices are not collinear, every triangle has an interior and an exterior.

collinear points
do not form triangles!

The Sum of the Angles of a Triangle

Primary Math 5B introduces students to some initial facts about triangles, squares, and other quadrilaterals. Almost immediately, students begin using these facts to solve multi-step geometry problems. There is a pedagogical problem here: students are comfortable using "facts" only after they are certain of their correctness, yet 5th graders lack the background to understand geometric proofs. How is this paradox avoided?

The Primary Math books have an ingenious solution called *picture proofs.* A picture proof is an illustration or activity, often involving folding or cutting-and-rearranging, that makes some fact evident. It both *clarifies the meaning of the fact* and *convinces students that it is true.* A good picture proof conveys the essential ideas of a mathematical proof without words.

Many elementary textbooks demonstrate that the sum of angles in a triangle is 180° using one or both of the following activities. The first is a picture proof.

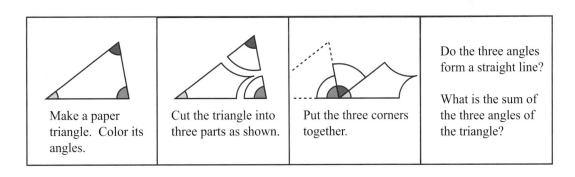

| Make a paper triangle. Color its angles. | Cut the triangle into three parts as shown. | Put the three corners together. | Do the three angles form a straight line?

 What is the sum of the three angles of the triangle? |

This activity gives compelling evidence that the sum of the three cut-out angles is 180°. But the triangle is destroyed in this process, so it is not clear that the fact is a result about triangles. Consequently, textbooks often provide a second activity in which students measure and add the angles of several triangles.

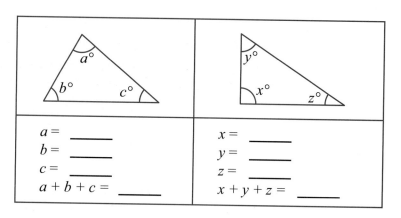

Measure and add
the angles.

What did you notice?

$a =$ _____	$x =$ _____
$b =$ _____	$y =$ _____
$c =$ _____	$z =$ _____
$a + b + c =$ _____	$x + y + z =$ _____

EXERCISE 2.2. *Read pages 57-58 of Primary Mathematics 5B. Which exercise(s) on these pages is similar to the first activity? To the second activity? Roughly how much class time do you think is spent on doing the activities shown on pages 57-58?*

The purpose of these activities is *not* to provide experimental evidence about the sum of the angles — geometry is not an experimental subject! Rather, these activities are designed to ensure that all students completely understand the meaning of the following statement.

In any triangle, the sum of the measures of the interior angles is 180°.

(Abbreviation: ∠ **sum of** Δ.)

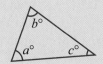

$a + b + c = 180.$

This is one of the most important facts in all of geometry. Almost all subsequent work in geometry depends upon it.

Here is a different teaching sequence leading to the same fact. This approach starts by studying *right triangles*. Students begin by doing the following folding exercise.

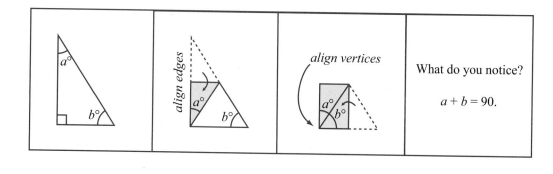

align edges

align vertices

What do you notice?

$a + b = 90.$

When one angle of a triangle is a right angle, the measures of the other two angles add up to 90°.

(Abbreviation: ∠ **sum of rt.** Δ.)

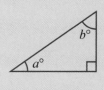

$$a + b = 90.$$

Students can then use this fact to find the sum of the angles of any triangle. The trick is to realize that every triangle can be split into two right triangles. The pictures below show how to use a set square to draw the splitting. *Be sure that you understand the reasoning depicted in the right-hand picture.*

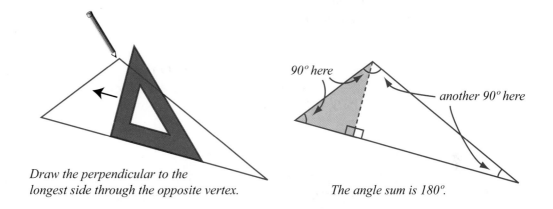

Draw the perpendicular to the longest side through the opposite vertex.

The angle sum is 180°.

Many geometric facts, like this one, become clear if one first thinks about right triangles, and then decomposes general figures into right triangles. The idea of decomposing figures into right triangles is an important recurring theme in geometry; we will use it repeatedly in Chapters 5 through 8. Teachers can add coherence to classroom discussions by emphasizing the role of right triangles in geometry.

Exterior Angles

An angle formed by one side of a triangle and the straight extension of another side is called an **exterior angle** of the triangle. In the picture below, one side of triangle *ABC* has been extended, creating an exterior angle *e*. This exterior angle *e* is supplementary to the interior angle *C*.

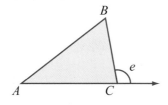

Every triangle has 3 pairs of exterior angles.

At each vertex, interior and exterior angles are supplementary.

Now look again at the cut-out triangle on page 37. What do you notice?

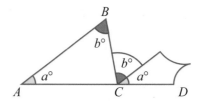

The picture proof above shows that the measure of the exterior angle $\angle BCD$ is $a+b$ degrees, which is the sum the two interior angles along the opposite side of the triangle.

The measure of each exterior angle of a triangle is the sum of the measures of the opposite interior angles.

(Abbreviation: **ext. $\angle$ of $\triangle$**.)

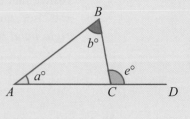

$$e = a + b.$$

Homework Set 6

In this homework set you will study two presentations of the facts about the angle sum of a triangle: one for 5th graders and one for 7th graders.

1. (*Study the Textbook!*) The fact that the sum of the measures of the angles of a triangle is 180° is introduced in pages 57-60 of Primary Math 5B.

   a) Do the experiment described on page 57. Is this a "picture proof" as defined in this section?

   b) The statement (at bottom of page 57) abbreviates language in the interest of clarity. Use the words "measure" and "interior" to expand this statement to make it complete and correct.

   c) Using a protractor, measure the angles of triangles A and B in Problem 1 on page 58. What do you get for the sum of the interior angles?

   d) What do students gain by doing this problem? (Hint: read this section!)

2. (*Study the Textbook!*) Continue reading and doing the problems in Primary Math 5B pages 58-60. Notice that the students are no longer measuring angles. Instead they are *figuring out angles using the given information*.

   a) Answer Problems 2 and 3 on page 58.

   b) Do the folding experiment described on page 59. Again, according to this section, what is the purpose of such picture proofs?

   c) Answer Problems 5 and 6. Write the answers as a list of numbers.

   d) Here is another 5th grade explanation of the boxed statement on page 59. Justify the first step by filling in the blank using the abbreviation for one of the boxed facts in this section

   The figure shows a right triangle.
   To Prove: $a + b = 90°$.

   $a + b + 90 = 180$ _____

   Therefore $a + b = 90$.

3. Find the value of c in the figure.

   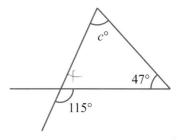

4. In the figure, $\overline{AB}$, $\overline{CD}$ and $\overline{EF}$ are segments. Find the value of d.

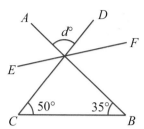

5. Find the value of e in the figure.

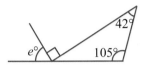

6. Find the value of f in the figure.

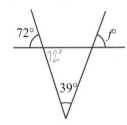

7. Find the value of g in the figure.

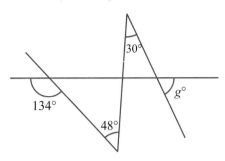

8. *(Study the textbook!)* In NEM, read pages 262-263 and study the solution to Worked Example 4 on page 263. Then in Exercise 10.2 (pages 263-266):

   a) Write solutions to Problems 3a, 3c, 3h, and 3i using the format of Worked Example 4. Be sure to include reasons in parentheses.

   b) Use the same format to write solutions to Problems 4a, 4h, and 4l.

2.3 Symmetry and Triangles

A major portion of geometry is the study of the logical relationships between lengths and angles in figures. It is an excellent avenue for teaching deductive reasoning: children learn reasoning skills as they solve geometry problems. In the homework of the previous section, we saw how three facts about triangles open up a wealth of interesting, instructive geometry problems. This section adds a new fact to the repertoire: base angles of isosceles triangles are equal.

There are several routes to introducing isosceles triangles in the classroom. One common approach uses symmetry and paper-folding exercises to avoid formalities that are inappropriate at the K-8 level. As a result, teachers can quickly present the key facts about isosceles triangles and immediately engage students in solving interesting geometry problems.

Lines of Symmetry

Our visual system enables even young children to match shapes and recognize symmetry. This ability can be used by teachers to introduce geometric concepts and provide intuitive justifications. For this reason, most elementary curricula include a discussion of symmetry.

Symmetry is taught through examples. The immediate goal is to introduce words for two types of symmetry. These words help make children aware of visual patterns that they intuitively recognize. They also provide vocabulary for classroom discussions.

line of symmetry

The idea of a *line of symmetry* can be explained by folding and cutting as shown. It is apparent that many familiar shapes have a line of symmetry. The pictures below show several facts about lines of symmetry that students should know.

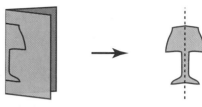

Cut folded paper along a path that begins and ends on the fold.

Unfolding creates a figure with a line of symmetry along the fold.

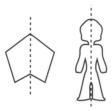

A line of symmetry separates the figure into two parts of equal size.

Lines of symmetry needn't be vertical.

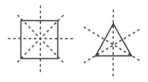

Some figures have several lines of symmetry.

rotational symmetry

A second type of symmetry is rotational symmetry. A figure has *rotational symmetry of order n* if there is some "center" point P so that a rotation with center P by $1/n$ of a turn carries the figure onto itself. This can be illustrated by overlaying two copies of a figure, one on cardboard and one on a transparency, inserting a pin at the center point, and rotating.

Rotational symmetry of order 5.

The center of symmetry needn't be part of the figure.

Many figures have both rotational symmetry and lines of symmetry.

Symmetry is an important but relatively easy idea. It can be introduced in any grade and needs only a few class sessions to teach. The Primary Mathematics curriculum includes two days on lines of symmetry in grade 4 and a week on symmetry in grade 7 (see Chapter 11 of NEM 1). The goal is to attune students to symmetry and to begin using symmetry to relate the measures of segments and angles in a figure.

When a figure has symmetry

- corresponding segments have equal length, and

- corresponding angles have equal measure.

Rotate: these angles have equal measure.

Reflect: these segments have equal length.

Teachers can use symmetry to clarify geometric reasoning. For example, symmetry helps students spot congruent triangles (such as the two "halves" of an isosceles triangle). Symmetry is also useful when computing areas: to find the area of a symmetric figure, one can find the area of half the figure, and double. As you continue reading this and later chapters, pay attention to the ways that you can use symmetry in the classroom.

Types of Triangles

Triangles can be classified by their angles:

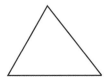

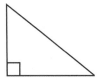

Acute Triangle
all angles are
less than 90°.

Right Triangle
one angle is 90°.

Obtuse Triangle
one angle is
greater than 90°.

Triangles can also be classified by their sides, or by their lines of symmetry:

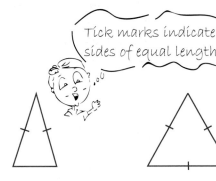

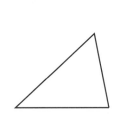

Scalene
all sides are unequal
no lines of symmetry

Isosceles
at least two sides equal
at least 1 line of symmetry

Equilateral
all sides are equal
3 lines of symmetry

EXERCISE 3.1. *Is every equilateral triangle an isosceles triangle?*

In an isosceles triangle, the sides of equal length are called the *legs* and the third side is called the *base*. The angles along the base are the *base angles* and the angle opposite the base is the *vertex angle*. Notice — and make sure that your students notice — that the base of an isosceles triangle need not be horizontal!

The base need
not be horizontal!

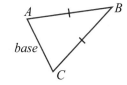

Isosceles and Equilateral Triangles

The definitions of an isosceles and equilateral triangles refer to side lengths, but say nothing about angles. But the definition determines a symmetry, which can be used to relate angles. An isosceles triangle has a line of symmetry, namely the line from the middle of the base to the opposite vertex. When an isosceles triangle is folded along its line of symmetry, the two sides and the two base angles match. Hence *the base angles are equal.*

Base angles of an isosceles triangle are equal.

(Abbreviation: **base ∠s of isos. Δ.**)

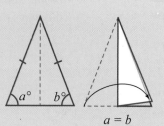

$a = b$

The same folding picture shows a second, logically different fact about isosceles triangles: If two angles in a triangle are equal then the opposite sides have the same length.

Equilateral triangles have rotational symmetry. If we rotate by 1/3 of a turn, the triangle matches itself. Thus all three angles are equal. Since their sum is 180°, each is a 60° angle.

Each angle in an equilateral triangle is 60°.
(Abbreviation: **equilat. Δ.**)

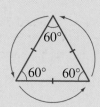

EXAMPLE 3.2. *In the figure, AB = AC = BC = CD. Find the value of a.*

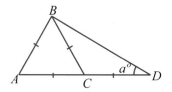

Solution:

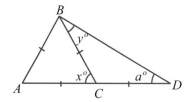

Mark angles x and y as shown.

$y + a = x$	ext. ∠ of Δ
$x = 60$	equilat. Δ
$y = a$	base ∠s of isos. Δ
∴ $2a = 60,$	
∴ $a = 30.$	

The symbol ∴ that appears above is a standard mathematical abbreviation for the word "therefore".

Homework Set 7

In this homework set you will study the presentation of the facts about angles of a triangle, first at the grade 5 level, then at the grade 7 level.

1. (*Study the Textbook!*) The basic facts about equilateral and isosceles triangles are introduced in Primary Math 5B. Read pages 61-64 carefully and answer the following questions.

   a) The fact that the base angles of an isosceles triangle are congruent is illustrated how?

   b) Read Problem 2 on page 62 carefully. This problem illustrates the fact that "if a triangle has two equal angles then _____".

   c) Write the answers to Problems 3 and 4.

   d) Problems 5, 6 and 7 are 2-step problems that combine facts about isosceles triangles with one other fact. For each, write the answer and state the "other fact" used.

   e) Write the answers to Problem 8.

2. Find the value of x in the figure.

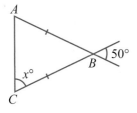

3. The figure shows a pentagon whose central angles are all equal: $a = b = c = d = e$. Find the value of y and the value of z.

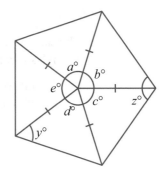

4. Find the value of r and of s in the figure.

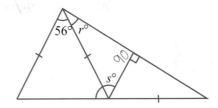

5. (*Study the textbook!*) Read Section 10.3 in NEM1, pages 268–270. Do Problems 1, 2a, 2b, 3a, 3b, 3c, 3d, and 3g.

6. (*Study the textbook!*) Read Sections 11.1 and 11.2 in NEM1 pages 290–298. Do problem 4 on page 297 by drawing the lines of symmetry in your NEM1 textbook (do not copy to your homework paper). Write your answer to part (xii) on your homework paper.

7. Do Problem 6 on page 298 of NEM1.

2.4 Parallelograms, Rhombuses and Trapezoids

According to the school definition given on page 36, a quadrilateral is a figure enclosed by 4 straight segments. In special quadrilaterals, such as parallelograms, the angle measures and side lengths are related in various ways. In grades 4–6 children learn about these relationships and begin applying them to solve problems. Real geometry begins!

The school definition of quadrilateral uses simple language that children can understand, but the school definition is ambiguous. Students are likely to wonder whether the interior is part of the quadrilateral, and whether a triangle with a fourth vertex along a straight edge is considered to be triangle or a quadrilateral. As with triangles, these perplexities are resolved by giving the correct mathematical definition.

DEFINITION 4.1. *A quadrilateral consists of 4 distinct points* A, B, C, D *in the plane, no three of which are collinear, and four segments* $\overline{AB}, \overline{BC}, \overline{CD}, \overline{DA}$ *that intersect only at their endpoints.*

The segments are called the sides *and the endpoints are called the* vertices *of the quadrilateral.*

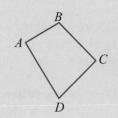

Elementary students are introduced to six types of special quadrilaterals.

A **parallelogram** is a quadrilateral in which both pairs of opposite sides are parallel.

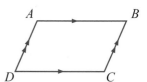

A **rectangle** is a parallelogram all of whose angles are right angles.

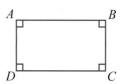

A **rhombus** is a parallelogram with all sides of equal length.

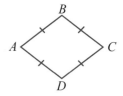

A **square** is a rectangle with all sides of equal length.

A **trapezoid** is a quadrilateral in which one and only one pair of opposite sides are parallel. The parallel sides are called the *bases* of the trapezoid and the other two sides are called *transversals*.

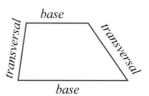

A **kite** is a quadrilateral in which two consecutive sides have equal length and the remaining two sides also have equal length.

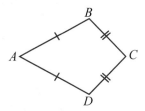

High school textbooks use slightly different definitions of rectangle and rhombus. They replace the condition "is a parallelogram" by the more general phrase "is a quadrilateral" and proceed to give proofs that a quadrilateral with four right angles must be a parallelogram, and that a quadrilateral with four sides of equal length also must be a parallelogram. But these proofs are unnecessary complications at the stage when children are first introduced to quadrilaterals. Thus elementary school definitions of rectangle and rhombus include the words "is a parallelogram" for pedagogical, not logical, reasons. In Chapter 4 we will revisit this issue at the grade 7 level.

Several of these terms may apply to one figure. For example, a square is automatically a rectangle and is also a parallelogram. Standardized tests often have questions that require students to know the above definitions and be able to give counterexamples. Here is such a question.

EXERCISE 4.2. *a) Is every parallelogram a kite? Why or why not?*
b) Is every rhombus a kite? Why or why not?

Solution: a) No. A 'thin' parallelogram is not a kite.

b) Yes. Every rhombus has four equal sides, therefore adjacent sides are equal.

Teaching Comment. The chart on the right shows how the various quadrilaterals are related. Students should not memorize this chart! The point of questions like those in Exercise 4.2 is to get students to learn and appreciate the importance of precise definitions, and to reason with those definitions. Memorization defeats this teaching goal.

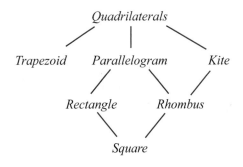

Angles in Parallelograms

If you know the measure of one angle in a parallelogram, then you can determine all of the other angles in the parallelogram. This is commonly presented as two separate facts, both introduced by folding and cutting activities.

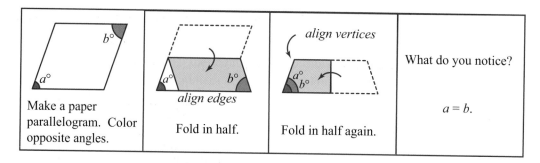

This gives convincing evidence for a simple fact about the angles in a parallelogram:

Opposite angles in a parallelogram are equal.

(Abbreviation: **opp. ∠s //-ogram.**)

$a = b$

Cutting exercises can also be used. The pictures below show a cutting exercise that leads students to a second fact in parallelograms and trapezoids.

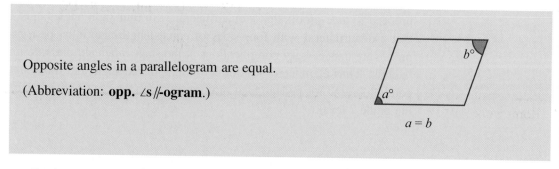

EXERCISE 4.3. *Try the cutting exercise above for a trapezoid. Some pairs of angles add up to 180° — which ones?*

Interior angles between two parallel sides in a trapezoid (or a parallelogram) are supplementary.

(Abbreviation: **int. ∠s, $\overline{BC} \parallel \overline{AD}$.**)

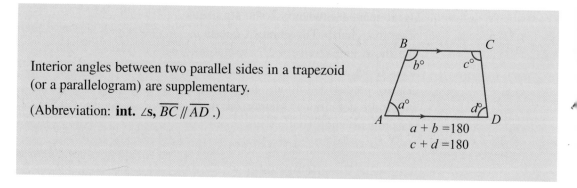

$a + b = 180$
$c + d = 180$

As a general principle, folding is better than cutting because the figure is not destroyed; after students see that angles match they can easily unfold and interpret the matching in terms of the original figure.

Both facts can be combined with the facts of the previous sections to solve "unknown angle" problems.

EXAMPLE 4.4. *The picture shows a trapezoid. Find angle a.*

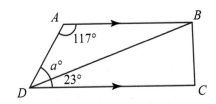

Solution:

$$(a + 23) + 117 = 180 \quad \text{int. } \angle s, \overline{AB} \parallel \overline{DC}$$
$$a + 140 = 180$$
$$a = 40.$$

Homework Set 8

1. To stay in practice, make the following conversions.

   a) 18 m 67 cm = _____ m

   b) 1 km 230 m = _____ m

   c) 86 mm = _____ cm

   d) 4 m 7 cm = _____ cm

   e) 23.8 cm = _____ mm

2. This exercise provides practice in creating "instructional counter-examples". Draw:

   a) a rectangle that is not a square.

   b) a parallelogram that is not a rhombus.

   c) a kite that is not a parallelogram.

   d) a trapezoid with two opposite sides that clearly have different lengths.

   e) a parallelogram whose diagonals are clearly not perpendicular.

3. Is this figure a kite? (Read the definition of kite carefully).

4. (*Study the Textbook!*) The basic facts about parallelograms and rhombuses are introduced on pages 68-71 of Primary Math 5B.

   a) Write down precise definitions for *parallelogram*, *rhombus* and *trapezoid*.

   b) What fact is illustrated on page 69? (see the pictured "student helper"). The illustrations show how to match up angles by cutting, _____ , and sliding.

   c) What fact is illustrated on page 70?

   d) Write answers for Problems 3 and 4.

   e) Problem 5 uses the fact established in Problem ___, now applied to a trapezoid instead of a parallelogram.

   f) Copy the picture in Problem 5 and show how to cut and slide to see each of the two facts needed to solve the problem. Can you show both in one picture?

   g) Write the answers to Problem 6.

5. Read pages 72–75 of Primary Math 5B. These give students practice in geometric constructions with ruler, set square, and compass. Using those tools, do the constructions called for in Problems 3 and 5 on page 75.

6. Now go to Primary Math 6B. Work through pages 62-65, answering Problems 1-7 in your book, then copying the answers onto your HW paper. Take time to understand the pictures. Notice how the questions take you through the intermediate steps *in order*.

7. Continuing in Primary Math 6B, answer Problems 1-5 of Practice 5A on page 66.

8. Continuing, answer Problems 1-5 on page 67.

9. Draw a kite and label the vertices *A, B, C, D*.

   a) Draw and name a line of symmetry.

   b) Describe a folding exercise that shows this symmetry.

   c) The symmetry shows which two angles are equal?

   d) The line of symmetry bisects which two angles?

10. In general, how many lines of symmetry do each of the following figures have? Draw sketches showing the lines of symmetry.

   a) isosceles triangle

   b) kite

   c) rectangle

   d) parallelogram

   e) square

   f) circle.

11. In general, does a parallelogram have rotational symmetry of order 2? of order 4? (see page 42) Draw a sketch.

2.5 Geometric Constructions

A part of geometry is concerned with techniques for constructing accurate diagrams. A **geometric construction** is a theoretically exact method of determining points, lines and figures that meet specified conditions. Constructions are traditionally made using two tools: a straightedge and a compass. In school, geometric constructions can be presented as challenging puzzles that provide insight into principles of geometry. They are included in almost every K-12 curriculum around the world.

A straightedge is a ruler without any markings and a compass is a tool for drawing circles with any desired center and radius. These tools do not measure lengths or angles, yet they are enough to draw *most* geometric figures. The eight constructions presented in this section underlie much of what will be done in later chapters.

Straightedge and compass constructions involve repeatedly applying two moves according to these instructions: Given two points P and Q, we can

- Use a straightedge to draw the segment $\overline{PQ}$.
  (Abbreviation: **Draw $\overline{PQ}$.**)

- Use a compass to draw the circle with center P and radius PQ.
  (Abbreviation: **Draw circle: center P, radius PQ.**)

These moves can be used to create new points, which we can label before proceeding (Abbreviation: **Mark point C where...**). In carrying out a compass move, we usually draw only the relevant part of the circle needed for the construction.

For a first example, imagine that someone gives you a piece of paper with a line segment $\overline{AB}$ drawn on it. Your task is to draw an equilateral triangle that has $\overline{AB}$ as one side.

CONSTRUCTION 1. *Construct an equilateral triangle with a given side $\overline{AB}$.*

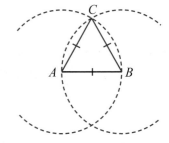

- Draw circle: center A, radius AB.

- Draw circle: center B, radius AB.

- These circles intersect at two points. Mark one of them C.

- Draw $\overline{AC}$ and $\overline{BC}$.

$\triangle ABC$ is an equilateral because all three sides have equal length.

Recall that "bisecting an angle" means drawing a ray that splits the angle into two congruent adjacent angles.

CONSTRUCTION 2. *Bisect a given angle with vertex A.*

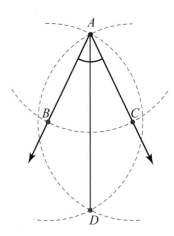

- Draw circle: center A, any radius. Mark points B and C where the circle intersects the sides of the angle.

- Draw circle: center B, radius AB.

- Draw circle: center C, radius AC.

- These circles intersect at A and at another point, D.

- Draw $\overline{AD}$.

Why is this a bisector? K-8 teachers can give a simple explanation: line $\overline{AD}$ is a line of symmetry, so the two halves of $\angle A$ have equal measure.

CONSTRUCTION 3. *Bisect a given segment $\overline{AB}$.*

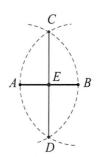

- Draw circle: center at A, radius AB.

- Draw circle: center B, radius AB. Mark the points C and D where the circles intersect.

- Draw $\overline{CD}$ and mark the point E where it intersects $\overline{AB}$.

By symmetry, E is the midpoint of $\overline{AB}$ and $\overline{CD}$ is perpendicular to $\overline{AB}$. Line $\overline{CD}$ is called the *perpendicular bisector* of segment $\overline{AB}$.

The next construction is the key to building squares and rectangles. The steps are almost the same steps as in the previous construction.

CONSTRUCTION 4. *Given a point A on a line L, construct the line perpendicular to L at A.*

- Draw circle: center A, any radius > 0. Mark points B and C where the circle intersects line L.

- Using Construction 1, construct an equilateral triangle $\triangle BCD$.

- Draw $\overline{AD}$.

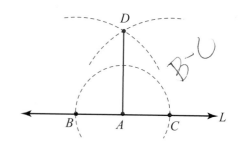

The next construction is similar, but with the given point A *not* on the given line.

CONSTRUCTION 5. *Given a point A not on a line L, construct the line perpendicular to line L passing through A.*

- Mark some point B on L.

- Draw circle: center A, radius AB. This intersects L at B and at another point C.

- Draw circle: center B, radius AB and circle: center C radius AB. These intersect at A and at another point D.

- Draw $\overline{AD}$.

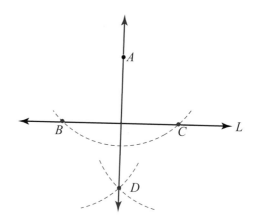

Alternatively, we can draw perpendicular lines using a set square, as we did in Section 2.1. Constructions 4 and 5 show that a set square, while convenient, is not necessary—anything done with the set square can also be done with a compass and straightedge, albeit with more steps.

One can also use a compass and a straightedge to make copies of a given triangle.

CONSTRUCTION 6. *Copy a triangle △ABC onto a specified side of a given ray* $\overrightarrow{DE}$.

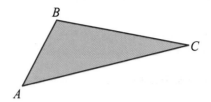

- Draw circle C_1: center D, radius AB. Mark F where the circle intersects ray $\overrightarrow{DE}$.

- Draw circle C_2: center D, radius AC.

- Draw circle C_3: center F, radius BC. Mark G at the intersection of circles C_2 and C_3 on the desired side of $\overleftrightarrow{DE}$.

- Draw segments $\overline{DG}$ and $\overline{FG}$.

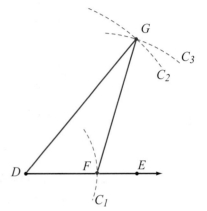

CONSTRUCTION 7. *Copy a given angle onto a given ray.*

This construction is Problem 7 in the homework for this section. The idea is to make the given angle part of a triangle, then duplicate the triangle using Construction 6.

Construction problems can often be solved in several ways. Here is an example.

CONSTRUCTION 8. *Construct the line parallel to a given line L through a given point A.*

This construction was done in Section 2.1 using a set square and straightedge to create the picture on the right. Alternatively, one can create the same picture using only a straightedge and a compass by combining Constructions 4 and 5. But it is simpler to proceed as follows.

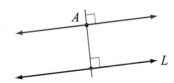

- Choose a point on L and label it B.

- Draw circle C_1: center A, radius AB. This intersects L at B and at another point C.

- Draw circle C_2: center A, radius BC.

- Draw circle C_3: center C, radius AB. This intersects C_2 at a point D.

- Draw $\overleftrightarrow{AD}$.

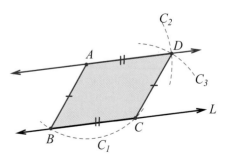

Then *ABCD* is a parallelogram because its opposite sides have equal length (as will be proved in Chapter 4).

EXERCISE 5.1. *Construction 8 can be shortened: only two circles are needed. Write down such a shortened construction.*

Homework Set 9

Build your own straightedge by folding a piece of construction paper in half twice. Use this tool (not a ruler!) in Problems 1 and 2. After that, you may use your ruler as a straightedge.

1. On your HW paper, mark two points *A* and *B* about 2 inches apart. Then do these steps:
   - Draw $\overline{AB}$. There is nothing more you can do with your straightedge, so pick up your compass.
   - With the information you have — just two points — you can draw only two circles. Draw them and mark all points of intersection.
   - There is nothing more you can do with your compass, so pick up your straightedge. Draw all the lines that your marked points determine.

   Which of the constructions described in this section can you see within your final drawing?

2. On your HW paper, draw a line *L* and mark a point *P* on that line. Using a straightedge and compass, follow the steps of Construction 4 of this section to draw a line through *P* perpendicular to *L*.

3. On your HW paper, draw a line *L* and mark a point *P* **not** on that line. Using a straightedge and compass, follow the steps of Construction 5 of this section to draw a line through *P* perpendicular to *L*.

4. a) Using straightedge and protractor, draw a 63° angle.
   b) Bisect your angle using straightedge and compass (no protractor!).

5. a) Using ruler and protractor, draw $\triangle PQR$ with $PQ = 6$ cm, $\angle P = 60°$ and $\angle Q = 50°$.
   b) Using straightedge and compass (no protractor!), draw a second copy of your triangle.

6. Using straightedge and compass:
   a) Copy segment $\overline{AB}$ below onto your HW paper.
   b) Construct an isosceles triangle with base $\overline{AB}$ whose legs are congruent to segment $\overline{CD}$.
   c) List your steps using the format used to describe constructions in this section.

7. In this problem you will supply the details of Construction 7.
   a) Draw an angle and label its vertex *A*. Then, elsewhere, draw a ray $\overrightarrow{PQ}$.
   b) Using straightedge and compass, construct ray $\overrightarrow{PR}$ so that $\angle QPR$ has the same measure as your angle with vertex *A*. (Experiment on scrap paper until you see what to do.)
   c) List your steps using the format used to describe constructions in this section.

8. On a blank sheet of paper, mark two points *A* and *C* with $AC = 11$ cm. Draw two circles with radius 6 cm: one with center *A* and one with center *C*. Complete your figure into a rhombus *ABCD*. Using scissors, cut out your rhombus and use it to answer the following questions:
   a) Name two lines of symmetry.
   b) Describe a folding exercise that shows these symmetries.
   c) Are the diagonals perpendicular? Do they bisect one another? Use folding and symmetry to explain your answer.

9. (*Study the Textbook!*) Read pages 276-277 of NEM 1. Then:
   a) Do Problem 1 on page 278 (using ruler, compass and set square).
   b) Is the figure a rectangle? Why?
   c) What fact about such figures does this suggest?

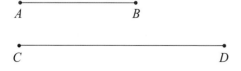

CHAPTER 3

Finding Unknown Angles

Geometry becomes more interesting when students start using geometric facts to find unknown lengths and angles. During this stage, roughly grades 5-8, students work on "unknown angle problems". These problems are learning bonanzas. They initiate students in the art of deductive reasoning, solidify their understanding of geometry and measurement, and help introduce algebra.

You have already solved some unknown angle problems and seen how they are integrated into the Primary Math curriculum in grades 5 and 6. This chapter examines how unknown angle problems are used to develop geometry in grades 6 and 7.

From a teaching perspective, unknown angle problems are not just part of the geometry curriculum, they *are* the curriculum in grades 5-8; everything else is secondary. In these grades, teachers and textbooks introduce facts about angles within triangles and polygons, about parallel lines, about congruent and similar figures, and about circles. These are not simply facts to memorize: understanding emerges as students use them to solve problems. Thus teaching centers on *solving problems*.

Unknown angle problems are superbly suited for this purpose. Solutions require several steps, each applying a known fact to the given figure. As students do these problems the geometric facts spring to life; these facts become friends that can be called upon to help solve problems. Unknown angle problems are also enormous fun!

3.1 Unknown Angle Problems

An unknown angle problem is a puzzle consisting of a figure with the measures of some sides and angles given and with one angle — the unknown angle — marked with a letter. The student's task is to find the measure of the unknown angle by applying basic geometric facts. Beginning exercises require only rudimentary facts, such as the fact that angles around a point add to 360°. As new geometric facts are introduced, they are added to the list of facts that are available as tools to solve unknown angle problems. As more knowledge is integrated, the problems become more challenging and more interesting.

This section examines the role of unknown angle problems in the Primary Math and New Elementary Math textbooks for grades 5-7. It includes a list of the geometric facts learned during this stage and a format for presenting "Teacher's Solutions" to unknown angle problems. You will be asked to use this format for many homework problems.

Many elementary textbooks, including the Primary Math books, introduce new concepts using the following specific process.

Teaching sequence for introducing geometric facts

1. Review background knowledge and introduce any new terms needed.

2. Introduce the fact by an activity (measuring, folding, or cutting-and-rearranging) that serves to *clarify what the fact says* and *convince students that it is true*.

3. Summarize by stating the geometric fact in simple clear language.

4. Have students solve dozens of unknown angle problems:

   a) simple problems using the fact alone,

   b) multi-step problems using the fact alone,

   c) multi-step problems combining the fact with previously-learned facts.

Step 3 takes only a few minutes, but it is the teacher's most important input. In geometry, words have precise meanings; students' success depends on knowing definitions and knowing how to apply them. One can even argue that geometry is included in the K-12 curriculum to teach students that *giving words precise meaning fosters clear thinking*. This lesson is applicable to all subjects.

After these preliminaries, the fun begins as students solve increasingly challenging problems (Step 4). As always in mathematics, the real learning occurs as students solve problems.

Geometry Facts — First List

As you have seen in homework problems, the basic facts about angles, triangles and quadrilaterals are presented in Primary Mathematics 5A and 5B. Below is a list of the facts learned at that stage. Each has a simple abbreviation. You will be expected to be consistent in using these abbreviations in your homework solutions.

The list of facts is built around three exercises. These questions ask you to observe how these facts are justified at the grade 5 level (using folding, cutting, and measuring exercises) and to observe the type of problems students are asked to solve.

EXERCISE 1.1 (Angle Facts). *The following three facts are introduced on pages 85–88 of Primary Mathematics 5A. How are these facts justified?*

Vertical angles have equal measure.
(Abbreviation: **vert. ∠s.**)

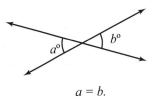

$a = b.$

The sum of adjacent angles on a straight
line is 180°.   (Abbreviation: **∠s on a line**.)

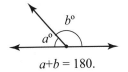

$a + b = 180.$

The sum of adjacent angles around a point is 360°.
(Abbreviation: **∠s at a pt.**)

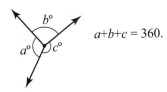

$a + b + c = 360.$

EXERCISE 1.2 (Triangle Facts). *The following five triangle facts are introduced on pages 57–64 in Primary Mathematics 5B. Locate the statement of each in your 5B book. What activity is used to justify the first fact? What wording is used for the fourth one?*

The angle sum of any triangle is 180°.
(Abbreviation: **∠ sum of △**)

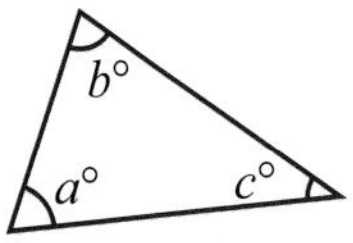

$a + b + c = 180.$

When one angle of a triangle is a right angle,
the other two angles add up to 90°.

(Abbreviation: **∠ sum of rt. △.**)

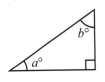

$a + b = 90.$

The exterior angle of a triangle is equal to
the sum of the interior opposite angles.

(Abbreviation: **ext. ∠ of △.**)

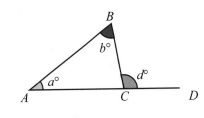

$d = a + b.$

Base angles of an isosceles triangle are equal.

(Abbreviation: **base ∠s of isos. Δ.**)

$a = b$

Each interior angle of an equilateral triangle is 60°.

(Abbreviation: **equilat. Δ.**)

EXERCISE 1.3 (Quadrilateral Facts). *The next section of Primary Math 5B (pages 68–71) introduces two facts about 4-sided figures. Study the folding and cutting exercises given on page 70. How would you use these exercises in your class?*

Opposite angles in a parallelogram are equal.

(Abbreviation: **opp. ∠s //-ogram.**)

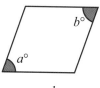

$a = b.$

Interior angles between two parallel sides in a trapezoid (or a parallelogram) are supplementary.

(Abbreviation: **int. ∠s, $\overline{BC} \parallel \overline{AD}$.**)

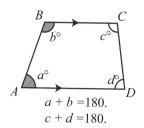

$a + b = 180.$
$c + d = 180.$

The "Teacher's Solution" Format for Unknown Angle Problems

Teachers are obliged to present detailed solutions to problems for the benefit of their students. The teacher's solutions must meet a different standard than the students' solutions. Both teachers and students are expected to get the reasoning and the answer correct. But teacher-presented solutions must also communicate the thought process as clearly as possible.

In this book, solutions that meet this high standard are called **Teacher's Solutions**. You will frequently be asked to write such Teacher's Solutions in homework. If you are unsure how to do this, *look in the textbooks*: almost every solution presented in the Primary Math books, and all of the "Worked Examples" in the New Elementary Mathematics book, are Teacher's Solutions.

You are already familiar with one type of Teacher's Solution — bar diagrams. Bar diagrams are extraordinarily useful for communicating ideas about arithmetic. Teachers need similar devices for communicating geometric ideas. As a start, in this chapter you will be writing Teacher's Solutions for unknown angle problems. Here is a simple example.

EXAMPLE 1.4. *The figure shows angles around a point. Find the value of x.*

Teacher's Solution to an Unknown Angle Problem

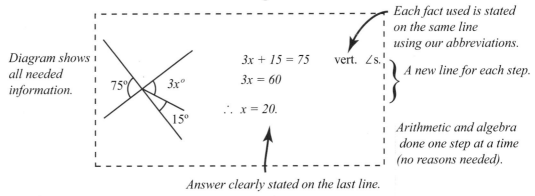

Diagram shows all needed information.

Each fact used is stated on the same line using our abbreviations.

$3x + 15 = 75$ vert. ∠s.

A new line for each step.

$3x = 60$

$\therefore x = 20.$

Arithmetic and algebra done one step at a time (no reasons needed).

Answer clearly stated on the last line.

This solution is short and clear, yet displays all the reasoning. It always begins with a picture showing all points, lines, and angles used in the solution, and it always ends with a clear answer to the question asked.

Notice what happens with the degree signs. The angles in the picture have degree signs, so 75, 15 and $3x$ are all numbers. Thus we can drop the degree signs in the equations. This saves work and makes the solution clearer. Degree signs are handled in the same way in the next two examples.

EXAMPLE 1.5. *The figure shows a parallelogram. Find the value of x.*

Teacher's Solution:

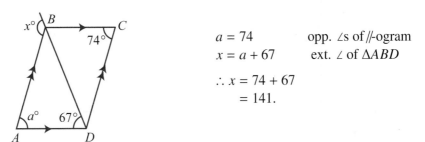

$a = 74$ opp. ∠s of //-ogram

$x = a + 67$ ext. ∠ of $\triangle ABD$

$\therefore x = 74 + 67$

$\quad = 141.$

EXAMPLE 1.6. *Find the values of a and b in the following figure.*

Teacher's Solution:

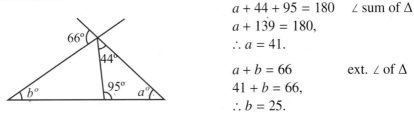

$a + 44 + 95 = 180$ ∠ sum of $\triangle$

$a + 139 = 180,$

$\therefore a = 41.$

$a + b = 66$ ext. ∠ of $\triangle$

$41 + b = 66,$

$\therefore b = 25.$

Elementary students are not usually asked to record reasons in the manner done in these examples. But in the New Elementary Mathematics textbook, middle school students are expected to present solutions exactly as above — middle school students use the same format as elementary school teachers!

This Teacher's Solution format is used by

- *Teachers* in elementary school,

- *Teachers and students* in middle school.

Unknown angle problems in grades 5-7 also help introduce algebra. These geometry problems expose students to the idea of using letters to stand for numbers (notice that the whole alphabet, not just x and y, are used!). They often require solving simple linear equations, as you see in Example 1.4. This is a sneaky trick: giving students practice in algebra as they do geometry. Solving for unknown angles also gives students a visual way to understand what it means to "solve for x" and appreciate why one would want to.

Homework Set 10

1. (*Study the Textbook!*) Give one-sentence answers to Exercises 1.1, 1.2, and 1.3 in this section.

2. (*Study the Textbook!*) Turn to page 87 of Primary Math 5A.

   - Do all of the problems on pages 87 and 88. Write your answers as a single list of numbers, separated by commas, but *not* labeled by the problem numbers.

   - Note the variation: on pages 87 and 88, how many different letters are used to stand for numbers?

3. On page 109 of Primary Math 6B, answer Problems 35, 36, and 37.

4. Answer Problem 2 on page 264 of NEM1. Show your reasoning.

5. For Problem 3 on page 264 of NEM 1, write Teacher's Solutions to parts b, d, e, g, and j.

6. For Problem 4 on the next page (page 265) write Teacher's Solutions to parts b, c, f and g.

7. (*Study the Textbook!*) Compare the grade 6 and grade 7 problems you did in this HW Set. Name two new features required in solving the grade 7 problems that are not present in the grade 6 problems.

3.2 Finding Angles Using Parallel Lines

After completing Primary Mathematics 5 and 6, students enter grade 7 with two years' experience solving unknown angle problems. They understand that geometry is a game in which one uses a few simple facts to find relations among the lengths and angles in figures. The grade 7 textbook (New Elementary Mathematics 1) revisits the material learned earlier, putting it in a condensed, structured form. It then moves on to new ideas.

The revision begins with lines and angles (Chapter 9 of NEM1). Folding and measuring exercises are no longer primary; the discussion is built on facts about parallel lines and congruent triangles, and is broadened to include area. The transition is subtle: the spirit of the subject is unchanged and student work remains focused on solving short geometric puzzles.

This section describes the basic facts about parallel lines. It ends with discussions of two sources of student confusion: the distinction between a statement and its converse, and the technique of drawing auxiliary lines.

Transversals and Parallel Lines

In the figure below, T is a *transversal* to the lines L and M. More precisely: Given a pair of lines L and M in a plane, a third line T is a **transversal** if it intersects L at a single point P and intersects M in a different point Q.

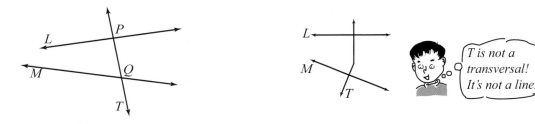

A transversal forms eight angles with the two lines. Pairs of angles are named according to their relative positions. Angles on the same side of the transversal and on the same side of the lines are called **corresponding angles**. Four pairs of corresponding angles are shown below.

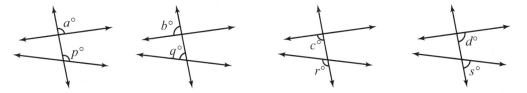

The key fact about parallel lines is that *when a transversal intersects parallel lines, corresponding angles are equal.* Here is an activity introducing the idea.

A sheet of lined paper has many parallel lines.
Draw a slanted line.
Compare the corresponding angles.
Are they equal?

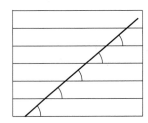

This lined paper activity provides experimental evidence, but it is not the kind of logical argument required in geometry. Instead, the value of the activity is psychological: it serves to make the stated fact clear and believable to students.

> If a transversal intersects two parallel lines, then corresponding angles are equal, i.e.,
>
> if $\overline{AB} \parallel \overline{CD}$, then $a = p$.
>
> (Abbreviation: **corr. ∠s, $\overline{AB} \parallel \overline{CD}$.**)

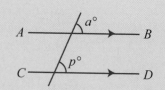

In the blue box, the same fact is stated three times: first in words, then as a labeled picture, and then again as an abbreviation. This presentation gives students three ways to understand and remember the fact.

Notice that the abbreviation says "corr. ∠s" and *then identifies which pair of parallel lines we are using.* Asking students to name the parallel lines is important for clarity. It reminds them that this fact requires parallel lines. It is also a courtesy to the teacher who is trying to follow the student's reasoning.

The statement in the box above has a partner called its converse. For the converse, we consider a transversal intersecting two lines that are not necessarily parallel. We then measure corresponding angles. If these are equal, then we can conclude that the lines are parallel.

> If $a = p$, then $\overline{AB} \parallel \overline{CD}$.
>
> (Abbreviation: **corr. ∠s converse.**)

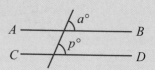

Recall the principle that when two lines cross, each of the angles formed determines the other three. The above fact gives a similar principle about the eight angles formed by a transversal that intersects two parallel lines: *any one angle determines all 8.* In fact, among the eight angles, four have the same measure as the given angle, and the other four have the supplementary measure.

EXAMPLE 2.1. *In the figure below, $\overline{AB} \parallel \overline{CD}$. Find $b, c, d, p, q, r,$ and s.*

Teacher's Solution:

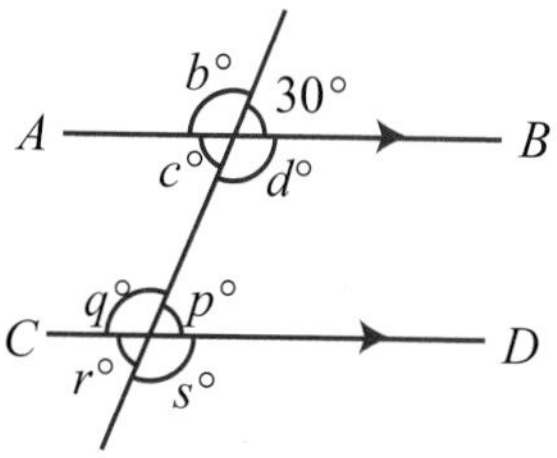

$$30 + b = 180, \quad \text{∠s on a line}$$
$$b = 150.$$

$$\left. \begin{array}{l} c = 30 \\ d = 150 \end{array} \right\} \quad \text{vert. ∠s.}$$

$$\left. \begin{array}{l} p = 30 \\ q = 150 \\ r = 30 \\ s = 150 \end{array} \right\} \quad \text{corr. ∠s, } \overline{AB} \parallel \overline{CD}.$$

The reasoning in Example 2.1 combines corresponding angles with familiar facts about vertical and supplementary angles. To avoid having to determine all eight angles each time, it is convenient to restate the "corresponding angles are equal" fact in two ways. Each restatement begins by naming a type of angle pair.

First Restatement: Two angles are a pair of **interior angles along a transversal** if they are between the two lines and on the same side of a transversal.

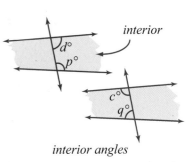

interior

interior angles

One sees that *if the lines are parallel, the interior angles are supplementary*. The pictures below show two classroom explanations: one using corresponding angles, the other using the grade 5 fact about adjacent interior angles in a parallelogram. In contrast, in the pictures on the right, the lines are not parallel and the interior angles are not supplementary.

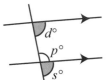

The shaded angles are equal.
$p+s=180$.
Therefore $p+d=180$.

Draw a line to make a parallelogram.
Then $p+d=180$.

If a transversal intersects two parallel lines, then the interior angles on the same side of the transversal are supplementary, i.e.,

if $\overline{AB} \parallel \overline{CD}$, then $d + p = 180$.

(Abbreviation: **int. ∠s, $\overline{AB} \parallel \overline{CD}$** .)

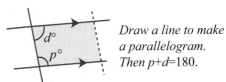

Conversely, if $d + p = 180$, then $\overline{AB} \parallel \overline{CD}$.

(Abbreviation: **int. ∠s converse.**)

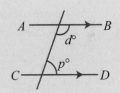

Second Restatement: Pairs of angles on the opposite sides of a transversal are called **alternate angles**. The left-hand pictures below show two pairs of alternate angles. The example on the right shows why, when a transversal intersects parallel lines, alternate interior angles are equal.

In the figure, AB//CD. Find p.

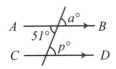

alternate
interior angles

alternate
exterior angles

$a = 51$ vert. ∠s,
$p = 51$ corr. ∠s, $\overline{AB} \parallel \overline{CD}$.

If a transversal intersects two parallel lines, then alternate interior angles are equal, i.e.,

if $\overline{AB} \parallel \overline{CD}$, then $c = p$.

(Abbreviation: **alt. ∠s, $\overline{AB} \parallel \overline{CD}$** .)

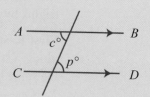

Conversely, if $c = p$, then $\overline{AB} \parallel \overline{CD}$.

(Abbreviation: **alt. ∠s converse.**)

EXERCISE 2.2. *Read Class Activity 4 (pages 245-246) of New Elementary Mathematics 1. What terms are introduced in this activity? On page 246, match the statements in the blue box with the statements in the blue boxes above.*

Converses

Each fact in this section is paired with its converse. All students should be able to distinguish a statement from its converse. The distinction is a simple point of logic that arises in many contexts, but is rarely taught outside of geometry. A complete explanation requires only a few sentences and some examples.

Every "if...then" statement has a **converse**. The converse of the statement "If A is true then B is true" is the statement obtained by reversing the roles of A and B, namely "If B is true then A is true". Here are three simple examples.

Statement: If an animal is a woman then it is human. (TRUE)
Converse: If an animal is human then it is a woman. (FALSE)

Statement: If two angles are vertically opposite, then they have equal measure. (TRUE)
Converse: If two angles have equal measure, then they are vertically opposite. (FALSE)

Statement: If a triangle is isosceles then it has two equal sides. (TRUE)
Converse: If a triangle has two equal sides then it is isosceles. (TRUE)

In the first two cases, the statement is true but its converse is false. In the third case, both the statement and its converse are true. Thus one should not confuse a statement with its converse. Knowing that one is true tells us nothing about the other.

The blue boxes in this section give three statements about parallel lines, each paired with its converse. For all three facts, both the statement and its converse are true.

Auxiliary Lines

Some geometry problems can be solved easily after modifying the given figure. If you are stuck, it may help to extend an existing line or to add a new line; both are called *auxiliary lines*. You can also give letter names to angles not named in the original figure.

Hint: Look for an auxiliary line that *forms a new triangle*, or one that *is parallel or perpendicular to an existing line*.

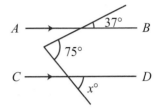

EXAMPLE 2.3. *In the figure,* $\overline{AB} \parallel \overline{CD}$. *Find the value of x.*

Below are three student solutions. Each uses an auxiliary line (the dotted line).

a)
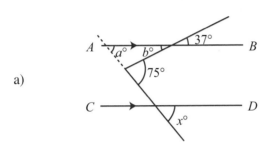

$a = x,$ corr. ∠s, $\overline{AB} \parallel \overline{CD},$
$b = 37,$ vert. ∠s,
$a + b = 75,$ ext. ∠s of a Δ,
$x + 37 = 75,$
$\therefore x = 38.$

b)
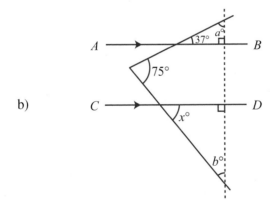

$a + 37 = 90,$ ∠ sum of rt. Δ,
$\therefore a = 53.$

$a + b + 75 = 180,$ ∠ sum of Δ,
$53 + b + 75 = 180,$
$b + 128 = 180,$
$\therefore b = 52.$

$x + 52 = 90,$ ∠ sum of rt. Δ,
$\therefore x = 38.$

c)
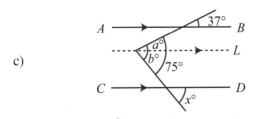

$a = 37,$ corr. ∠s, $\overline{AB} \parallel L.$

$37 + b = 75,$ ∠s add,
$\therefore b = 38.$

$\therefore x = 38,$ corr. ∠s, $L \parallel \overline{DC}.$

Caution: In c), the line L was draw parallel to $\overline{AB}$. *It does not bisect the center angle.* (One could draw the actual angle bisector, but then it would not be parallel to $\overline{AB}$ or $\overline{CD}$).

In many figures there are several possibilities for auxiliary lines and it may not be immediately clear which is best. Often it doesn't matter: many problems can be solved in several ways, using different auxiliary lines. Some approaches may be more efficient than others. For the solutions in Example 2.3, the auxiliary line in b) leads to a complicated solution, while the one in c) yields a short efficient solution.

The existence of different routes to the same conclusion is one of the joys of geometry. As a teacher, it is important to give your students opportunities to compare approaches. When solving unknown angle problems, students can learn just as much from seeing a second and a third solution as they can from the first. There is pleasure in watching different approaches unfold and end with exactly the same conclusion. Students, working alone or in small groups, can enjoy a friendly competition to come up with the simplest solution, and can enjoy showing off their solutions to the class.

Homework Set 11

1. Write the converse to the following statements. State whether the converse is true or false.

    a) If a baby is hungry, then it cries.

    b) If it rained, the grass is wet.

    c) If a triangle has 3 congruent sides, then it has 3 congruent angles.

2. Convert to an "if-then" statement, then give the converse:

    a) All tall men play basketball.

    b) An angle measuring less than 90° is acute.

    c) A square is a rhombus.

Open NEM1 to page 247. Carefully read the solution to parts (a) and (b) of Worked Example 4. Notice that these follow the Teacher's Solution format, and that the solutions require

- *adding a new line to the figure.*

- *giving letter names to some angles that are not present or not named in the original figure.*

3. Write a Teacher's Solution for Problem 2 on page 248. Your first line should be "Draw line $L \parallel$ to $\overline{BA}$".

4. Answer Problem 7 on page 249. Include a reason for each pair of parallel lines.

5. Teacher's Solutions for parts (a) through (f) on page 250. Be sure to include a picture for each.

6. Find x for Problems (g) through (j) on the same page (no need for a Teacher's Solution).

7. On page 251, write Teacher's Solutions to Problems 9a, 9b and 10d.

    Look over pages 262–263 of NEM1. These quickly review the triangle facts students learned in grade 5 and give examples — in Teacher's Solution format — that use these facts to solve multi-step unknown angle problems.

8. On page 264-265, write Teacher's Solutions to Problems 3f, 4d, 4i, 4j, 4m, 4n and 4p.

9. Give a Teacher's Solution to Problem 1 on page 286 of NEM1.

3.3 Angles of a Polygon

Children first encounter polygons in pre-school or kindergarten when they learn to name triangles, squares, rectangles, pentagons, etc. Polygons remain central objects of study throughout the K-12 geometry curriculum. Curiously, as we will explain, the word "polygon" has two different meanings in school mathematics, and the meaning shifts depending on context.

The main focus of this section is on finding the sum of the interior and exterior angles of an *n*-sided polygon, and applying the results. This topic is included in most middle school curricula. It is a simple example of "building new facts from known ones", and the facts learned can be used to solve interesting unknown angle problems. Here, for the first time, students learn to make statements about n-sided polygons without specifying the number n. It is an ideal place in the curriculum for discussing the distinction between inductive and deductive reasoning.

In the early grades, polygons are usually regarded as regions in the plane whose boundary is a union of straight segments. Students are given the school definition below, and lots of examples (as described in Section 2.2). In the school definition, polygons have interiors, so the meaning of "interior angles" is clear.

School Definition: A region enclosed by 3 straight segments is a triangle. A region enclosed by n straight segments is an n-sided **polygon**.

Children also learn to use the correct mathematical definition, in which a polygon is a collection of line segments. The definition is based on the same idea as connect-the-dots puzzles: draw a segment from the first point to the second, from the second to the third, etc., and end by connecting the last to the first point, thereby "closing up" the figure. The definition is clearest when given in two parts.

DEFINITION 3.1. *Given $n \geq 3$ points P_1, P_2, ..., P_n, all different, the corresponding closed polygonal path is the collection of segments $\overline{P_1P_2}$, $\overline{P_2P_3}$, ..., $\overline{P_nP_1}$. The points are called the vertices and the segments are called the sides of the polygonal path.*

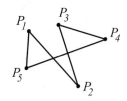

a closed polygonal path

DEFINITION 3.2. *An n-sided polygon or n-gon is a closed polygonal path in a plane with $n \geq 3$ vertices such that*

> *(i) the sides intersect only at their endpoints and*

> *(ii) no adjacent sides are collinear.*

Conditions (i) and (ii) may seem awkward, but they are needed to make this definition compatible with the school definition above.

polygon

Polygons separate the plane into two regions, the interior and the exterior. A polygon together with its interior is called a **polygonal region**; the school definition is actually the definition of a polygonal region. Condition (ii) ensures that the count of sides and vertices is the same as the count obtained from the school definition.

polygonal region

EXERCISE 3.3. *Which of the figures below is a polygon? Which violates the requirement that the vertices be distinct? Is figure D a triangle or a quadrilateral?*

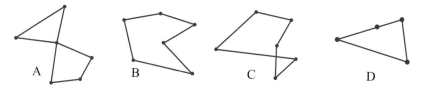

Definition 3.2 is different from the school definition, yet the two coexist through elementary and middle school. Sometimes the word "polygon" refers to a union of segments, and sometimes it means a region. In most textbooks, including the always-careful Primary Mathematics and New Elementary Mathematics books, the meaning of words like "triangle", "rectangle" and "polygon" shifts according to the topic being covered.

- When discussing area, "polygons" are regions.

- When finding unknown angles, polygons are unions of segments.

- For some topics, the distinction is not important. One example is the topic on the next page: the sum of interior angles.

Teachers should be alert to possible confusion. When clarity is needed, both teachers and students should speak of "triangular regions" and "polygonal regions". This long-winded terminology becomes tiresome in studying topics, such as area, where one is *always* considering regions. In such situations, it is fine to say "triangle" and "quadrilateral" instead of "triangular region" and "quadrilateral region" provided that all students are aware that the words refer to regions.

The parts of a polygon are named using terms students learned when studying triangles and quadrilaterals: vertex, side, diagonal, interior angle, and exterior angle. Look at page 271 in New Elementary Mathematics 1 to see how the terms (*vertex, side, diagonal, interior angle,* and *exterior angle*) are reviewed for 7th grade students simply by drawing a single picture.

Two other terms frequently enter discussions of polygons. The first gives a name to the most commonly-seen examples of polygons.

DEFINITION 3.4. *A polygon is **regular** if (i) all sides have equal length, and (ii) all angles have equal measure.*

Most children are familiar with the regular polygons below. In fact, teachers should be sure that students realize that words like "pentagon" do not automatically refer to a regular pentagon.

equilateral triangle

square

regular pentagon

regular hexagon

EXERCISE 3.5. *A regular pentagon has rotational symmetry. What is an angle of rotation for this symmetry?*

A polygon is **convex** if, for any two points P and Q in the interior of the polygon, the segment $\overline{PQ}$ lies completely in the interior of the polygon. Any polygon with an interior angle greater than $180°$ is not convex.

convex　　　*not convex*

Sum of the Interior Angles

We already know that the sum of the interior angles of a triangle is $180°$ ("one straight angle"). One can ask the analogous question for polygons: What is the sum of the interior angles of an n-sided polygon? This question is a standard middle school topic, and it has an elegant answer.

As a first step, notice that any quadrilateral has a diagonal that splits its interior into two triangles. Hence the angle sum of a quadrilateral is "two straight angles", which is $360°$.

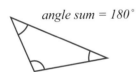
angle sum = 180°

180° in top triangle
180° in bottom triangle
total: 360°

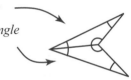

EXERCISE 3.6. *Find the sum of the interior angles of a pentagon by splitting it into triangles.*

One can continue on to 6-gons, 7-gons, and so forth, until a pattern emerges. This is the approach taken in New Elementary Mathematics 1 on page 272. It is an example of inductive reasoning. In general, **inductive reasoning** is the type of reasoning in which one uses a limited number of cases to draw a conclusion or make a prediction. Inductive reasoning supports a conclusion, but does not guarantee that it is correct because not all cases have been examined.

Geometry is based on **deductive reasoning** — reasoning in which a conclusion follows logically from previously known facts. For the case of the angle sum of an n-gon, an argument using deductive reasoning gives the definitive answer for all n. Here are two deductive arguments for showing the sum of interior angles in an n-gon is $180(n-2)$. In both, we assume that the polygon is convex.

Vertex Method. Choose one vertex. Draw lines from that vertex to each of the other vertices, thereby decomposing the n-gon into triangles. Darken the opposite side (with respect to the vertex) of each triangle to help count triangles.

The n-gon has n-2 dark sides.

Each triangle has 1 dark side.

∴ there are n-2 triangles, so

Sum of interior angles = 180×(n-2).

2 sides not dark.

Interior Point Method. Choose a point in the interior. Draw lines from that interior point to every vertex, thereby decomposing the *n*-gon into *n* triangles.

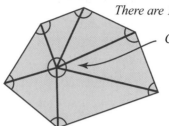

There are 180° in each triangle.

Center angles total 360°.

The remaining angles form the interior angles of the polygon.

$\therefore$ *Sum of interior angles* $= 180 \times n - 360$
$= 180 \times (n\text{-}2).$

The case of non-convex polygons is more complicated. But by drawing pictures like the one below, you should be able to convince yourself that every non-convex polygonal region with *n* sides can be partitioned into (*n* − 2) triangular regions — in fact there are often many ways of doing this.

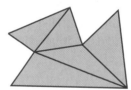 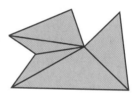

A 7-gon decomposed into 5 triangles (in two different ways).

The sum of the interior angles of an *n*-gon is 180(*n* − 2) degrees.

(Abbreviation: ∠ **sum of *n*-gon.**)

EXERCISE 3.7. *Do Problem 1 in Class Activity 3 of NEM1 on page 272.*
   a) What do you conclude about the sum of interior angles of an n-sided polygon?
   b) Is this activity an example of building a fact inductively or deductively?

Sum of the Exterior Angles

At each vertex of a convex polygon there is an interior angle and also two exterior angles. There is a formula for the sum of the exterior angles that is analogous to the one for interior angles, but simpler. Here are three classroom explanations.

Racetrack Method. Imagine the polygon as a racetrack. A car starts on one side and moves around the track counter-clockwise. At the first vertex it turns left through an angle equal to the exterior angle at that vertex. When it gets to the second vertex it turns again, by an amount equal to the second exterior angle. When the car returns to its starting point it has completed one full turn — 360 degrees. Thus the sum of the exterior angles of the polygon is 360°.

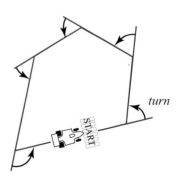

turn

Zoom-out Method. Moving around the polygon in one direction, extend each side to a ray. Then "zoom-out", looking at the polygon from farther and farther away. From 1000 miles away, the figure looks like a point and the exterior angles clearly add to 360°.

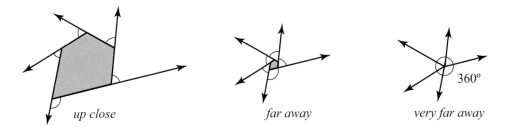

up close   *far away*   *very far away*

Base Point Method. Fix a point P and draw segments at P parallel to the sides of the polygon as shown. This creates angles congruent to the exterior angles of the polygon whose sum is 360°.

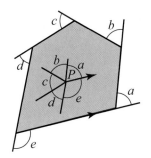

The sum of the exterior angles, one at each vertex, of a convex polygon is 360°.

(Abbreviation: **ext. ∠s of polygon.**)

EXERCISE 3.8. *In the above "Base Point Method" picture, why are the two angles labeled a congruent to each other?*

Recall that there are two exterior angles at each vertex. In the above explanations, the exterior angles were chosen in a consistent manner (the ones that arise by "turning left" at each vertex). But there is no need to be consistent: because the two exterior angles at each vertex are congruent, we can arbitrarily choose one external angle at each vertex and still have a sum of 360°.

EXAMPLE 3.9. *What is the measure of each interior angle of a regular 9-gon?*

Teacher's Solution:

Sum of exterior angles: 360,
Each exterior angle: 360÷9 = 40,
Each interior angle: 180-40=140.

∴ *Each interior angle of a regular 9-gon is 140°.*

In your homework, you will consider whether the sum of the exterior angles is 360° for polygons that are not convex.

Which is Taught First?

For convex polygons, we now have a number of ways of calculating the two numbers:

$$I = \text{sum of the interior angles,}$$

$$E = \text{sum of the exterior angles.}$$

In fact, the numbers I and E are related. At each vertex there is an interior and an exterior angle that, together, make a straight angle. Adding up the angles associated with each of the n vertices of an n-gon shows that

$$I + E = n \text{ straight angles} = 180n.$$

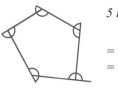

5 interior angles
+ 5 exterior angles
= 5 straight angles
= 5 × 180°.

This formula relates I and E: if we already know I we can use it to find E, and if we already know E we can use it to find I. For example, one might use the racetrack method to find that $E = 360°$; the above relation then gives

$$I = 180n - 360 = 180(n - 2).$$

Some textbooks first focus on the sum of the interior angles, while others start with the sum of the exterior angles. Others give separate discussions, as if these were two unrelated facts. All of these approaches are correct, but teachers and students should be aware that the sum formulas for interior and exterior angles are two sides of the same coin.

Homework Set 12

1. Read Problem 1 of Class Activity 3 on page 272 of NEM1. Fill in the table in the book (but not in your homework). What do you obtain for the sum of the angles of an n-gon? Is this an example of inductive or deductive reasoning?

2. (*Study the textbook!*) Read pages 270-274 in NEM 1. Do Problems 1-11 on pages 274-5.

3. Continuing, do parts (a), (b) and (c) of Problem 12. *Hint:* For (b), mark the angles a, b, etc. and then express other angles in the figure in terms of these. For example, you might label one angle $180 - a - b$.

4. Continuing, turn the page and do Problems 13 and 14 (the given ratios are multiples of some unit; call that unit x).

5. Find the measure of an interior angle of a regular polygon with
   a) 5 sides   b) 6 sides   c) 20 sides   d) n sides

6. A polygon has m sides. If one of its interior angles is 80 degrees and the other interior angles are each equal to 160 degrees, find the value of m.

7. Give a Teacher's Solution to the following problem.

   The figure is a regular pentagon. Find, in order, angles a and b, angle c, angle d, and angle e. Conclude that $c = d = e$, so the top interior angle is *trisected*.

8. Draw a non-convex 10-sided polygon. Partition your polygon into triangles as in the example on page 70. How many triangles did you get?

9. Here is a non-convex polygon. Is the sum of the measures of its exterior angles 360°? Explain.

10. ✳ Solve problem 5 on page 287 of NEM1.

11. ✳ Solve problem 6 on page 287 of NEM1.

CHAPTER 4

Deductive Geometry

Deductive geometry is the art of deriving new geometric facts from previously-known facts by using logical reasoning. In elementary school, many geometric facts are introduced by folding, cutting, or measuring exercises, not by logical deduction. But as we have seen, fifth and sixth grade students are already practicing — and enjoying — deductive reasoning as they solve unknown angle problems.

In geometry, a written logical argument is called a *proof*. Section 4.1 introduces one type of proof: "unknown angle proofs". Unknown angle proofs are natural continuations of students' experience in solving unknown angle problems; the transition is a small step that requires no new concepts. Indeed, as you will see, unknown angle proofs are almost identical to the "Teacher's Solutions" that you wrote in the previous chapter!

Section 4.2 describes how congruent triangles are introduced in middle school. Congruence is a powerful geometric tool that opens a door to new aspects of geometry, as explained in Sections 4.3 and 4.4. These sections also describe how the facts about triangles and quadrilaterals that students learned in grades 5 and 6 are revisited at a higher level in middle school.

In this chapter we reach the last stage in the preparation of students for high school geometry. As you read and do problems, think about how these problems are part of a story line that goes back to learning to measure angles in grade 4 and learning to measure lengths in grade 1. You will be teaching part of this story, and it is important to know how it unfolds.

Background Knowledge

Here is a list of the geometric facts at our disposal at this point. These facts will be used in the examples and homework problems in this chapter. Several additional facts will be added to this list in Section 4.2.

• The measures of adjacent angles add.
($c = a + b$.)
Abbreviation: ∠s **add**.

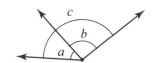

• The sum of adjacent angles on a straight line is 180°.
(If L is a line then $a + b = 180°$.)
Abbreviation: ∠s **on a line**.

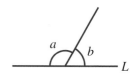

• The sum of adjacent angles around a point is 360°.
($a + b + c + d = 360°$.)
Abbreviation: ∠s **at a pt.**

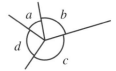

• Vertically opposite angles are equal.
(At the intersection of two straight lines, $a = c$ and $b = d$).
Abbreviation: **vert. ∠s.**

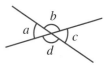

• When a transversal intersects parallel lines, corresponding angles are equal.
(If $\overline{AB} \parallel \overline{CD}$ then $a = b$.)
Abbreviation: **corr.** ∠s, $\overline{AB} \parallel \overline{CD}$.

• Conversely, if $a = b$ then $\overline{AB} \parallel \overline{CD}$.
Abbreviation: **corr.** ∠s **converse**.

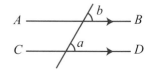

• When a transversal intersects parallel lines, alternate interior angles are equal.

(If $\overline{AB} \parallel \overline{CD}$ then $a = c$.)
Abbreviation: **alt.** ∠s, $\overline{AB} \parallel \overline{CD}$.

• Conversely, if $a = c$ then $\overline{AB} \parallel \overline{CD}$.
Abbreviation: **alt.** ∠s **converse**.

• When a transversal intersects parallel lines, interior angles on the same side of the transversal are supplementary.

(If $\overline{AB} \parallel \overline{CD}$ then $a + d = 180°$.)
Abbreviation: **int.** ∠s, $\overline{AB} \parallel \overline{CD}$.

• Conversely, if $a + d = 180$ then $\overline{AB} \parallel \overline{CD}$.
Abbreviation: **int.** ∠s **converse**.

• The angle sum of any triangle is 180°. (*)
($a + b + c = 180°$.)
Abbreviation: ∠ **sum of** Δ.

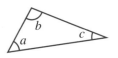

• Each exterior angle of a triangle is the sum of the opposite interior angles. (*)

($e = a + b$).
Abbreviation: **ext.** ∠ **of** Δ.

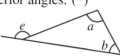

• Base angles of an isosceles triangle are equal. (*)
(If $AC = BC$ then $a = b$.)
Abbreviation: **base ∠s of isos.** △.

• Each interior angle of an equilateral triangle is 60°. (*)
Abbreviation: **equilat.** △.

• Opposite angles in a parallelogram are equal. (*)
($a = b$).
Abbreviation: **opp.** ∠s //-**ogram.**

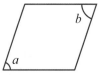

• The sum of the interior angles of an n-gon is $(n - 2) \cdot 180°$.
Abbreviation: ∠ **sum of** n-**gon.**

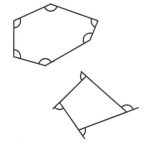

• The sum of the exterior angles of a convex n-gon is 360°.
Abbreviation: **ext.** ∠s **of cx.** n-**gon.**

(*) The starred facts were established by fifth grade classroom demonstrations. Later in this chapter we will give deductive proofs for them.

4.1 Unknown Angle Proofs

The previous chapter introduced the idea of a "Teacher's Solution", which you then used for homework solutions. This specific format is designed to help make you aware of all the aspects of a solution that must be communicated to students and to emphasize that this communication requires only a few words. Many problems in the New Elementary Math textbooks lead students to write teacher solutions themselves.

The Teacher's Solution format serves another purpose: it helps pave the way for proofs. In fact, a Teacher's Solution can be made into a proof by simply changing one specific measurement (such as 31°) into a measurement specified by a letter (such as $x°$). Beyond that, there are only stylistic differences between unknown angle problems and unknown angle proofs.

Examples 1.1 and 1.2 illustrate the transition from unknown angle problems to unknown angle proofs. This section also introduces a format for writing simple proofs in a manner that is almost identical to the Teacher's Solutions you have done already.

EXAMPLE 1.1. *In the figure, angles A and C are right angles and angle B is 78°. Find d.*

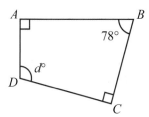

Teacher's Solution:

$$90 + 78 + 90 + d = 360 \quad \angle \text{ sum in 4-gon}$$
$$180 + 78 + d = 360$$
$$78 + d = 180$$
$$\therefore \quad d = 102.$$

Example 1.1 is a fact about one particular shape. But if we replace the specific measurement 78° by an unspecified angle measure $b°$, then the identical reasoning yields a general fact about quadrilaterals with two 90° interior angles.

EXAMPLE 1.2. *In the figure, angles A and C are right angles. Prove that d = 180 − b.*

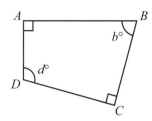

Proof. $\quad 90 + b + 90 + d = 360 \quad \angle \text{ sum in 4-gon}$
$$180 + b + d = 360$$
$$b + d = 180$$
$$\therefore \quad d = 180 - b.$$

Notice the distinction between the above examples. Example 1.1 is an unknown angle problem because its answer is a number: $d = 102$ is the number of degrees for the unknown angle. We call Example 1.2 an **unknown angle proof** because the conclusion $d = 180 - b$ is a relationship between angles whose size is not specified.

EXAMPLE 1.3. *In the figure, $\overline{AB} \parallel \overline{EC}$ and $\overline{BD} \parallel \overline{EF}$. Find b.*

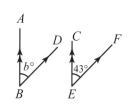

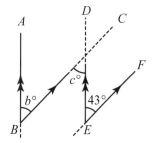

Teacher's Solution: Extend the lines as shown. Mark angle c as shown.

$$c = 43 \quad \text{alt. } \angle s, \ \overline{BC} \parallel \overline{EF}$$
$$b = c \quad \text{alt. } \angle s, \ \overline{BA} \parallel \overline{ED}$$
$$\therefore \quad b = 43.$$

There is nothing special about the number 43. The same reasoning shows that $b = a$ in the picture on the right. The proof below is a Teacher's Solution with two embellishments. First, it is "launched" by a preamble that states, in very few words, what we are assuming as known and what we wish to show. Second, the solution involves two auxiliary lines, as we explain to the reader on a line labeled "construction".

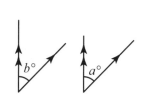

Given: $\overline{AB} \parallel \overline{ED}$ and $\overline{BC} \parallel \overline{EF}$.
To prove: $b = a$.

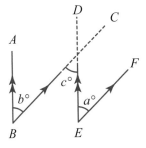

Construction: Extend sides $\overline{BC}$ and $\overline{ED}$.
  Mark angle c as shown.

Proof. $c = a$ alt. $\angle$s, $\overline{BC} \parallel \overline{EF}$
    $b = c$ alt. $\angle$s, $\overline{BA} \parallel \overline{ED}$
  $\therefore$ $b = a$.

We have just turned Example 1.3 into a proof. The proof requires no additional effort!

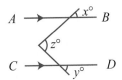

EXAMPLE 1.4. *In the figure, $\overline{AB} \parallel \overline{CD}$.*
Prove that $z = x + y$.

You have seen this problem before: it is almost identical to Example 2.3 on page 65. The previous version was an unknown angle problem: two of the three angles x, y, and z were given (one was 37° and another was 75°) and the problem was to find the third. The version above leaves x, y, and z unspecified and the problem is to prove that they are related.

Just as before, the proof requires a construction, and several different constructions will work. Here is one proof.

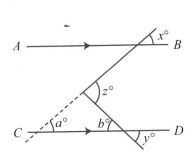

Given: $\overline{AB} \parallel \overline{CD}$.
To prove: $z = x + y$.

Construction: Extend line as shown.
    Mark angles a and b as shown.

Proof. $a = x$ corr. $\angle$s, $\overline{AB} \parallel \overline{CD}$
    $b = y$ vert. $\angle$s
    $z = a + b$ ext. $\angle$s of a Δ
  $\therefore$ $z = x + y$.

A polygon whose vertices lie on a circle is said to be **inscribed** in the circle. The next example proves a famous fact about inscribed triangles.

EXAMPLE 1.5. *Any inscribed triangle with a side passing through the center of the circle is a right triangle.*

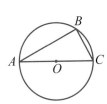

Given: $\triangle ABC$ is inscribed in a circle.
$\overline{AC}$ contains center O.

To prove: $\angle B = 90°$.

Construction: Draw segment $\overline{OB}$.
Mark angles as shown.

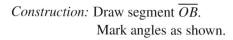

Proof.	$OA = OB = OC$	def. of circle
		(each is a radius)
$\therefore$	$\triangle OAB$ and $\triangle OBC$ are isosceles $\triangle$s	
	$a = x$	base $\angle$s of isos. $\triangle$
	$b = y$	base $\angle$s of isos. $\triangle$
	$x + y + a + b = 180°$	$\angle$ sum of $\triangle ABC$
	$x + y + x + y = 180°$	
	$2(x + y) = 180°$	
$\therefore$	$\angle B = x + y = 90°$	$\angle$s add.

There are two standard ways for writing angles in geometric figures. One possibility is to label angles in figures with a letter and a degree sign, as in $x°$. Then x stands for a number, for example, x might be 42. The alternative is to label angles in figures with a letter only, as was done in Example 1.5. Then x stands for a quantity, x might be 42 degrees. Both are correct *provided the notation is consistent within each problem*. In particular, equations should be written so that every term is a number, or every term is a quantity.

EXERCISE 1.6. *In which of the solved examples in this section do letters stand for numbers? In which to they stand for quantities?*

For elementary students, it is best to make the units — the degree signs — plainly visible in the figure. But for unknown angle proofs, the presentation is often clearer when letters stand for quantities. Accordingly, we scrupulously included degree signs in Chapters 1, 2 and 3, but we will now begin using both notations freely.

The "Elementary Proof" Format

Proofs are exercises for students! The challenge — and the fun — lies in figuring out the sequence of steps that take you to the desired conclusion. But, as with multi-step problems, it is easy for students to get confused unless they *systematically record their steps in writing*. Students who have learned a specific format for recording steps can devote more attention to geometric thinking and less to organizing their writing. A uniform format also facilitates classroom discussions and makes it easier for teachers to read and evaluate student work.

Which format is best? There is no single answer, but several principles are important. Writing proofs shouldn't be a chore, so the chosen format should be simple, minimal, and natural. It is useful to include a preamble stating the hypotheses and the goal, because this *helps students clearly understand the task* before starting. A clearly-marked picture obviously helps students work out the solution. Finally, the completed proof should make the reasoning clear to the reader.

And who is this mysterious reader? At all levels of K-12 mathematics, students write for two readers: *themselves and their teacher*. For students, clear writing aids clear thinking. For teachers, asking students to use a simple, clear format is a matter of self-interest: it makes student work easier to read. In fact, this applies to everything written by mathematics students.

In this book, we will adopt the format used in the examples in this section. We will call a proof written in this format an **Elementary Proof**. You will be expected to use this in all homework problems that ask for an Elementary Proof. The following template shows the features of an Elementary Proof.

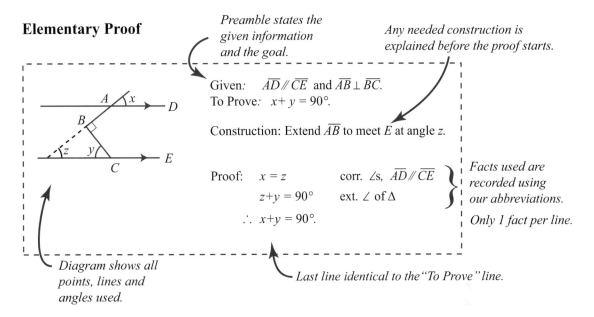

Elementary Proof

Preamble states the given information and the goal.

Any needed construction is explained before the proof starts.

Given: $\overline{AD} \parallel \overline{CE}$ and $\overline{AB} \perp \overline{BC}$.
To Prove: $x + y = 90°$.

Construction: Extend $\overline{AB}$ to meet E at angle z.

Proof: $x = z$ corr. $\angle$s, $\overline{AD} \parallel \overline{CE}$
        $z + y = 90°$ ext. $\angle$ of Δ
   $\therefore$ $x + y = 90°$.

Facts used are recorded using our abbreviations.

Only 1 fact per line.

Diagram shows all points, lines and angles used.

Last line identical to the "To Prove" line.

Hints.   Clear proofs are short and simple. To that end,

- Do not label the two columns "statement" and "reason" (everyone already knows this!).
- Do not include reasons for simple arithmetic and algebra steps.
- To avoid cluttering the picture, label *only* those points, lines and angles used in the proof.

Establishing Facts Using Proofs

The next two examples show how two familiar facts about triangles follow from the properties of parallel lines. In fifth grade, students justified the "angle sum of triangle" fact by cutting and re-arranging paper triangles. Middle school students can give a purely geometric argument for this fact. These are very important proofs: learn them.

THEOREM 1.7. *In any triangle, the sum of the interior angles is* $180°$.

Given: ΔABC.
To prove: $a + b + c = 180°$.

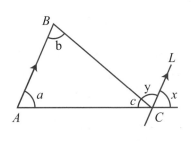

Construction: Draw line L through C parallel to $\overline{AB}$. Mark angles x and y as shown.

Proof. $a = x$ corr. $\angle$s, $L \parallel \overline{AB}$
       $b = y$ alt. int. $\angle$s, $L \parallel \overline{AB}$
       $c + x + y = 180°$ $\angle$s on a line
 $\therefore$ $a + b + c = 180°$.

THEOREM 1.8. *Each exterior angle of a triangle is the sum of the opposite interior angles.*

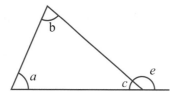

Given: $\triangle ABC$.
To prove: $e = a + b$.

Proof.	$e = 180° - c$	$\angle$s on line
	$a + b = 180° - c$	$\angle$ sum of $\triangle$
$\therefore$	$e = a + b.$	

EXERCISE 1.9. *Compare both theorems with the "picture proof" of the same fact described in Section 2.2 of Chapter 2. Are they compatible? Do these proofs elaborate on the picture proofs?*

The next proof is different from the fifth-grade paper-folding explanation, but is still easy to understand.

THEOREM 1.10. *Opposite angles in a parallelogram are equal.*

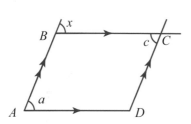

Given: $ABCD$ is a parallelogram.
To prove: $a = c$.

Construction: Extend sides $\overline{AB}$, $\overline{DC}$, and $\overline{BC}$.
Mark angle x as shown.

Proof.	$a = x$	corr. $\angle$s, $\overline{BC} \parallel \overline{AD}$
	$x = c$	alt. int. $\angle$s, $\overline{CD} \parallel \overline{AB}$
$\therefore$	$a = c.$	

Theorems and Proofs in the Classroom

Students often acquire misconceptions about the meaning of the words "theorem" and "proof". Many believe that a theorem is "a mathematical fact" and a proof is "an explanation of why a fact is true." This viewpoint embodies a subtle misunderstanding that teachers should try to prevent from taking root.

Theorems are not statements of universal truths. Rather, they are "if-then" statements: *If* certain assumptions are true *then* a stated conclusion is true. The assumptions are of two types: those explicitly stated as hypotheses (after the word *Given* in our format), and a collection of "background knowledge" facts (often not explicitly mentioned) that have already been accepted or proven true. A proof is a sequence of deductive steps that explain how the conclusion follows from the hypothesis. In summary,

DEFINITION 1.11. *A **proof** of a mathematical statement is a detailed explanation of how that statement follows logically from other statements already accepted as true.*

*A **theorem** is a mathematical statement with a proof.*

Theorems are the building blocks of geometry. Once a theorem has been proved, it can be added to the list of background facts and used in subsequent proofs. For example, after proving

Theorem 1.7 we were able to use it as a step in the proof of Theorem 1.8. In this way one builds, bit by bit, a large body of knowledge.

This structure puts a burden on textbooks and teachers. A proof only makes sense in the context of a particular collection of accepted background facts, and that collection changes grade by grade. Teachers should devote some time to clarifying the already-accepted background facts for their grade.

Homework Set 13

Following the format described in this section, give an "Elementary Proof" of each statement.

1. In the figure, prove that $a + b = 90$.

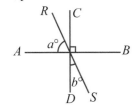

2. In the figure, $\overline{AB} \parallel \overline{CD}$. Prove that $a = b$.

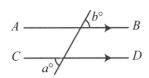

3. In the figure, $\angle B = 90°$. Prove that $a + c = 90$.

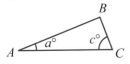

4. In the figure, prove that $z = x + y$.

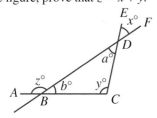

5. In the figure, $\angle A = \angle X$, $\angle B = \angle Y$. Prove that $\angle C = \angle Z$.

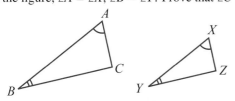

6. In the figure, $a = b$. Prove that $c = d$.

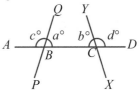

7. In the figure, prove that $d + e = b + c$.

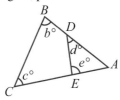

8. In the figure, prove that $d = a + b + c$.

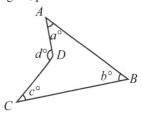

9. In the figure, $\overline{AB} \parallel \overline{CD}$ and $\overline{CB} \parallel \overline{ED}$. Prove that $\angle ABC = \angle CDE$.

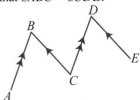

10. In the figure, $\overline{AB} \parallel \overline{CD}$ and $\overline{BC} \parallel \overline{ED}$. Prove that $b + d = 180$.

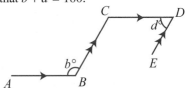

11. In the figure, $\overline{AB} \parallel \overline{XY}$ and $\overline{BC} \parallel \overline{YZ}$. Prove that $\angle ABC = \angle XYZ$.

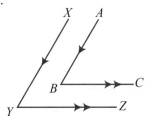

12. In the figure, $\overline{PQ} \parallel \overline{TS}$. Prove that $\angle QRS = q + s$.

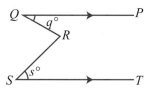

4.2 Congruent Triangles

Two line segments are called congruent if they have equal lengths. Two angles are congruent if they have equal measures. Similarly, two triangles are called congruent if their sides have the same lengths and their angles have the same measures. The first part of this section explores how curricula build up to this notion of congruent triangles. The second part focuses on the criteria that ensure that two triangles are congruent.

A Curriculum Sequence

Early Grades. In geometry, figures that are duplicates – exact copies of one another – are called *congruent*. Duplicate figures can be drawn in different positions and orientations. Thus, to check whether two figures are congruent one must realign them to see if they match.

Young children are taught to match shapes, first with figures made of cardboard or thin plastic, then visually with pictures. The phrase "same size and same shape" is often used to mean "congruent". The grade 1 Primary Mathematics books contain exercises like this:

Do the figures have the same size and same shape?

a) ▬ ▬ b) ▲ ◣ c) ▬ ▮ d) ◼ ◆

Such exercises use visualization only; students are not expected to make measurements. The goal is to convey the idea that matching requires first sliding and rotating, and then comparing lengths and angles. The term congruence is not used, but the seed of the idea is planted.

Teaching comment: Children may misinterpret the term "same shape" to mean "shapes with the same name". But the word "shape" refers to the angles and proportions in a figure, not just its name. Thus, the figures in b) above are both triangles, but do not have the same shape.

Matching exercises also introduce ideas that are used later for defining area and for modeling fractions. For example, a regular hexagon, decomposed into 6 congruent triangles, can be used to illustrate fractions whose denominator is 6.

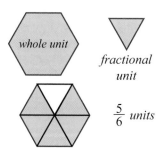

Middle School Introduction. The Primary Mathematics curriculum introduces congruence in grade 7 (some curricula start as early as grade 5). One approach starts with see-through tracing paper or overhead transparency sheets as in the following exercise.

EXERCISE 2.1. *Trace triangle A on a transparent sheet and lay it over figures B and C. Can you make them match? Flip the sheet over and try again.*

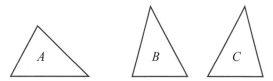

Exercise 2.1 makes the idea of "same size, same shape" more precise, yet it still relies on visual matching. But notice that "matching" can be described purely in terms of the 3 side lengths and 3 angle measures: two triangles match if they can be aligned so that *all six of these measurements exactly agree.* In diagrams, such matching can be shown by marking the triangles as in the figure below.

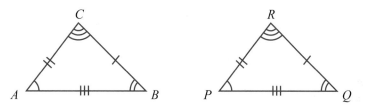

The next step is to express matching in terms of the vertices of the triangle. To proceed, we need (i) a symbolic way of describing how to align two triangles, and (ii) a definition for what is meant by "exactly match".

To align triangles, one pairs up their vertices. Such a pairing is called a correspondence. More precisely, a **correspondence** between two triangles pairs each vertex of one triangle with one and only one vertex of the other. The figure shows triangles $\triangle PQR$ and $\triangle XYZ$ aligned in a way that suggests the correspondence $P \leftrightarrow X$, $Q \leftrightarrow Y$, and $R \leftrightarrow Z$.

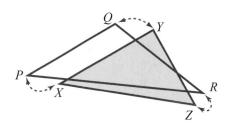

Once a correspondence is chosen, we can talk about *corresponding sides* and *corresponding angles.* For the correspondence $P \leftrightarrow X$, $Q \leftrightarrow Y$, and $R \leftrightarrow Z$, $\angle P$ corresponds to $\angle X$, side $\overline{QR}$ corresponds to side $\overline{YZ}$, etc. In this way we can compare the six measurements of two triangles, even if they don't have the same shape or size. When the corresponding measurements are equal, the correspondence gives us a precise way of stating that the triangles are exact copies of each other.

DEFINITION 2.2. *Two triangles are **congruent** if, under some correspondence,*

- *all pairs of corresponding sides are equal, and*

- *all pairs of corresponding angles are equal.*

To indicate that two triangles are congruent we use the symbol $\cong$ and write the vertices of the triangles in corresponding order. Thus $\triangle ABC \cong \triangle PQR$ means that $\triangle ABC$ and $\triangle PQR$ are congruent under the correspondence $A \leftrightarrow P$, $B \leftrightarrow Q$, $C \leftrightarrow R$. To see the correspondence, one can visualize arrows pairing up the vertices in order.

$$\triangle ABC \cong \triangle PQR$$

Here is a grade 7 exercise that helps students move from checking congruence visually to thinking about the measurements of corresponding parts:

EXERCISE 2.3. *These triangles are congruent. Fill in the blanks by matching side lengths and estimating angle measures.*

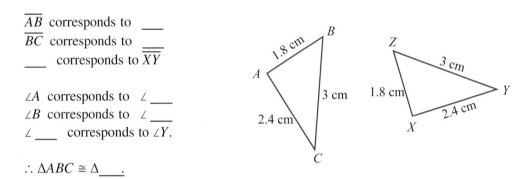

$\overline{AB}$ corresponds to ____
$\overline{BC}$ corresponds to ____
____ corresponds to $\overline{XY}$

$\angle A$ corresponds to $\angle$ ____
$\angle B$ corresponds to $\angle$ ____
$\angle$ ____ corresponds to $\angle Y$.

$\therefore \triangle ABC \cong \triangle$ ____ .

Hint: In such a congruence, one can associate each letter with an interior angle, and then the smallest angle of one triangle is paired with the smallest angle of the other, the largest is paired with the largest, and the mid-sized with the mid-sized.

Symmetry can be expressed as a congruence of a triangle *with itself*. For example, the isosceles triangle below has a line of symmetry. Reflecting across the line of symmetry interchanges A and C and does not move B. Thus this reflection is described by the correspondence

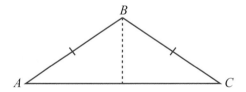

$A \leftrightarrow C$, $C \leftrightarrow A$, and $B \leftrightarrow B$. The reflection takes the 3 sides of the triangle to sides of equal length (since $AB = BC$) and takes the 3 angles to angles of equal measure (since base angles are equal). Consequently, the reflection is a congruence, which we write as $\triangle ABC \cong \triangle CBA$.

EXERCISE 2.4. *An equilateral triangle $\triangle ABC$ is congruent to itself in six ways. Write down all six, beginning with $\triangle ABC \cong \triangle ABC$. Write "R" next to the congruences that are rotations and "LS" next to those that are reflections across a line of symmetry. It will help to draw pictures.*

Congruence Tests for Triangles: a Teaching Sequence

Congruent triangles have six pairs of equal measurements (3 pairs of angles and 3 pairs of side lengths). However, to show that triangles are congruent, it isn't necessary to check all six pairs. Four **congruence criteria** make the task easier. The criteria are often called "tests" and are named by triples: the Side-Side-Side Test, Angle-Side-Angle Test, Side-Angle-Side Test and the Right-Hypotenuse-Leg Test. Each test states that two triangles are congruent whenever the named measurements match under some correspondence.

Congruence tests are often introduced in middle school by activities that ask students to construct triangles with specified measurements. The aim is to make the meaning of the tests clear and convince students of their validity.

Side-Side-Side Test.   Construction 6 on page 53 showed how to use the 3 side-lengths of a triangle to create a duplicate triangle with the same side-lengths. To verify that the two triangles are congruent, one must also know that corresponding angles have equal measure.

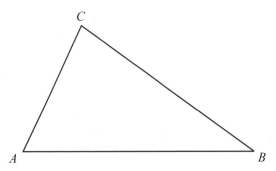

EXERCISE 2.5. *Using a compass and a straightedge, copy △ABC onto a blank paper as in Construction 6 on page 53. Then make the following checks:*

First Check: *Measure the angles in the copied triangle with a protractor. Are they equal to the corresponding angles in △ABC? Are the two triangles congruent?*

Second Check: *Cut out your triangle and place it on top of the original triangle in this book. Align the sides. Are all angle measures equal? Are the triangles congruent?*

In Exercise 2.5, both checking methods refer directly to the definition of congruence — both require verifying that all corresponding angles and sides are equal. The teaching goal at this stage is to make students explicitly aware of the definition: congruence means 6 matching measurements.

Side-Side-Side Test

Two triangles are congruent if corresponding sides are equal under some correspondence, i.e.,

If $AB = PQ$, $BC = QR$, $CA = RP$, then $\triangle ABC \cong \triangle PQR$.

(Abbreviation: **SSS.**)

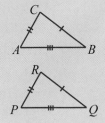

Angle-Side-Angle Test. In the next example, students duplicate a triangle by copying two angles and the side between them.

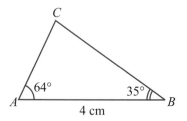

EXERCISE 2.6. *Using a straightedge and protractor, copy △ABC onto a blank paper as described below. Then make the two checks stated beneath the picture.*

Ruler and Protractor Construction:

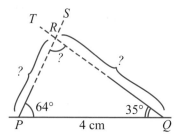

- Draw $\overline{PQ}$ of length AB.

- Draw ray $\overrightarrow{PS}$ so $\angle SPQ = 64°$.

- Draw ray $\overrightarrow{QT}$ so that $\angle TQP = 35°$, as shown.

- Mark R where the two rays intersect and draw $\overline{PR}$ and $\overline{QR}$.

First Check: *Use a protractor to measure $\angle R$; is it equal to $\angle C$? Use your compass to compare lengths QR and PR; are they equal to BC and AC? Are the two triangles congruent?*

Second Check: *Cut out your triangle and place it on top of △ABC. Align the sides. Are all angles and side lengths equal? Are the two triangles congruent?*

Angle-Side-Angle Test

Two triangles are congruent if two pairs of corresponding angles and their included sides are equal, i.e.,

If $\angle A = \angle P$, $\angle B = \angle Q$, $AB = PQ$, then $△ABC \cong △PQR$.

(Abbreviation: **ASA.**)

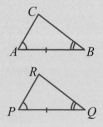

The ASA Test should really be called the "two angles and a side" test. After all, if two pairs of angles are equal, then the third pair is also equal (because the angles of a triangle total 180°). Consequently, each side lies between two pairs of corresponding angles, and we can apply the ASA Test. Some books distinguish between the ASA and AAS conditions, but we will the term "ASA Test" for both.

Side-Angle-Side Test. In the next exercise, students copy a side, the included angle and side of a triangle to create a copy of △ABC above.

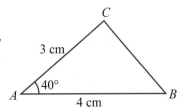

EXERCISE 2.7. *Using a ruler and protractor, copy △ABC onto a blank paper using the construction below and make the check described.*

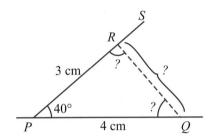

Ruler and Protractor Construction:

- Draw a segment $\overline{PQ}$ of length 4 cm.

- Draw ray $\overrightarrow{PS}$ with $\angle SPQ = 40°$.

- Mark point R on $\overrightarrow{PS}$ with $PR = 3$ cm.

- Draw $\overline{RQ}$.

First Check: *Measure angles $\angle Q$ and $\angle R$; are they equal to $\angle B$ and $\angle C$? Use your compass to compare the lengths QR and BC; are they equal? What do you conclude about the two triangles?*

Second Check: *Cut out your triangle and place it on top of △ABC. Align the sides. Are the two triangles congruent?*

Side-Angle-Side Test

Two triangles are congruent if two pairs of corresponding sides and their included angle are equal, i.e.,

If $AB = PQ$, $AC = PR$, $\angle A = \angle P$, then $\triangle ABC \cong \triangle PQR$.

(Abbreviation: **SAS.**)

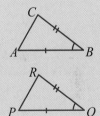

Some sets of three equal corresponding measurements do not guarantee congruence. In particular, triangles with three matching angles needn't be congruent.

These triangles have the same Angle-Angle-Angle data but are not congruent.

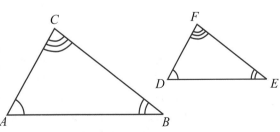

Likewise, triangles with one pair of equal corresponding angles and two pairs of equal corresponding sides needn't be congruent, as the following "swinging girl" picture shows.

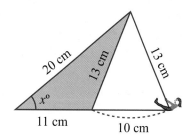

The shaded triangle (base 11 cm) and the large triangle (base 21 cm) have the same Angle-Side-Side data but are not congruent.

The fact that Angle-Side-Side measurements do not determine a unique triangle is easily said: *there is no A.S.S. test.* This phrasing is not recommended for classroom use. Typically, textbooks tell students that "A.A.A. and S.S.A. do not confirm congruence of triangles."

Right-Hypotenuse-Leg Test. For pairs of *right* triangles, it is enough to compare two pairs of sides. In a right triangle, the side opposite the 90° angle is called the *hypotenuse* and the other sides are called *legs*. The following exercise shows that two right triangles are congruent if they have equal hypotenuses and a leg of one has the same length as a leg of the other.

EXERCISE 2.8. *Copy the right triangle △ABC onto some tracing paper using the construction below.*

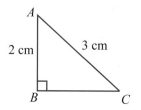

Construction:

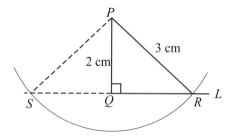

- Draw a segment $\overline{PQ}$ of length 2 cm.
- Draw line L perpendicular to $\overline{PQ}$ passing through Q.
- Draw circle, center P, radius 3 cm.
- Mark as R one of the two points where the circle intersects L.

Measure angles ∠P and ∠R; are they equal to ∠A and ∠C? Use your compass to compare the lengths QR and BC; are they equal? What do you conclude about the two triangles?

Right-Hypotenuse-Leg Test

If two right triangles have hypotenuses of the equal length and a pair of legs with equal length, then the triangles are congruent, i.e.,

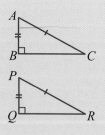

If $∠B = ∠Q = 90°$, $AC = PR$, $AB = PQ$, then $△ABC ≅ △PQR$.

(Abbreviation: **RHL.**)

The RHL Test uses two sides and a non-included angle — Angle-Side-Side measurements. In general, for such measurements, the swinging girl picture produces two non-congruent triangles with the same Angle-Side-Side measurements. But the RHL Test is true because, when the angle x is a right angle, the swinging girl picture becomes the diagram in Exercise 2.8, and the triangles are actually congruent.

Homework Set 14

1. Do Exercise 2.3 in this section (just fill in the blanks in your textbook). Then fill in all of the blanks in the exercises below. (On your homework sheet, just state the correspondence for each part.)

a)

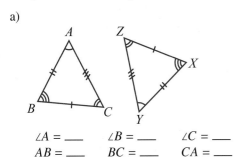

$\angle A = \underline{\quad}$ $\quad \angle B = \underline{\quad}$ $\quad \angle C = \underline{\quad}$
$AB = \underline{\quad}$ $\quad BC = \underline{\quad}$ $\quad CA = \underline{\quad}$

Correspondence: $\triangle ABC \cong \triangle \underline{\qquad}$

b)

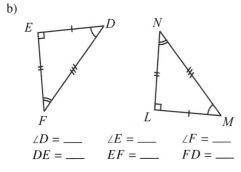

$\angle D = \underline{\quad}$ $\quad \angle E = \underline{\quad}$ $\quad \angle F = \underline{\quad}$
$DE = \underline{\quad}$ $\quad EF = \underline{\quad}$ $\quad FD = \underline{\quad}$

Correspondence: $\triangle DEF \cong \triangle \underline{\qquad}$

c)

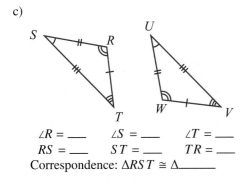

$\angle R = \underline{\quad}$ $\quad \angle S = \underline{\quad}$ $\quad \angle T = \underline{\quad}$
$RS = \underline{\quad}$ $\quad ST = \underline{\quad}$ $\quad TR = \underline{\quad}$
Correspondence: $\triangle RST \cong \triangle \underline{\qquad}$

2. Do Exercise 2.5 on page 85 of this section. Answer the "First Check" and "Second Check" questions beneath the picture.

3. Is there an "SSSS Test" for quadrilaterals? That is, is it true that two quadrilateral with four pairs of corresponding sides of equal length are necessarily congruent? Explain and illustrate.

4. Do Exercise 2.6 in this section. First do the construction (in the first step, use your compass to carry the "4 cm" length from your book to your HW paper). Then answer the "First Check" and "Second Check" questions.

5. Do Exercise 2.7 on page 87, this time using *ruler and protractor*. Then answer the "Check" questions.

6. For each figure, name the congruent triangles and state the reason they are congruent (i.e., SSS, ASA, SAS, RHL).

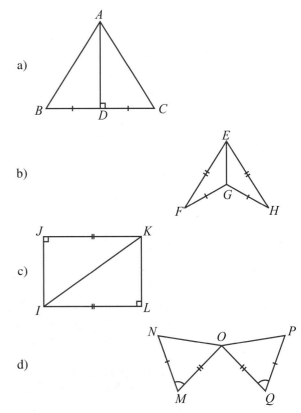

a)

b)

c)

d)

e)

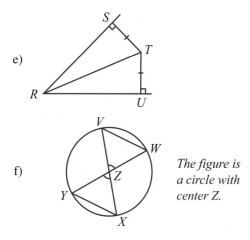

f)

The figure is a circle with center Z.

7. For each figure, find the values of the unknowns.

a) $\triangle ABC \cong \triangle DCB$

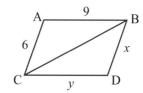

b) $\triangle RST \cong \triangle VUT$

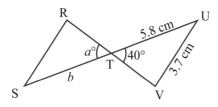

8. In the figure below, which triangles are congruent? Write down each congruence.

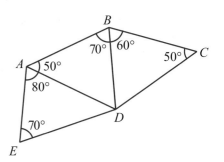

9. Given any three positive real numbers, $a, b,$ and c, with b less than 180 and c less than 180, can you construct a triangle having two interior angles whose measures are b and c, respectively, and the included side having measure a? Illustrate.

10. Given any three positive real numbers, $a, b,$ and c, with c less than 180, can you construct a triangle having two sides whose measures are a and b with the included angle having measure c? Illustrate.

11. Prove or give a counterexample: If two triangles both have interior angle measures equal to 32°, 100° and 48°, and both have a side of length 10 cm, then the triangles are congruent.

4.3 Applying Congruences

Once students have learned the triangle tests, they can move beyond unknown angles problems to the next stage in the curriculum: proving facts about side-lengths and angles within figures. This section is an introduction to the simplest proofs. At this point, students appreciate and perhaps enjoy unknown angle problems and short proofs. They are prepared for high school geometry.

EXAMPLE 3.1. *Let $\triangle ABC$ be an isosceles triangle with $AB = BC$. Let X and Y be distinct points on $\overline{AC}$ such that $AX = YC$. Prove that $\triangle XBY$ is also isosceles.*

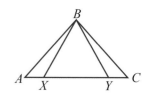

Given: $AB = BC$ and $AX = YC$.
To Prove: $BX = BY$.

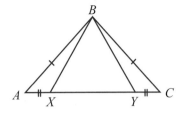

Proof.	$AB = BC$	given
	$\angle A = \angle C$	base $\angle$s of isos. $\triangle$
	$AX = YC$	given
	$\therefore \triangle AXB \cong \triangle CYB$	SAS.
$\therefore$	$BX = BY$	corr. sides of $\cong \triangle$s.

The triangle tests can also be used in unknown angle proofs.

EXAMPLE 3.2. *In the figure, $\angle A = \angle D$ and $AE = DE$. Prove $\angle ECB = \angle EBC$.*

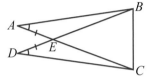

To prove this, mark angles as shown and concentrate your attention on the two shaded triangles.

Given: $a = d$ and $AE = DE$.
To Prove: $b = c$.

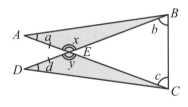

Proof.	$a = d$	given
	$AE = DE$	given
	$x = y$	vert. $\angle$s
	$\therefore \triangle AEB \cong \triangle DEC$	ASA.
	$\therefore EB = EC$	corr. sides of $\cong \triangle$s.
$\therefore$	$b = c$	base $\angle$s of isos. $\triangle$.

Study Examples 3.1 and 3.2 for a moment. In each proof, Line 4 states that two triangles are congruent by a congruence test, Lines 1-3 are the facts needed to apply the test, and Line 5 is a conclusion based on this congruence. In this chapter, almost all of the proofs will have this format. It is simple, but it has many applications!

As students learn to construct proofs, it is easy for them to make a "false start" — their first approach doesn't work. *This is completely normal!* Proofs are like puzzles: the fun lies in trying different strategies to find a solution. The reward, like the reward in solving a tricky puzzle, is a feeling of accomplishment. In fact, geometric proofs were a common amusement of educated people in the 19th century, just as crossword and sudoku puzzles are today.

false starts
in proofs

The next example is a problem in which it is easy to make a false start. The figure contains several pairs of congruent triangles; which pair should be used in the proof? Try to find a strategy before you look at the proof written below. Here is a strategy that helps: color, highlight or shade the segments that appear in the "Given" and the "To Prove" statements. *Look for a pair of congruent triangles that contain these sides.*

EXAMPLE 3.3. *In the figure, CA = CB. Prove that AS = BR.*

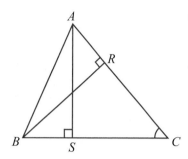

Given: $CA = CB$.
To Prove: $AS = BR$.

Proof. In $\triangle ACS$ and $\triangle BCR$,
$CA = CB$	given
$\angle C = \angle C$	common angle
$\angle R = \angle S = 90°$	given
$\therefore \triangle ACS \cong \triangle BCR$	AAS.

$\therefore \quad AS = BR$ corr. sides of $\cong$ $\triangle$s.

EXERCISE 3.4. *This proof used the congruence $\triangle ACS \cong \triangle BCR$. Name (without proof) two other pairs of congruent triangles in this figure (use the letter T to label the intersection point in the middle of the figure).*

These examples indicate that there are two levels of congruent triangle proofs: ones that are especially simple because the figure contains only one pair of congruent triangles, and ones in which students must find the appropriate congruent triangles from among several pairs. Careful textbooks (and careful teachers!) provide plenty of practice at the first level before challenging students with problems at the second level. The problems in the homework for this section (HW Set 15) are similar to a well-written eighth grade textbook. As you do these proofs, notice how they are arranged so that they slowly increase in difficulty.

Proofs for Symmetry Explanations

Congruence tests can be used to prove many of the facts that were introduced in fifth and sixth grade using symmetry arguments. We will give three examples. As you will see, the elementary school "folding proofs" contain the key ideas of a complete mathematical proof.

For example, the following proof is just the detailed explanation of the fifth grade "picture proof" shown on page 62 of Primary Math 5B and on page 44 of this book.

THEOREM 3.5. *In an isosceles triangle, base angles are congruent.*

*(Abbreviation: **base ∠s of isos.** △.)*

The proof applies the Side-Side-Side Test to confirm that the two "halves" of the triangle are congruent. We begin by labeling vertices.

Given: $\triangle ABC$ with $AC = BC$.
To prove: $a = b$.

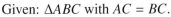

Construction: Let D be the midpoint of $\overline{AB}$.
Draw $\overline{CD}$.

Proof.

$AC = BC$	given
$AD = DB$	D is the midpoint
$DC = DC$	common.
$\triangle ADC \cong \triangle BDC$	SSS
$\therefore a = b$	corr. $\angle$s of $\cong \triangle$s.

When we first introduced compass and straightedge constructions in Section 2.5, we focused on the steps required and used symmetry to argue that the construction accomplished its intended purpose. We can now replace those symmetry arguments with proofs based on congruent triangles. For example, the construction below shows how to bisect an angle.

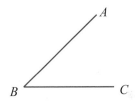

EXAMPLE 3.6. *Bisect* $\angle ABC$.
(Abbreviation: **bisect $\angle$ constr.***)*

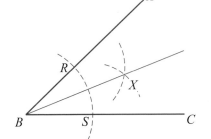

- Draw circle, center B, any radius. Mark R and S where the circle intersects the sides of the angle.

- Draw circle, center R, radius RS. Draw circle, center S, radius RS.

- Mark X where these two circles intersect.

- Draw $\overrightarrow{BX}$, $\overrightarrow{RX}$ and $\overrightarrow{SX}$.

We claim that this construction works: that $\overrightarrow{BX}$ bisects $\angle ABC$. Symmetry suggests that $\triangle BRX$ and $\triangle BSX$ are congruent. Here is a proof:

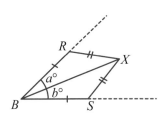

Given: $BR = BS$, $RX = SX$.
To prove: $a = b$.

Proof.

$BR = BS$	given
$RX = SX$	given
$BX = BX$	common
$\triangle BRX \cong BSX$	SSS.
$\therefore a = b$	corr. $\angle$s of $\cong \triangle$s.

All constructions are theorems. When written down in complete form, each entails a construction followed by a proof that the construction works. We can therefore use constructions as reasons in proofs. Here is an example:

THEOREM 3.7. *If two angles of a triangle are congruent, then the triangle is isosceles.*

(Abbreviation: **base ∠s converse***.)*

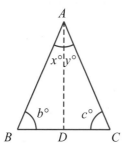

Given: $\triangle ABC$ with $b = c$.
To Prove: $AB = AC$.

Construction: Bisect $\angle A$ and mark
angles x and y as shown.

Proof.

$b = c$		given
$x = y$		bisect ∠ constr.
$AD = AD$		common
$\therefore \triangle BAD \cong \triangle CAD$		AAS.
$\therefore \quad AB = AC$		corr. sides of $\cong \triangle$s.

Homework Set 15

This homework set gives more practice with proofs using congruent triangles. Please write Elementary Proofs to the following problems. Most of these problems are similar to homework problems found in Japan and Hong Kong in eighth grade.

1. In the figure, prove that $\angle ABC = \angle EDC$.

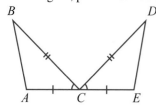

2. In the figure, prove that $BD = DC$.

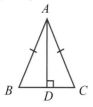

3. In the figure, O is the center of the circle. Prove that $TA = TB$.

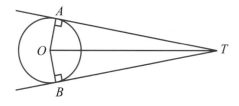

4. In the figure, $AB = AC$, $AP = AQ$. Prove that $BQ = CP$.

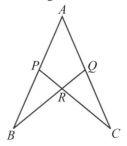

5. In the figure, $\angle B = \angle C = 130°$. Prove that $AB = AC$.

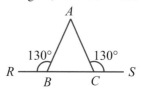

6. In the figure, $AB = AC$ and $\overline{AB} \parallel \overline{HK}$. Prove that $HK = HC$.

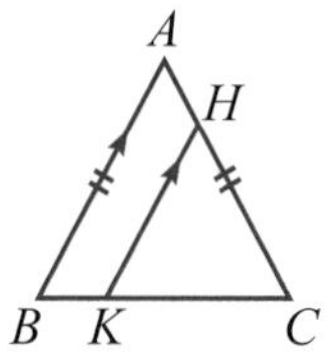

7. In the figure, $BP = QC$, $AP = AQ$, and $x = y$. Prove that $AB = AC$.

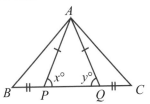

8. In the figure, $a_1 = a_2$, $e_1 = e_2$. Prove that

   a) $\triangle ABE \cong \triangle ACE$.

   b) $AB = AC$ and $\overline{AD} \perp \overline{BC}$.

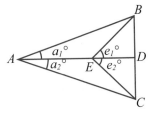

9. In the figure, $a = d$, $b = c$, and $CB = CD$. Prove that

   a) $\triangle ADC \cong \triangle ABC$.

   b) $e = f$.

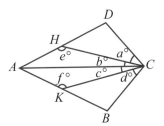

10. In the figure, $a_1 = b_1$, $a_2 = b_2$. Prove that $AC = BE$.

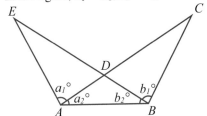

11. In the figure, $AV = BV$, $AP = BP$. Prove that

    a) $\angle APV = \angle BPV$.

    b) $AQ = BQ$.

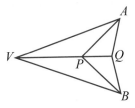

12. In the figure, $AB = CD$, $BC = AD$. Prove that

    a) $\angle ADB = \angle DBC$.

    b) $\overline{AC}$ and $\overline{BD}$ bisect each other.

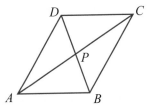

13. In the figure, P is equidistant from the lines OA and OB (i.e. $PA = PB$). Prove that OP bisects $\angle AOB$.

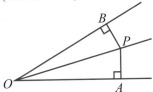

14. In the figure, OX and OY are the perpendicular bisectors of AB and AC respectively. Prove that

    a) $\triangle OAX \cong \triangle OBX$.

    b) $OA = OB = OC$.

    c) What can you say about the circle with center O and radius OA? (Hint: Draw it in your book.)

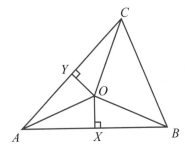

4.4 Congruences in Quadrilaterals

You have already seen how the Primary Mathematics textbooks present facts about parallelograms in grades 5 and 6 (page 68 of Primary Math 5B and pages 62–64 of Primary Math 6B). Middle school students can dig deeper and see that the facts they learned about parallelograms and other quadrilaterals are actually consequences of basic facts, namely those listed as "Background Knowledge" at the beginning of this chapter. This section shows how the background knowledge facts can be used to prove various properties of quadrilaterals. It ends with a review of the K-8 curriculum sequence that leads to deductive geometry.

Parallelograms

By definition, a parallelogram is a quadrilateral in which both pairs of opposite sides are parallel. Using this definition and congruent triangles, we can prove additional properties of parallelograms, as in the following proofs.

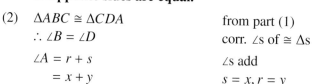

(1) In $\triangle ABC$ and $\triangle CDA$,

$s = x$	alt. $\angle$s, $\overline{AB} \parallel \overline{CD}$
$r = y$	alt. $\angle$s, $\overline{AD} \parallel \overline{BC}$
$AC = AC$	common
$\triangle ABC \cong \triangle CDA$	ASA
$\therefore AB = CD$ and $AD = BC$	corr. sides of $\cong$ $\triangle$s.

∴ **Opposite sides are equal.**

(2)

$\triangle ABC \cong \triangle CDA$	from part (1)
$\therefore \angle B = \angle D$	corr. $\angle$s of $\cong$ $\triangle$s
$\angle A = r + s$	$\angle$s add
$\quad = x + y$	$s = x, r = y$
$\quad = \angle C$	$\angle$s add.

∴ **Opposite angles are equal.**

(3)

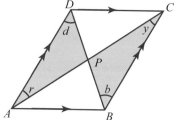

$\triangle ABC \cong \triangle CDA$	from part (1)
$r = y$	corr. $\angle$s of $\cong$ $\triangle$s
$AD = CB$	corr. sides of $\cong$ $\triangle$s
$b = d$	alt. $\angle$s, $\overline{AD} \parallel \overline{BC}$.
$\triangle ADP \cong \triangle CBP$	ASA
$\therefore AP = PC$ and $BP = PD$	corr. sides of $\cong$ $\triangle$s.

∴ **The diagonals bisect each other.**

These three properties can also be seen by symmetry — but it is not a folding symmetry. Instead, put a pin at the center of parallelogram (the point where the diagonals intersect) and rotate 180° around that point. Do you see why this symmetry gives all three properties (opposite sides equal, opposite angles equal, diagonals bisect)?

EXERCISE 4.1. *Try the activity suggested above using transparency sheet.*

The converse of each of these three properties is also true: If a quadrilateral satisfies any one of the conditions (1), (2), (3) above, then that quadrilateral is a parallelogram. Students can be led to this conclusion by working through the following eighth-grade activity.

EXERCISE 4.2. *The chart below gives four different criteria for recognizing parallelograms. Fill in the blanks to complete these sketches of proofs:*

If both pairs of opposite angles are equal, then the figure is a parallelogram. 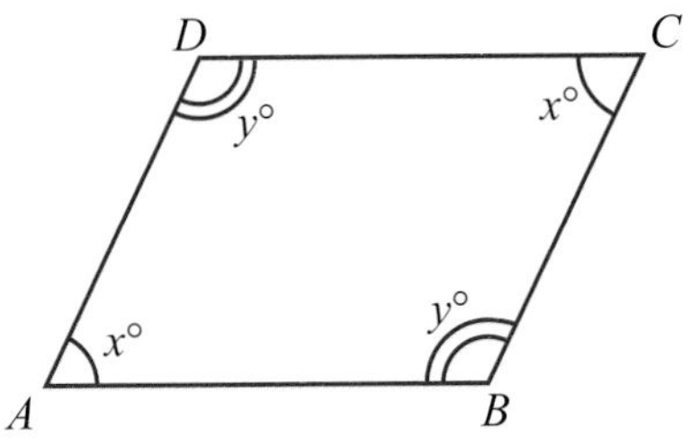 D C $y°$ $x°$ $x°$ $y°$ A B	$x + y + x + y =$ ____ $\angle$ sum n-gon $x + y = 180$ $\therefore \overline{AB} \parallel \overline{CD}$ int. $\angle$s converse. $\therefore \overline{AD} \parallel \overline{BC}$ _____ $\therefore ABCD$ is a parallelogram.
If both pairs of opposite sides are equal, then the figure is a parallelogram. 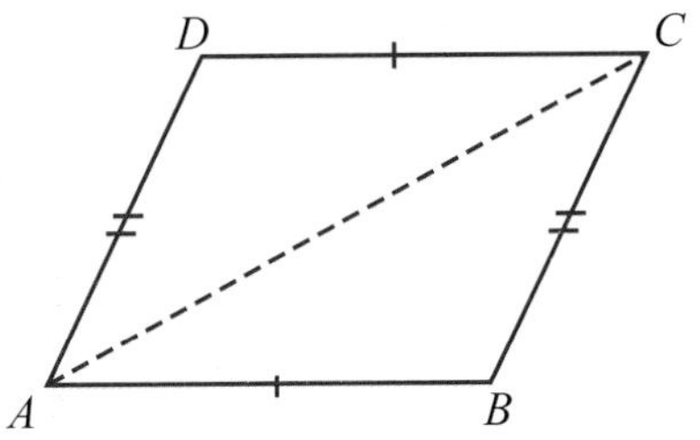 D C A B	$\triangle ABC \cong \triangle CDA$ _____ $\angle BAC = \angle DCA$ _____ $\angle CAD = \angle ACB$ _____ $\therefore \overline{AB} \parallel \overline{CD}$ alt. $\angle$s converse $\therefore \overline{AD} \parallel \overline{BC}$ alt. $\angle$s converse $\therefore ABCD$ is a _____
If the diagonals bisect each other, then the figure is a parallelogram. 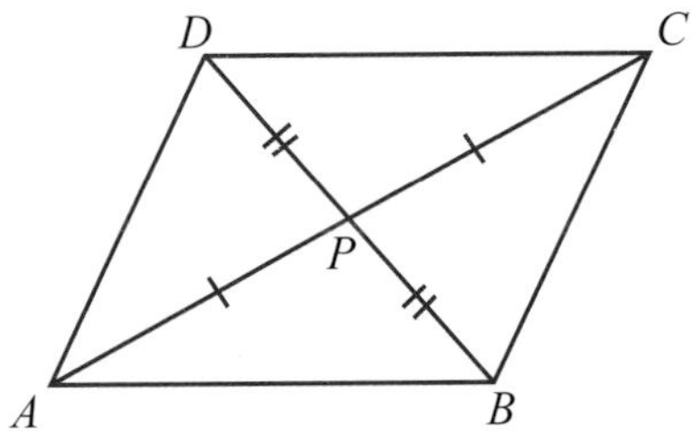 D C P A B	$\triangle APB \cong \triangle CPD$ _____ $\angle PAB = \angle PCD$ _____ ____ $\parallel$ ____ _____ Similarly, $\triangle APD \cong \triangle CPB$ _____ $\angle ADP = \angle CBP$ _____ ____ $\parallel$ ____ _____ $\therefore ABCD$ is a _____
If two opposite sides are equal and parallel, then the figure is a parallelogram. 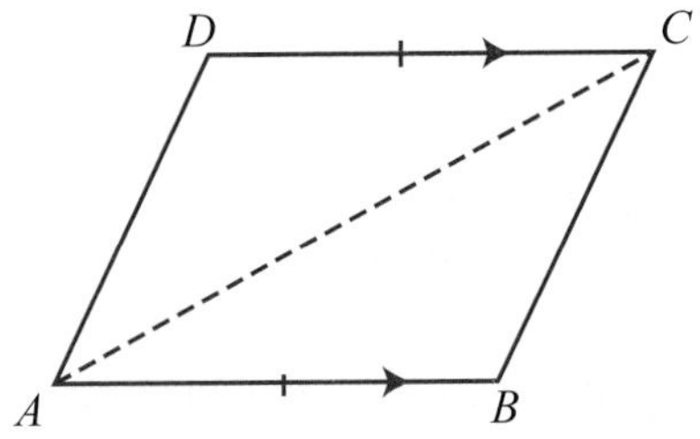 D C A B	$DC = AB$ given $\angle DCA = \angle BAC$ alt. $\angle$s, $\overline{AB} \parallel \overline{DC}$ $AC = AC$ common $\triangle ACD \cong \triangle CAB$ SAS $\angle DAC =$ ____ corr. $\angle$s, $\cong \triangle$ $\overline{AD} \parallel \overline{BC}$ _____ $\therefore ABCD$ is a _____

These criteria justify the "school definitions" of rhombus and rectangle (see page 46 and the comment on page 47). The standard definitions used in high school geometry are:

- A rhombus is a quadrilateral with all four sides equal in length.

- A rectangle is a quadrilateral with four right angles.

With these definitions, the second boxed criterion on the previous page shows that *every rhombus is a parallelogram* and the first criterion shows that *every rectangle is a parallelogram*. Thus we lose nothing by defining a rhombus to be "a parallelogram with four equal sides" and a rectangle to be "a parallelogram with four right angles", as we did on page 46.

Kites

By definition, a kite is a quadrilateral in which two adjacent sides have equal length and the remaining two sides also have equal length. A kite has the following properties:

1. There is a pair of equal opposite angles.

2. One of its diagonals bisects a pair of opposite angles.

3. The two diagonals are perpendicular.

The first two of these properties are obvious from symmetry. In the kite on the right, the line of symmetry is $\overline{BD}$; it splits the kite into two triangles that are congruent by SSS (or by symmetry). Therefore, $\angle A = \angle C$, which shows the first statement. Furthermore, $\overline{BD}$ bisects $\angle B$ and $\angle D$ (by symmetry or because these are corresponding angles of congruent triangles), which shows the second statement.

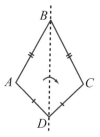

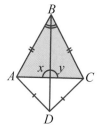

To see that the diagonals are perpendicular, note that the two shaded triangles pictured on the left are congruent by SAS. Angles x and y are therefore equal, so both are 90°. Thus the diagonals are perpendicular.

Quadrilateral Properties

We have seen that rectangles, rhombuses, and squares are also parallelograms. These figures therefore have all the properties of parallelograms. Likewise, rhombuses and squares are kites, so the properties of a kite also hold for rhombuses and squares. Below is a summary of the properties of quadrilaterals that are learned in grades K-8.

By definition, a *parallelogram* is a quadrilateral in which both pairs of opposite sides are parallel. For parallelograms,
 	
   1. both pairs of opposite sides are equal,
 	
   2. both pairs of opposite angles are equal,
 	
   3. the diagonals bisect each other, and
 	
   4. two opposite sides are equal and parallel.
 	
     Furthermore, any quadrilateral satisfying (1), (2), (3), or (4) is a parallelogram.	

By definition, a *kite* is a quadrilateral with two consecutive sides of equal length and the other two sides also of equal length. For kites,
 	
   1. at least one pair of opposite angles are equal,
 	
   2. there is a diagonal that bisects a pair of opposite angles, and
 	
   3. the diagonals are perpendicular to each other.
 	
     Furthermore, any quadrilateral satisfying (2) is a kite.	

By definition, a *rhombus* is a quadrilateral with all sides of equal length. A rhombus has all the properties of a parallelogram and of a kite, and the diagonals bisect the interior angles.	

By definition, a *rectangle* is a quadrilateral all of whose angles are right angles.
 	
   A rectangle has all of the properties of a parallelogram, and its diagonals are equal.
 	
   Furthermore, any quadrilateral whose diagonals are equal and bisect each other is a rectangle.	

By definition, a *square* is a rectangle with all sides of equal length. A square has the properties of a rectangle and of a rhombus.	

Curriculum Overview

Look how far we've come! In four chapters, we have followed the main thread of the geometry curriculum starting in Kindergarten and now we are reaching the level of beginning high school geometry. This upward path is built on two themes: solving word problems involving measurements, and solving unknown angle problems.

The part of the curriculum we have studied so far can be organized into four phases:

- **Grades 1–4.** Students learn to measure and calculate with lengths and angles.

- **Grades 4–6.** Students learn angle, triangle, and parallelogram facts (convincingly introduced by brief paper-folding, cutting, and measurement exercises). They use those facts to solve many unknown angle problems.

- **Grades 6–7.** Students learn parallel line facts and use them to give geometric proofs of some of the angle and triangle facts learned in grades 4–6. Students continue to solve many unknown angle problems, which now involve simple algebra.

- **Grades 7–8.** Congruence and similarity tests are introduced using constructions and measurement, and the Pythagorean Theorem is introduced with a simple proof. Students continue working on unknown angle problems and begin doing simple proofs.

Students with this background are well-prepared for a 9th or 10th grade geometry course that concentrates on the logical structure of geometry. By that time they have spent five years developing knowledge and intuition for geometry and logical deduction. This built-up intuition and knowledge make learning the "axiomatic approach" to geometry in high school courses *enormously easier.*

We have reached the limits of elementary school mathematics. The next section briefly describes some aspects of the "transformation" approach to geometry that are included in some elementary school curricula. After that, we will return to second grade and study how area is developed in elementary school.

Homework Set 16

1. Do Problem 2 on page 282 of NEM1. Copy only the letters for the properties (you don't need to write the sentence). For example, the first line of the table should start: "(a) T F T …".

2. Do all parts of Problem 3 on pages 283-284 of NEM1. Do not give proofs or Teacher's Solutions —just find the unknowns x and y in each figure.

3. Prove that $ABCD$ is a parallelogram.

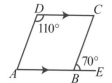

4. In the figure, $\overline{SR} \parallel \overline{PQ}$, $PS = SR$, and $PQ = QR$. Prove that $PQRS$ is a rhombus, i.e., prove that $PS = SR = PQ = QR$.

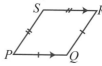

5. In the figure, $ABCD$ is a parallelogram, and $\overline{AE}$ and $\overline{CF}$ are perpendicular to $\overline{BD}$. Prove that $AE = CF$.

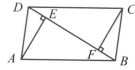

6. In the figure, *ACDF* is a rectangle and *BCEF* is a parallelogram. Prove that $\triangle ABF \cong \triangle DEC$.

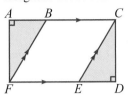

7. In the figure, *ABCD* is a rectangle, and *AP* = *CR* and *AS* = *CQ*. Prove that *PQRS* is a parallelogram.

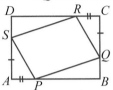

8. Give an Elementary Proof: the diagonals of a square are perpendicular. Start by drawing a picture and writing:

Given: Square *ABCD* with diagonals $\overline{AC}$ and $\overline{BD}$
To Prove: $\overline{AC} \perp \overline{BD}$.

9. Prove that a parallelogram with one right angle is a rectangle.

4.5 Transformations and Tessellations

This section describes two topics often used for "enrichment": transformations (which sometimes appear under the title "motion geometry") and tessellations (also called "tilings"). Both are serious subjects whose study is college-level mathematics. Both are also frequently taught in K-8 mathematics classes. At the K-8 level, these topics are rich in classroom activities, but the mathematical content sometimes gets lost. This section explains the mathematics that is involved and includes some additional "teacher-knowledge" information.

Here is one way to introduce the idea of transformations in the classroom. Begin by drawing a figure on a piece of cardboard. Lay an overhead projector transparency on it and trace the figure.

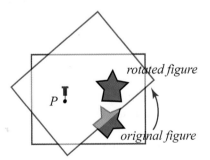

(1) At some point *P*, insert a pin through the transparency into the cardboard (this is the reason for using cardboard). Rotate the transparency. The traced figure moves to a new position. This motion is called a *rotation about P* and the moved figure is called a *rotation* of the original figure. (In many elementary school illustrations, the rotation is around a point *P* that lies inside the figure and is often the center of the figure.)

(2) Instead of inserting a pin, draw a line *L* on the cardboard and trace the line on the transparency. Slide the transparency along the line, keeping the traced line exactly on top of the line *L* while moving the figure to a new position. This motion is called a *translation parallel to L* and the moved figure is called a *translation* of the original figure.

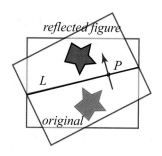

(3) Now mark a point P on L and the corresponding point on the traced copy of L. Turn over the transparency and align the traced line exactly on top of L with the two marked points aligned. This produces a mirror image of the original figure. The motion is called a *reflection across L*, and the moved figure is called a *reflection* of the original figure.

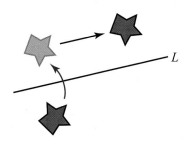

A *composite motion* is any succession of rotations, translations, and reflections. For example, reflecting across a line L and then translating in the direction of L is a composite motion called a *glide reflection*.

Transformations move the entire plane, including all figures within it. The transformed figure is called the *image* of the figure under the transformation. Notice that if you trace a segment or angle, moving the transparency does not affect the length or angle. Thus:

> For rotations, translations, reflections and their composites:
>
> - the image of a segment is a segment of equal length,
>
> - the image of an angle is an angle of equal measure,
>
> - the image of a figure is a congruent figure.

rigid motion

There is a more elementary version of these ideas that involves moving figures (rather than moving the entire plane). If students cut a figure out of cardboard and lay it on a sheet of paper, they are able to slide the figure around. The various ways of sliding and turning are called the *motions* of the figure. These are sometimes called *rigid motions* because the cardboard figure is rigid — it does not stretch or distort, and hence does not change lengths and angles.

In classroom language, a translation "moves the figure parallel to a line", a rotation "spins the figure", and a reflection "turns the figure over and places it on the other side of a given line". These descriptions are not precise, but they are enough for students to recognize two key points:

- A motion takes a figure to a figure with the "same size and shape".

- Every motion can be obtained as a succession of rotations, translations, and reflections.

These two points are the basis for the informal elementary school definition of congruence.

> Two figures are *congruent* if one is obtained from the other by a rigid motion.

The required motion can be thought of as a way of picking up the first figure and laying it down so that it exactly covers the second figure. Alternatively, one can think of sliding and flipping the first figure through a succession of rotations, translations, and reflections until it exactly matches the second figure.

Middle school students learn that congruence is defined by the requirement that corresponding sides and angles are equal. At that point a mathematical question arises: is it true that any two congruent figures are related by a succession of rotations, translations, and reflections? The answer is "Yes, that is a mathematical theorem" — but the proof is beyond K-8 mathematics. Nevertheless, the basic ideas, discussed next, are important teacher knowledge.

Isometries

One unifying idea in geometry is the notion of an "isometry". The mathematical study of isometries begins with the precise definition of a (general) *transformation* of the plane, which is defined in college-level mathematics as an "invertible mapping from the plane to the plane". For our purposes, it is enough to say that a transformation is any succession of rotations, translations, reflections and any kind of stretching and pulling that might be possible with a transparency sheet made of stretchable plastic.

transformation

DEFINITION 5.1. *A transformation that takes every line segment to a line segment of equal length is called an* isometry.

Thus isometries are "length-preserving transformations". They also preserve distances because the distance between two points is the length of a segment. The congruence tests for triangles show that isometries also preserve angles.

THEOREM 5.2. *Isometries preserve angles.*

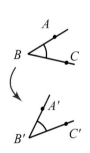

Given: A', B', and C' are obtained from
$\quad\quad$ A, B and C by an isometry.
To prove: $\angle B' = \angle B$
Constr.: Draw $\overline{AC}$ and $\overline{A'C'}$.

Proof. $\left.\begin{array}{l} A'B' = AB \\ B'C' = BC \\ A'C' = AC \end{array}\right\}$ isometries preserve lengths

$\triangle A'B'C' \cong \triangle ABD$ $\quad$ SSS

$\therefore \quad \angle B' = \angle B.$

Theorem 5.2, together with Definition 5.1, shows that isometries preserve both lengths and angles. Consequently, they take triangles to congruent triangles. In fact, *isometries move any figure to one that is congruent to the original.*

Rotations, translations and reflections preserve lengths, so are isometries. What other kinds of isometries are there? The following theorem, which is proved in college geometry courses, provides a complete list. The statement involves two new terms. The isometry that does nothing — that does not move points, lines, and figures at all — is called the *identity*. In general, an isometry will move most points of the plane; the points that are not moved are called the *fixed points* of the isometry.

identity

fixed points

THEOREM 5.3. *All isometries are composites of rotations, translations and reflections. In fact, every isometry is one of four types: a rotation, a translation, a reflection or a glide reflection. Specifically,*

a) *The only isometry that fixes 3 non-collinear points is the identity.*

b) *Any isometry that fixes 2 points is a reflection across the line through those points or is the identity.*

c) *Any isometry that fixes exactly 1 point P is either a rotation around P, or the composite of a rotation around a point P and a reflection across a line through P.*

d) *Any isometry that fixes no points is either a translation or a glide reflection.*

To get a sense of a), put 3 pins through your tracing paper and try to move it. You can't! Inserting 2 pins, then 1 pin, will similarly provide intuition (but not a mathematical argument) for b) and c). Statement d) is less intuitive. It includes the fact, which is not at all evident, that the composite of a rotation and a glide reflection along a line *L* is a glide reflection along a different line.

The details are complicated. Understanding the reasoning requires mathematical knowledge and maturity beyond the K-8 level. In other countries, transformations are not introduced until after students have begun using coordinate systems in the plane. At that point, students have the geometric tools and experience to study transformations *as mathematics*. In contrast, many U.S. curricula and state standards introduce motions at the level of cutting and folding paper in elementary or middle school, and then abandon it. These are fine activities for enrichment and building intuition, but teachers should be aware that the study of transformations is not part of the main story-line of geometry in the lower grades, which focuses on measurement and deduction.

Tessellations

One often sees floor tiles and wall decorations arranged in geometric patterns formed by joining together copies of geometric figures without gaps or overlaps. These patterns are called *tessellations* (the ancient Romans made mosaics from clay and glass tiles called *tessella*).

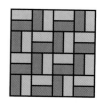

regular tessellation

More precisely, a *tessellation* or *tiling* of the plane is a collection of polygonal regions whose union is the entire plane and whose interiors do not intersect. A tessellation made of congruent regular polygons is called a *regular tessellation*.

It is a useful exercise to give students examples of tessellations and have them shade exactly one of the congruent polygons in the tiling. They can then visually test whether the tessellation is regular by checking the two requirements: a) is the tile a regular polygon? and b) are all the tiles in the tessellation congruent to the shaded one?

There are only three regular tessellations. The three possibilities are formed by equilateral triangles, squares, and regular hexagons as shown.

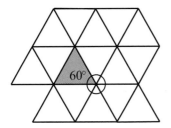 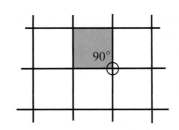 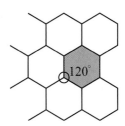

The proof that these are the only regular tessellations is an interesting classroom exercise in grades 5-7. The proof is based on the fact, which is evident from the pictures, that each vertex is surrounded by congruent angles. Thus, in a regular tessellation by n-gons

    (i) every interior angle of each tile is a factor of $360°$

and we know (from Section 3.3) that

    (ii) interior angles have equal measure, and

    (iii) the sum of interior angles is $180°(n-2)$.

With these facts students can show, as you will in a homework problem, that the only regular tessellations are the three pictured above.

symmetry of a tessellation

A *symmetry* of a tessellation is a transformation that moves the tessellation onto itself. For example, a tessellation by squares can be moved onto itself by translating one or more units up, down, left, or right, or by rotating $90°$ around the center point of one square. Fancy tessellations can be created by modifying simple tessellations by such transformations. Here is an example.

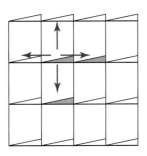 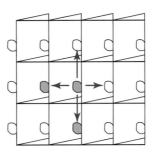 

Choose part of one rectangle and translate it to all rectangles.

Translate another part.

Paint your tiles for visual appeal.

A *semi-regular tessellation* is a tiling using two or more tile shapes, each a regular polygon, so that the arrangement of polygons at every vertex point is identical (i.e., the same tiles surround each vertex in the same order). It is a mathematical theorem (too difficult for school mathematics) that there are exactly 11 such semi-regular tessellations (including the 3 regular tessellations). There are also non-periodic tessellations called "Penrose tilings".

Elementary students can have fun with tessellations. Making and coloring tessellations is an excellent project for the end of the school year when summer is coming and students need a break from learning mathematics.

Homework Set 17

1. In this problem you will determine which regular n-gons tessellate. The steps outline a typical classroom exercise.

   a) Recall that the sum of the interior angles of any n-gon is $(n-2)180°$. Use this fact and a sketch to explain why the measure of each interior angle for any n-gon is
   $$I_n = 180° - \frac{360°}{n}.$$

   b) List all the factors of 360 greater than or equal to 60.

   c) Fill in the following table.

# of sides	Interior angle	Factor of 360°?	Tessellate?
3	60°	✓	✓
4			
5		✗	
6			
7			
8			
9			
10			

   d) Use the formula for I_n and some algebra to show that whenever n is bigger than 6, I_n is between 120° and 180°.

   e) Explain why your answers to parts a)-d) show that regular n-gons tessellate only for $n = 3, 4$ and 6.

2. Study the last picture of this section. Follow the same procedure to make two simple tessellations. Draw at least 6 tiles for each. Coloring may make your picture clearer.

3. Do the following constructions.

   a) Draw a triangle $\triangle ABC$ and a ray $\overrightarrow{DE}$. Show how to move the triangle $\triangle ABC$ 4 cm in the direction $\overrightarrow{DE}$ using only a compass, ruler, and a set-square.

   b) Draw a triangle $\triangle ABC$ and a line l. Show how to reflect the triangle $\triangle ABC$ across the line l using a compass and straightedge.

   c) Draw a triangle $\triangle ABC$ and mark a point D. Show how to rotate the triangle $\triangle ABC$ about the point D an angle measure of 45°, using a compass and straightedge.

4. (Study the textbook!)   Read pages 76–79 in Primary Math 5B. Use graph paper to show how Shape B on page 78 can tessellate (graph paper can be obtained from www.printfreegraphpaper.com).

5. (Study the textbook!)   Assuming that 1 to 2 pages can be covered in a day's lesson, estimate how many class days fifth grade Primary Math teachers spend on tessellations.

6. Explain, with pictures, why every parallelogram tessellates.

7. Explain why every triangle can tessellate (this can be done with one sentence and one picture using your answer to Problem 6).

8. ✳ This problem takes you through a classroom explanation of the fact that every quadrilateral tessellates.

   On a sheet of thin cardboard, draw a quadrilateral about 3 inches across. Make the sides straight (use a ruler) and make the four interior angles have clearly different measures (your quadrilateral needn't be convex). Label the interior angles w, x, y, z in clockwise order.

   a) What is the sum $w + x + y + z$ of the interior angles?

   Cut out your quadrilateral with scissors; this is your "template". On a large blank sheet of paper, make a copy of your quadrilateral by tracing around your template. Call this figure "Tile 1" and label its interior angles w, x, y, z as on the template. Draw additional tiles by repeatedly applying the following step (which is named to indicate the edge we fill across).

   STEP xy: Without flipping the template, align the template along the edge between interior angles x and y of one of the previously-drawn tiles so that y on the template matches with x on the tile and vice versa. Trace around the template to create a new tile. Label the interior angles of the new tile w, x, y, z as on the template.

   Do STEP xy to draw Tile 2. Then do STEP wx on Tile 1 to draw Tile 3.

   (b) Look at the vertex of Tile 1 labeled by angle x. It is surrounded by 3 tiled angles and an un-tiled angle. The un-tiled angle has the same measure as which interior angle of your template? Why?

   (c) Fill in the blanks: one can fill in this un-tiled angle either by doing STEP ___ on Tile ___ or by doing STEP ___ on Tile ___. Do these give the same result?

   (d) After drawing Tile 4 by your first answer to (c), explain why the paired sides of Tiles 2 and 4 have equal length.

   (e) Similarly, explain why the paired sides of Tiles 3 and 4 have equal length.

   (f) Draw at least 6 tiles. Can this tiling procedure be continued indefinitely?

CHAPTER 5

Area

Young children can intuitively judge the size of flat objects. They have no trouble spotting the biggest cookie or the largest picture. But it is difficult to turn this intuition into numbers and measurements. There are simple devices to measure length, weight and capacity (rulers, scales and measuring cups), but no device for measuring area, which is a more complicated process. As a result, area enters the curriculum later than length, weight, and capacity, and requires far more time to develop.

To measure length, one fixes a unit segment and uses the fact that any segment is congruent to a multiple of the unit segment. To measure area, we similarly fix a unit square and define area of a region as the number of unit squares (and fractions of unit squares) needed to fill the region. Thus second and third grade children are taught to find areas by counting unit squares.

However, one cannot get far by simply counting squares. Most regions are not rectangular and cannot easily be decomposed into unit squares. Consequently, instruction in grades 4 and 5 emphasizes the abstract properties of area listed in Section 5.2. The properties are used in grades 5-7 to derive formulas for the area of triangles, parallelograms, trapezoids, and circles.

This chapter examines the initial stages in the curriculum sequence for area. The story is continued in Chapter 8.

5.1 Area Units

disk
composite region

A portion of the plane is called a **region**. A triangular region is a triangle together with its interior, and a polygonal region is a polygon together with its interior. A circular region is a *disk*. A region formed from several pieces is a *composite region*.

triangle *triangular region* *rectangular region* *disk or circular region* *composite region*

Area is a way of associating to each region R a quantity Area(R) that reflects our intuitive sense of "how big" the region is without reference to the shape of the region. Area is defined by the same two-step scheme used to define length, weight, and capacity:

- Choose a "unit region" and declare its area to be 1 *unit of area*.

- Express the areas of other regions as multiples of this unit area.

In this way, area is expressed as a number times a unit of area, just as length is a number times a unit of length. In particular, *whenever an area is stated, the unit of area must be specified.*

In common English, one sometimes speaks of a "triangular area". But it is important not to confuse a figure with a measure of its size. Therefore, in mathematics geometric figures are always called regions, never "areas". Teachers can bring clarity to classroom discussions by insisting that the terms "region" and "area" be used correctly.

Choosing a Unit Region: What Shape?

In all measurement systems, the unit region is always chosen to be a square. Elementary students are likely to wonder: Why squares? Here is a classroom exercise that encourages students to think about the advantages of squares.

EXERCISE 1.1. *An interior designer wants to compare the areas of two rooms in a house. Her plan is to cover the floors with identical tiles and count the tiles. She has available boxes of tiles in four different shapes. Which shapes are convenient for her purpose?*

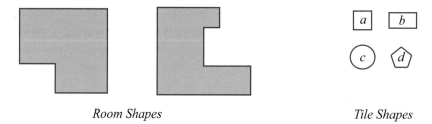

Room Shapes   *Tile Shapes*

Tiles (a) and (b) can be fitted together with *no gaps* — they tessellate. Tiles (c) and (d) cannot be fitted together without gaps.

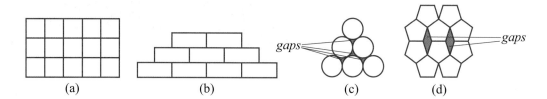

Thus squares and rectangles make convenient area units because they tessellate, while circles and pentagons do not. Squares are the most convenient for two other reasons:

- squares tessellate the plane, and little squares can tessellate big squares,
- this choice results in simple formulas for the areas of triangles and parallelograms.

Square Units

For each unit of length, a **unit square** is any square whose sides are 1 unit long. The corresponding unit of area, called a **square unit**, is defined as the area of a unit square. The pictures show two such units: one square centimeter, written 1 cm^2, and one square inch, written 1 in^2.

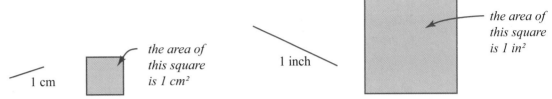

The notation is designed so that one "squares" units in the same way one squares numbers. For example, for a square whose sides are all 1 cm long,

$$\text{Area} = 1\text{ cm} \times 1\text{ cm} = (1 \times 1)\text{ cm} \times \text{cm} = 1\text{ cm}^2.$$

One gets other units similarly: 1 square meter, 1 square kilometer, 1 square foot, 1 square yard, 1 square mile. The procedure is the same: choose a unit of length, construct the corresponding unit square and declare the area of this unit square to be a unit of area. Note the terminology: a unit square is a geometric figure (a square) while a square unit is a unit of area.

square unit

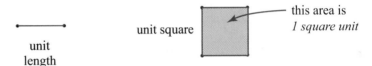

A Teaching Sequence—The Area of a Rectangle

Grade 2 — Counting Square Units. The Primary Mathematics curriculum introduces area in second grade with square tiles. This is the first step in a teaching sequence of the form described in Section 1.2. Standard area units like in^2 and cm^2 are not discussed; after all, second graders are still learning about length measurements. There are no area "formulas" yet. Students are simply directed to count the tiles in a region; the total number is called the area. The key fact is announced by a pictured "student helper" in the margin of the textbook:

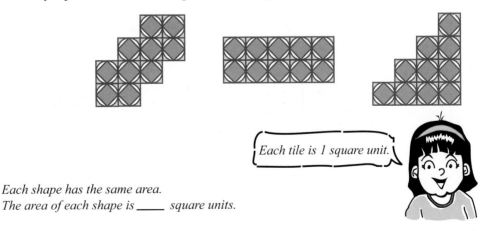

Each tile is 1 square unit.

Each shape has the same area.
The area of each shape is _____ square units.

Second grade students compare the size of regions by counting squares. In these activities, they are using the following definition of area.

DEFINITION 1.2 (School Definition). *The* area *of a region tiled by unit squares is the number of squares it contains.*

Grade 3 — Rectangles whose side lengths are whole numbers.   Third grade students again find areas by counting squares, but now begin using standard units: square centimeters and square meters. There is another twist to these exercises:

EXERCISE 1.3. *Read pages 96 to 100 of Primary Math 3B. How do the students find the areas of the triangles in these pictures?*

Many of these grade 3 problems are designed to make it difficult to guess which region is largest. Such problems help students by emphasizing that area is defined by counting units, not by visualization. They also allow teachers to assess whether students are counting or guessing.

The next conceptual step occurs at the end of Primary Math 3B. A single picture, shown below, uses the rectangular array interpretation of multiplication (learned in grade 2) to show that *areas can be calculated by multiplication.*

Find the area of each of the following rectangles.

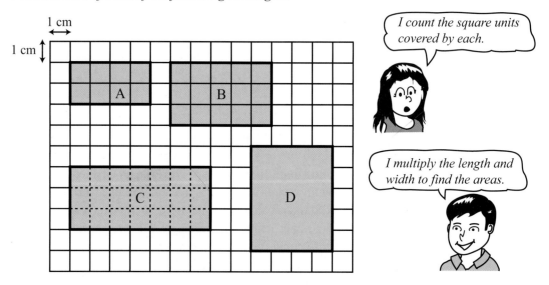

In this cleverly-drawn picture, the rectangular array is visible inside figures *A* and *B*, fades in figure *C*, and has disappeared in figure *D*. Figure *D* shows students that area can be calculated by multiplication *even without visible square units.*

Area of a Rectangle = Length × Width.

This formula is not a definition; area continues to be defined as the number of unit squares. Instead, the formula is a procedure — a quick way to calculate area without actually counting every individual square. Its value is obvious: one wouldn't want to find the area of the rectangle on the right by counting squares!

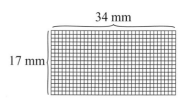

Teaching Comments. After students have begun using multiplication to find areas, it is helpful for the teacher to occasionally reverse the fading process to remind students that they are still counting "hidden" unit squares. Thus Primary Math 4A includes some pictures like this:

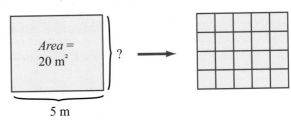

The rectangle has area 20 m². What is its perimeter?

distributive property

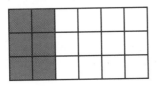

Recall that multiplication is introduced in grades 1 and 2 using three models: repeated addition, groups of objects, and rectangular arrays. Rectangular arrays are useful for illustrating the properties of multiplication, including the distributive property (see Section 1.5 of *Elementary Mathematics for Teachers*).

$3 \times (2 + 4) = 3 \times 2 + 3 \times 4$

After area is introduced, rectangular arrays have a new role: they link the product of $a \times b$ to the area of a rectangle with side lengths a and b. This viewpoint is called the *area model* of multiplication.

Grade 5 — Rectangles with fractional side lengths. Fifth grade teachers use area models to explain the algorithm for multiplying fractions. Exactly the same pictures are used later in the school year to show why the same "Length × Width" procedure correctly gives the area of rectangles whose side lengths are fractions. Study the teacher's demonstration below to understand the explanation.

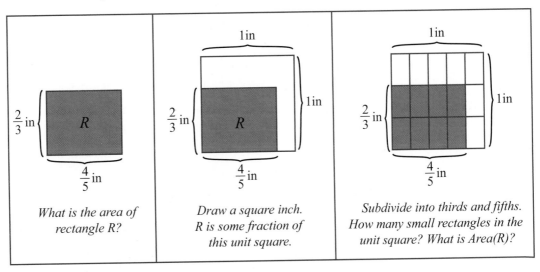

What is the area of rectangle R?

Draw a square inch. R is some fraction of this unit square.

Subdivide into thirds and fifths. How many small rectangles in the unit square? What is Area(R)?

The third picture shows that R is composed of 8 small rectangles, each with area $\frac{1}{15}$ in², so Area(R) = $\frac{8}{15}$ in². This is indeed the same as

$$\text{Length} \times \text{Width} = \frac{2}{3} \text{ in} \times \frac{4}{5} \text{ in} = \frac{2 \times 4}{3 \times 5} \text{ in}^2 = \frac{8}{15} \text{ in}^2.$$

In fact, the third picture is exactly the type of diagram used in Primary Math 5A to explain multiplication of fractions.

Middle School—Rectangles with real number side lengths. At this point, we know that "Length × Width" gives the area of rectangles whose side lengths are whole numbers, fractions and decimals. What about irrational side lengths? What, for example, is the area of the darkly-shaded rectangle in the first picture below? We can use the following multi-step approach, which is based on the decimal expansions.

$$\sqrt{2} = 1.41421\ldots \qquad \text{and} \qquad \sqrt{5} = 2.23606\ldots .$$

- First, round off the side lengths to the nearest whole number: $\sqrt{2} \approx 1$ and $\sqrt{5} \approx 2$. As the middle picture shows, the darkly-shaded region is almost covered by a 1 cm × 2 cm rectangle, so its area is approximately 2 cm².

- Rounding to the nearest tenth, we have $\sqrt{2} \approx 1.4$ and $\sqrt{5} \approx 2.2$. Approximating the darkly-shaded region by a 1.4 cm × 2.2 cm rectangle as in the third picture gives a better approximation: Area ≈ 3.08 cm².

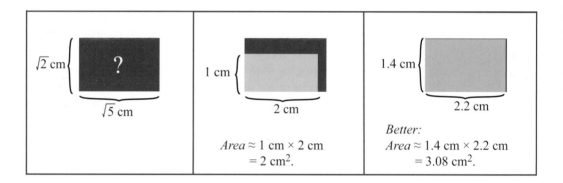

The next four approximations to the area are

$$
\begin{aligned}
1.41 \times 2.23 &= \mathbf{3.1}443\ldots \\
1.414 \times 2.236 &= \mathbf{3.16}170\ldots \\
1.4142 \times 2.2360 &= \mathbf{3.162}1512\ldots \\
1.41421 \times 2.23606 &= \mathbf{3.162}258\ldots
\end{aligned}
$$

At each step we use the area formula with finite decimals. Looking at the boldface digits, it is clear in this example—and it can be proved in general—that this process yields better and better approximations to the decimal expansion of a single number, namely the product

$$\sqrt{2} \times \sqrt{5} = \sqrt{10} = 3.162277\ldots$$

In fact, this method of ever-better approximations is exactly the way one finds the product of any two irrational numbers (see Section 9.3 of Elementary Mathematics for Teachers). We conclude that the area of a rectangle is Length × Width when the side lengths are any real number.

In the end, the formula Area = Length × Width is the same regardless of whether the side lengths are whole numbers, fractions, or irrational numbers. However, the *explanations are different.* All three cases must be addressed to justify the formula. Textbooks usually give pictures that illustrate the cases of whole number and fractions, and do not discuss irrational lengths. But in all curricula students are expected to understand that the formula applies even when the side lengths are irrational.

Homework Set 18

Work with area starts early in the Primary Mathematics curriculum. Students find areas by counting unit squares in grade 2. In Primary Math 3B, area units are defined and used. Area and perimeter are introduced in the same set of lessons, bringing out the similarities and the differences between length and area.

1. (*Study the Textbook!*) Read pages 96–100 in Primary Math 3B. In the first exercise, students use a "non-standard unit" — a square card of unspecified size.

   a) After that, which standard units are introduced?

   b) How many class days are spent on this material? (The arrows at the bottom of the pages refer students to 1-night homework exercises in the Workbooks.)

2. (*Study the Textbook!*) In Primary Math 3B, answer Problems 1-6 on pages 96-100. What is the point of Problem 1 on page 97?

3. Draw — actual size — a square of size 1 cm by 1 cm and a square of size 1 in by 1 in.

4. (*Study the Textbook!*) Read pages 101-103 in Primary Math 3B.

   a) Write down the 3rd grade definition of perimeter given here.

   b) The three examples on page 101 all have the same perimeter. What point does this illustrate?

   c) What practical difficulties will students have doing Problem 1 on page 102? (If you aren't sure, try doing the problem!)

   d) After doing Problems 3-5, students should understand what fact about the relationship between area and perimeter?

5. (*Study the Textbook!*) Page 105 of Primary Math 3B illustrates the formula for the area of a rectangle whose sides have whole number lengths. Examine the pictures carefully. Describe how this sequence of pictures evolves:

what is the difference between rectangles A and B and rectangle C, and between rectangles C and D?

6. (*Study the Textbook!*) Continuing in Problem 2 on page 106, what is the difference between the rectangles in parts (a) and (b) versus those in parts (c) and (d)? The rectangle in part (e) is tilted; what do students learn from this?

7. Do all problems in Practice 9A on page 107 of Primary Math 3B.

8. In terms of area, the commutative property can be interpreted as the statement: *The area of a rectangle is Length × Width and is also Width × Length.* What is the interpretation of the distributive property in terms of area? (See the picture in this section.)

9. Use the area model to justify the statement that $2\frac{1}{2} \times 3\frac{1}{4} = 8\frac{1}{8}$. (Draw a diagram and show the reasoning).

10. Recall that one decimeter is 10 centimeters (1 dm = 10 cm). Draw — actual size – a square of size 1 dm by 1 dm.

11. Draw a rectangle 1.5 dm by 0.7 dm (actual size). Give a series of pictures and 1-sentence instructions for a class that show how to calculate the area in square decimeters (dm^2) by the following steps. *Suggestion: look over pages 331-332 of NEM1 before starting.*

    a) Divide length and width into centimeters and make a grid of 1 cm squares.

    b) Find the area in cm^2 by multiplication.

    c) Separately find the number of cm^2 in 1 dm^2.

    d) Express the area of your rectangle in dm^2.

5.2 Rectangles and Area Properties

We saw in the previous section that area is measured in two steps. One first chooses a unit length (e.g., 1 cm, 1 m, 1 in, 1 ft, 1 mile) and constructs the corresponding unit square (1 cm², 1 m², etc.). The area of this unit square is called *one square unit* and written (name of unit)².

The area of this square is 1 square centimeter.

Area = 1 cm².

The next step is to express areas of other polygonal regions in terms of the area unit. It is not efficient — or even possible — to find areas of polygons by counting unit squares. Thus, beginning around grade 4, curricula begin developing more useful methods for finding areas. The key ideas are neatly summarized in the four "Area Properties" described in this section. At the end of the section we also look at common misconceptions about the relationship between area and perimeter.

The Properties of Area

Three vocabulary words are useful in discussions about regions and area. The **union** of two regions R and S, written $R \cup S$, consists of all points that lie in R or in S. The **intersection** of R and S, written $R \cap S$, consists of all points that lie in both R and S (the word intersection is already familiar from phrases such as "the point where the two lines intersect"). Finally, recall that two polygonal regions are *congruent* if, under some correspondence, all corresponding segments and angles have equal measure.

intersection $R \cap S$ *union* $R \cup S$

Intuition about area is built up in the Primary Mathematics curriculum in grades 2, 3 and 4. Four key principles are introduced. Teachers should never assume that the principles are obvious; all four must be explicitly stated, practiced in problems, and understood by every student.

1. Area is positive for regions that "have interiors". Points and segments have area 0.

2. From the time area is first introduced, exercises and models implicitly use the fact that *congruent regions have the same area*. This principle is being used in the grade 3 fraction problem on the right, even though the problem does not mention either area or congruence!

What fraction of the pentagon is shaded?

3. Grade 3 students learn that the area of rectangles can be found by multiplying Length $\times$ Width (see page 105 of Primary Math 3B).

4. Grade 4 students compute areas by decomposing them into rectangles and adding areas. Regions that can be decomposed into simple pieces are called **composite regions**.

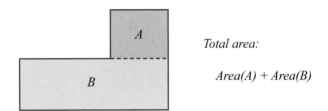

Total area:

Area(A) + Area(B)

These four properties underlie all discussions of area from grade 3 on. We will refer to them often, using the following short form:

AREA PROPERTIES. To each polygonal region R we associate a number, written Area(R) and called the **area of** R, with the following properties:

1. For any region R, Area(R) ≥ 0 (Abbreviation: **area $\geq$ 0**).

2. Congruent figures have equal area (Abbreviation: $\cong$ **figs**).

3. If two figures R and S intersect only in vertices and sides (or not at all), then their areas add:
$$\text{Area}(R \cup S) = \text{Area}(R) + \text{Area}(S) \quad \text{(Abbreviation: } \textbf{areas add}\text{)}.$$

4. The area of a rectangular region R is the product of the lengths of two adjacent sides:
$$\text{Area}(R) = \text{Length} \times \text{Width} \quad \text{(Abbreviation: } \textbf{area of rect.}\text{)}.$$

All facts about the area of polygonal regions are consequences of these four properties. Some consequences are intuitive and some are not. Here is one fact that children know instinctively; the proof shows how it follows from the area properties.

THEOREM 2.1. *If region R is contained in region S, then*
$$\text{Area}(S) \geq \text{Area(R)}.$$

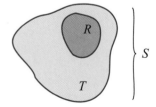

Proof. Let T be the lightly shaded region pictured; T is the set of points in S but not in R. Then $S = R \cup T$ with no intersection, so

$$\begin{aligned} \text{Area(S)} \quad &= \quad \text{Area}(R) + \text{Area}(T) \quad &\text{areas add} \\ &\geq \quad \text{Area}(R) \quad &\text{Area}(T) \geq 0. \quad \square \end{aligned}$$

Property 3 ("areas add") is also intuitive except for one point of possible confusion: it does not hold for regions whose interiors overlap.

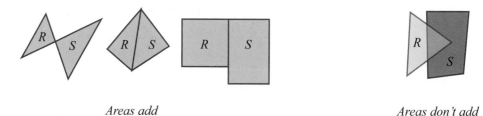

Areas add   *Areas don't add*

There is a refined version of the "areas add" property that that *does* apply to overlapping regions. It also is a consequence of the four properties. It is stated in the following theorem as a formula, but it is the reasoning used in the proof that is most valuable for students. (The formula is also used in probability; see Chapter 10.)

THEOREM 2.2. *For any two regions R and S,*

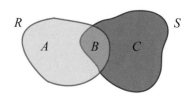

$$\text{Area}(R \cup S) = \text{Area}(R) + \text{Area}(S) - \text{Area}(R \cap S).$$

Proof. Let A be the set of points in R but not in S, let B be the intersection $R \cap S$, and let C be the set of points in S but not in R. Then

$\text{Area}(S) = \text{Area}(B) + \text{Area}(C)$	areas add
$\text{Area}(R \cup S) = \text{Area}(R) + \text{Area}(C)$	areas add
$\quad = \text{Area}(R) + (\text{Area}(S) - \text{Area}(B))$	from the first line
$\quad = \text{Area}(R) + \text{Area}(S) - \text{Area}(R \cap S)$	def. of B.

Area of Regions with Holes.

Students begin calculating the area of regions with holes in Primary Mathematics 4A. A preliminary step is finding the area of a region that *almost* has a hole in it.

EXERCISE 2.3. *The following pictures illustrate a 4th grade class as they find the area of a composite region. Which area properties are they using?*

The third student has used an important idea: instead of decomposing and adding areas, he has *extended* the region and *subtracted* the area of a "missing part". Subtraction can be used in many problems involving "regions with holes". The method can be summarized this way:

regions
with holes

$$\text{Area(Region)} \ = \ \text{Area(Region} \cup \text{Hole)} \ - \ \text{Area(Hole)}.$$

EXERCISE 2.4 (4th grade). *A rectangular carpet is placed on a wood floor which measures 7 m by 8 m. It leaves a margin 1 m wide around it. Find the area of the visible wood floor.*

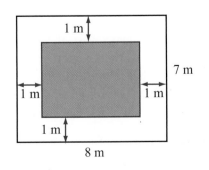

Teacher's Solution:

Area of Floor: $8 \text{ m} \times 7 \text{ m} = 56 \text{ m}^2$.

Carpet has: Width: $8 \text{ m} - 2 \text{ m} = 6 \text{ m}$,
                   Length: $7 \text{ m} - 2 \text{ m} = 5 \text{ m}$,
                   Area: $6 \text{ m} \times 5 \text{ m} = 30 \text{ m}^2$.

Difference: $56 \text{ m}^2 - 30 \text{ m}^2 = 26 \text{ m}^2$.

There are 26 m^2 of wood floor visible.

Regions-with-holes problems are extended to triangular regions in grade 5 and to circular regions in grade 6. Seventh grade students use the same method to find the volume of solids with holes. The figures below illustrate the sequence (in the actual problems, side lengths and radii are given).

Grade 5   *Grade 6*   *Grade 7*

Here is a cautionary note for teachers. Students often indicate areas by writing numbers in sub-regions, as in the left-hand picture below. Such shorthand notations help them solve problems quickly. But when teachers use the same shorthand, other students may misinterpret the numbers as lengths unless units are also written, as in the right-hand picture. Remember, *whenever a measurement is stated, the units should be included.*

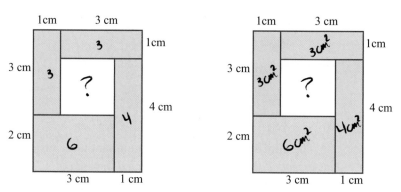

Area and Perimeter

A homework problem in the previous section pointed out that third grade students learn to find the perimeter of simple figures.

> The **perimeter** of a polygon is the sum of the lengths of the sides of the polygon.

Does perimeter determine area? For a square, yes: if you know the perimeter you can find the side length and hence the area. For a circle, yes: if you know the perimeter (i.e., the circumference) you can find the radius and hence the area. It also seems intuitive that regions with larger perimeter should have larger area. But for general shapes, *perimeter is not related to area*. They are different types of measurements, and they are expressed using different units.

Here are some instructional counterexamples emphasizing the fact that perimeter is unrelated to area. It is not hard to draw figures with

- Same area but different perimeters:

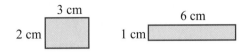

- Same perimeter but different areas:

Also notice that one can decrease area without changing the perimeter by "flattening":

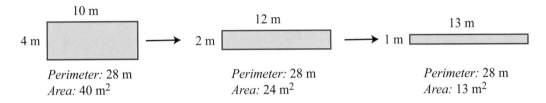

We can continue, making the height 1 cm, then 1 mm. In fact, by flattening enough we can make the area as close to zero as we might want!

EXAMPLE 2.5. *What are the side lengths of the largest rectangular field that can be enclosed with 20 meters of fencing?*

If the field is a rectangle with perimeter 20, then half the perimeter is 10. One possibility is a 5×5 square S. Any other possibility has one side more than 5 and one side less than 5. If we write the longer side as $5 + x$ then the shorter side is $5 - x$ (since the sum of these is 10). Then

$$\begin{aligned} \text{Area}(R) &= (5 + x)(5 - x) \\ &= 25 - x^2. \end{aligned}$$

When $x = 0$ the rectangle is a square with $\text{Area}(S) = 25$. For any other case, x^2 is positive and the equation says that

$$\text{Area}(R) < 25 = \text{Area}(S).$$

That is, the area of the rectangle is less than the area of the square. Thus the rectangular field with the largest area is the 5 m by 5 m square.

The result is similar if we fix the area and ask which rectangle of that area has the minimum perimeter. Either way, squares are the most efficient rectangles:

- Among rectangles with a fixed perimeter, squares have the largest area.

- Among rectangles with a fixed area, squares have the smallest perimeter.

Of all shapes, circles are the most efficient shape, as stated below. The facts are almost identical to the ones for rectangles, but their proof is much more difficult and is well beyond the level of K-8 mathematics.

- Among all shapes with a fixed perimeter, circles have the largest area.

- Among all shapes with a fixed area, circles have the smallest perimeter.

Homework Set 19

1. Do Problems 3–5 on pages 102–103 of Primary Math 3B mentally. What idea is taught in these problems?

2. (*Study the Textbook!*) Answer the following questions about Primary Math 4A as you read and mentally do the problems.

   a) Page 84 recalls the meaning of the area and the _____ of a rectangle. Write down these definitions exactly as they are given.

   b) Answer problems 1-5 on pages 85-86. In which of these problems are we given the width and height and asked to simply calculate width × height?

3. (*Study the Textbook!*) In Primary Math 4A, page 87 introduces the idea of decomposing figures into rectangles to find their area.

   a) Answer the two questions on page 87.

   b) If you know only the perimeter of a figure (without a picture), can you determine its area? Why or why not?

   c) If you know only the area of a figure (without a picture), can you determine its perimeter? Why or why not?

4. (*Study the Textbook!*) Solve Problems 1 and 2 on page 88 (examine the method and write down 2 numbers for each). Note the hints given by the "student helpers" in the margin.

5. (*Study the Textbook!*) On pages 89-90 of Primary Math 4A:

   a) Answer Problem 3.

   b) Do Problem 4 first by dividing the shaded region into 3 rectangles, then by the method described by the student helper in the margin. Which is easier?

c) Answer Problem 5.

d) Answer Problem 6.

6. In Primary Math 4A, answer all Problems in Practice 7A, pages 91-93.

7. (*Study the Textbook!*) In Primary Mathematics 4A,

   a) Were there any problems that involved lengths or areas that were fractions or decimals?

   b) All measurements and answers involved which units?

8. Give a complete proof: In a parallelogram ABCD, the diagonal $\overline{AC}$ bisects the parallelogram into 2 congruent triangles $\triangle ABC$ and $\triangle CDA$.

9. Which two area properties allow you to conclude that

$$\text{Area}(\triangle ABC) = \frac{1}{2}\,\text{Area}(ABCD)?$$

10. Dana said that the shaded triangle has area 6 cm^2 because "it's half the area of the rectangle". Check *all* of the area properties she was implicitly using.

3 cm

4 cm

☐ area is ≥ 0

☐ $\cong$ figures

☐ areas add

☐ area of rect = $L \times W$.

11. Describe a rectangle whose perimeter is over 100 ft but whose area is less than 1 ft^2.

5.3 Area of Triangles, Parallelograms and Trapezoids

The original definition of area as a count of unit squares does not provide a practical way to find the area of most triangles. In fact, at this stage *thinking about unit squares is not productive.* The pictures below illustrate the difficulty. For isoceles right triangles, one can find the area by counting squares, but the process does not suggest the expression "$\frac{1}{2}$ base × height". For other right triangles, you cannot even find the area by counting squares!

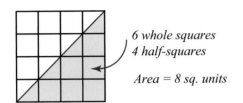

6 whole squares
4 half-squares

Area = 8 sq. units

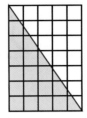

12 whole squares. How much area is in the partial squares?

Area = ??

To progress, one must use the area properties listed in the previous section. It is the area properties, not counting squares, that leads to the formulas for the area of triangles, parallelograms and trapezoids. Consequently, students should be adept at using the area properties *before* thinking about the area of triangles. All of the explanations in this section expect that students can solve multistep problems like those in Section 5.2.

Altitudes and Bases

Any side of a triangle can be called the *base*. The line containing the base is called the *baseline*. The corresponding *altitude* is the segment from the opposite vertex to the baseline that intersects the baseline perpendicularly. For every triangle, there are 3 choices for the base, and hence has 3 base-altitude pairs.

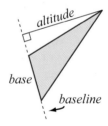

The terminology for parallelograms is similar. Again, any side of a parallelogram can be taken as a base. An **altitude** corresponding to this base is a segment perpendicular to the base from any point on the opposite side. For each base, there are many altitudes, all with the same length.

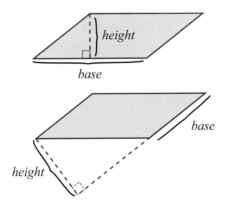

For both triangles and parallelograms, the **height** is the length of the altitude. The length of the base side is called either the base-length or, much more commonly, the '**base**'. Thus the word "base" sometimes means a segment, and sometimes means a length.

These terms can mislead students: the word "base" suggests something at the bottom of the figure, while "altitude" and "height" seem to refer to vertical distances. These impressions are reinforced when textbooks consistently display all triangles with horizontal bases. Yet, as you will see, it can be advantageous to choose a non-horizontal base.

First Approach: Triangles, then Parallelograms

An altitude line can be in the interior of the triangle, in the exterior, or it can be one of the sides of the triangle (as happens with right triangles). When rotated to make the base horizontal, the three possibilities look like this:

Case 1: Right Triangle   **Case 2: Altitude inside**   **Case 3: Altitude outside**

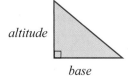   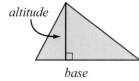   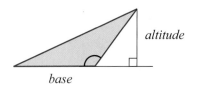

Case 3 occurs whenever one interior angle along the base is obtuse.

We will find the area of the triangle for each of these three types. The calculations move from easiest to hardest when done in the order pictured.

Case 1. The area of a right triangle is easily found:

Complete the right triangle to a retangle.

Area of Δ = ½ Area of rectangle

$\therefore$ *Area = ½ base × height.*

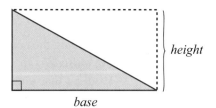

The expression "$\frac{1}{2}$ base × height" emerges from two properties of area: the fact that congruent regions have equal areas, and the fact that the area of a rectangle is the product of its sides.

Case 2. When the altitude lies inside the triangle, it is also easy to relate the triangle to a rectangular region:

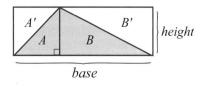

Area A' = Area A
Area B' = Area B
∴ the area of the triangle is half the area of the rectangle.

Area = ½ base × height.

Case 3. When the altitude lies outside the triangle, one can find the area as the difference of the areas of two right triangles:

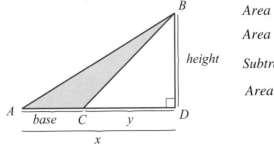

Area of big △ABD: $\frac{1}{2} x \cdot height$

Area of white △CBD: $\frac{1}{2} y \cdot height$

Subtract to get

Area of shaded △ABC $= \frac{1}{2}(x - y) \cdot height$

$\therefore Area \;\; = \;\; \frac{1}{2} base \times height.$

As teachers take their class through the three cases, the following points merit emphasis.

• From a strictly mathematical point of view, Case 1 is unnecessary because it is included in Case 2; it is Case 2 with the top vertex in a corner of the rectangle. But Case 1 is simple and it illustrates the key ideas used in the other cases.

• In both Case 2 and Case 3, we decomposed a triangle into two right triangles. As mentioned on page 39, the idea of decomposing figures into right triangles is useful in many contexts in geometry.

I split the figure into right triangles!

• Case 3 is more complicated because it requires using letters and because it involves subtraction. Both ideas are familiar to students who have been using letters in unknown angle problems and who have been finding areas of regions with holes.

• *Case 3 cannot be omitted* in class, even if textbooks leave it out (see Homework Problem 5).

Although the three cases require different reasoning, the final expression for the area is the same for all three cases.

THEOREM 3.1. *The area of a triangle is one-half the product of the length of the base and the corresponding height, regardless of which side is chosen as the base.*

$$Area\ of\ Triangle \;\; = \;\; \frac{1}{2} Base \times Height.$$

---

three crucial points

This area formula is simple and extraordinarily useful. But it contains subtleties that confuse students. Teachers can help by explicitly explaining the following crucial points.

First, one cannot simply *define* the area of a triangle to be "$\frac{1}{2}$ base × height". Every triangle already has a specific area; the area is defined by the area properties and the choice of a square unit, without reference to a formula. The area formula emerges later, after cleverly applying the area properties, as above.

Second, because any side of a triangle can be chosen as the base, Theorem 3.1 actually gives three different ways to compute the area of a given triangle, all giving the same result.

Third, while the expression "half base × height" is usually called a formula, it is better to think of it as a *procedure* for finding the area of a triangle. Presenting Theorem 3.1 as a procedure rather than a formula can clarify the first two points. Specifically, this procedure has three steps:

STEP 1. Choose one side of the triangle as the "base" and measure its length.

STEP 2. Find the corresponding height (this may require first drawing an altitude).

STEP 3. Compute half the product of these numbers.

After introducing the area formula, textbooks provide practice problems of two types: (i) given base and height, find the area, and (ii) given base and area, find the height. But learning to find the area of triangles is just one aspect of the teaching goal; the primary goal is developing students' facility at using the area properties. To progress, students need practice solving multi-step "find the area" problems like the ones below. The Primary Mathematics curriculum gives students many such area problems in grades 5–7. The area formula for triangles is simply one tool to use in solving such problems.

Multi-step area problems can often be solved in several ways. Such problems are wonderful for classroom discussions: students can present their solutions and the class can discuss the merits of each. Here is an example.

EXERCISE 3.2 (6th grade).
The diagram shows two adjacent squares.
Find the area of the region R in two ways:
• *by subtraction,*
• *by dividing R into two triangles.*

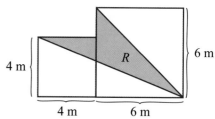

The area formula involves the base and height of the triangle, but not its shape. Therefore *triangles with equal bases and equal heights have equal areas.* This relates to the process of "skewing a triangle". Given triangle ABC, keep the base $\overline{AB}$ fixed and move vertex C along the line parallel to the base. The resulting family of skewed triangles all have the same area.

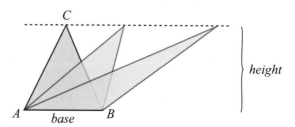

Skewing can be used to help find areas, as in the following problem. The idea is to "skew triangles" to change the given region into one with the same area but with a simpler shape.

EXERCISE 3.3 (7th grade).
The diagram shows several triangles
*in a rectangle. If the area of region R is 16 cm², *
find the total area of regions S and T.

Hint: skew S until it abuts T.

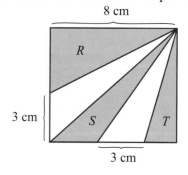

The area formula for triangles can be used to find the area of a parallelogram. The trick is to observe that a diagonal divides the parallelogram into two triangles, each with the same base and the same height as the parallelogram (the details are left for a homework problem).

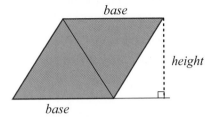

Second Approach: Parallelograms, then Triangles

In the above discussion we found the area formula first for triangles, then for parallelograms. Many curricula reverse this: they first find the area formula for parallelograms, then go on to triangles. Both approaches are common, and neither is clearly superior.

In the Primary Mathematics curriculum, students see *both* approaches. In fifth grade the area formula for triangles is derived by "folding proofs" for the three cases described above. Immediately afterwards, students begin solving single and multi-step area problems. Then in seventh grade the formula is re-derived, this time using the area of a parallelogram. This approach does not need three separate cases.

EXERCISE 3.4. *Read page 333 of New Elementary Math 1 and answer the questions in Class Activities 1 and 2.*

Textbooks typically introduce the area formula for parallelograms using the pictures below. The sliding-triangle shows that the area of the parallelogram is the same as the area of the rectangle with the same base and height.

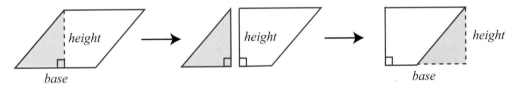

Area of Parallelogram = Area of Rectangle = base × height.

But wait! There's a flaw that students can readily spot: this picture proof doesn't work for parallelograms that "tilt too much" — specifically, when there is no altitude entirely inside the parallelogram, as in the leftmost figure below.

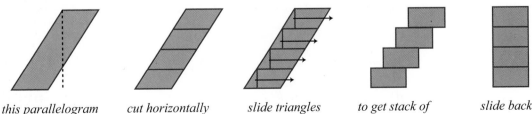

this parallelogram leans too much   *cut horizontally*   *slide triangles on each level*   *to get stack of rectangles*   *slide back to align*

To handle this case, decompose the parallelogram into several smaller parallelograms each of which don't "tilt too much". Then perform the cut-and-rearrange procedure on each small parallelogram. The resulting rectangles can be shifted to form a rectangle that is the same height, width, and area as the original parallelogram.

Here is another common approach. Given a parallelogram, construct the surrounding rectangle and rearrange as shown. This gives two expressions for the area of the surrounding rectangle which together show that Area(P) = base × height.

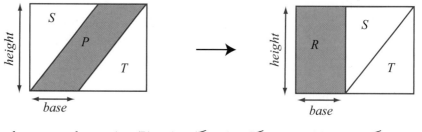

Total areas equal: *Area(P) + ~~Area(S)~~ + ~~Area(T)~~ = Area(R) + ~~Area(S)~~ + ~~Area(T)~~*

∴ *Area(P) = base × height.*

This argument is complete; there are no other cases to consider. In summary:

> **THEOREM 3.5.** *The area of a parallelogram is the product of the base and the corresponding height, regardless of which side is chosen as the base.*
>
> *Area of Parallelogram = Base × Height.*

Each picture proof in this section contains all the ideas needed for a complete mathematical proof. For example, here is a complete proof of the first "sliding triangle" proof above. The proof starts by proving that the two triangles are congruent, as was implicitly assumed in the picture proof. It then justifies the picture proof by citing area properties.

EXAMPLE 3.6. *Given: Parallelogram ABCD (shaded) with interior altitude $\overline{BF}$.*
Constr.: Draw rectangle AEFB as shown.
To Prove: Area(ABCD) = AB · BF (which is base × height).

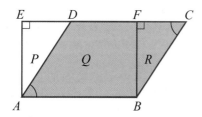

Proof. $\angle E = \angle F = 90°$ by construction
$AE = BF$ opp. sides of rectangle
$AD = BC$ opp. sides of //-ogram
$\triangle ADE \cong \triangle BCF$ RHL.

Now let *P*, *Q* and *R* be the areas of the three regions in this figure. Then

$$
\begin{aligned}
\text{Area of the parallelogram} \ &= \ Q + R &&\text{areas add} \\
&= \ Q + P &&\cong \text{ regions} \\
&= \ \text{Area}(EFBA) &&\text{areas add} \\
&= \ AB \cdot BF &&\text{area of rectangle.}
\end{aligned}
$$

Most of the parallelograms pictured in this section have horizontal bases. Textbooks begin this way for simplicity. But students are soon given problems that involve choosing a non-horizontal side as base, as in the following 2-step problem. This problem is solved by computing the area in two different ways — one for each choice of a base-altitude pair.

EXAMPLE 3.7. *The shaded figure below is a parallelogram. Find the unknown length x.*

Teacher's Solution: Find the area in 2 ways.

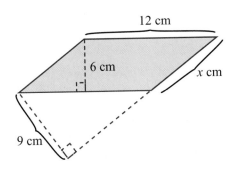

• Horizontal base 12 cm, corresp. height 6 cm
$$\text{Area: } 12 \text{ cm} \times 6 \text{ cm} = 72 \text{ cm}^2.$$

• Tilted base x cm, corresp. height 9 cm
$$\text{Area: } 9x \text{ cm}^2.$$

$$\therefore \ 9x = 72$$
$$x = 8.$$

Homework Set 20

1. Draw an obtuse triangle. Show the three base-altitude pairs (make three pictures if necessary).

2. It is common for students to erroneously apply the area formula for the triangle by interpreting "height" to mean the length of one side.

    In fact, the height of a triangle is *never* equal to the length of a side unless the triangle is a _____ triangle.

3. (*Study the Textbook!*) Read pages 65-70 in Prim Math 5A.

    a) On page 66, in all three cases, the area of the triangle is related to which rectangle?

    b) In the third of the five pictures on page 66, the first arrow indicates how folding shows that two triangles are congruent. Draw the same figure on your paper, give the vertices letter names and give a formal proof that these two triangles are indeed congruent (ignore the bottom two pictures on this page). *Do not use the grid shown; the grid applies only for triangles with certain side lengths.*

4. (*Study the Textbook!*) Call the three cases shown on page 66 of Primary Math 5A, "Case 1", "Case 2" and "Case 3".

    a) For each of the four parts of Problem 2 on page 68, identify whether one should apply Case 1, 2 or 3.

    b) Answer Problem 3 on page 68.

    c) Answer Problems 4 and 5 on page 69.

    d) Answer all problems in Practice 4A on page 70.

    e) Which of the problems on page 70 is an example of
    i) finding the area of a complicated polygon, and ii) finding the area of a composite figure.

5. Sarah claims that, when deriving the formula for the area of a triangle, it is not necessary to consider Case 3 because for any Case 3 triangle one can draw an altitude that lies inside the triangle, and that was considered in Case 2. What's wrong with Sarah's reasoning?

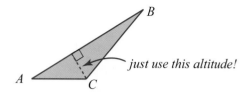

just use this altitude!

6. Write *Teacher's Solutions* to the four problems in Problem 28 on page 92 of Primary Math 5A. Make your solutions clear and complete and at the grade 5 level.

7. Do Exercises 3.2, 3.3 and 3.4 in this section.

8. Use the area formula for a triangle to obtain the area formula for a parallelogram by the approach suggested after Exercise 3.3 in this section. Write your answer in the "Teacher's Solution" format: draw and label a picture and give an explanation with equations and a few words.

9. Here are three methods for finding the area formula of a trapezoid. Show that all three methods lead to the same area formula. (In each picture, *a* and *b* are the base lengths and *h* is the height.)

   a) Divide the trapezoid into two triangles as illustrated below. Calculate the area of each triangle and add.

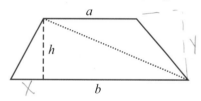

   b) Divide the trapezoid in half and put the top half next to the bottom half. Label and calculate the area of the parallelogram created.

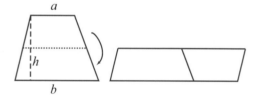

   c) Divide the trapezoid into two triangles and a rectangle. Calculate the area of each and add them together.

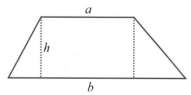

10. (*Study the Textbook!*) In NEM1, read Class Activity 3 at the top of page 334. Answer all the questions. Justify your answers to parts (c), (d) and (e).

11. Give Teacher's Solutions to Problems 12 – 15 on page 338 of NEM1.

12. Find the area of the shaded figures below.

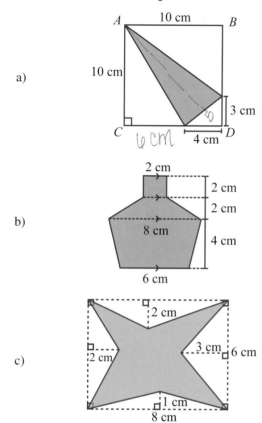

a)

b)

c)

13. Using Example 3.6 as a guide, write a complete proof for the area formula for a parallelogram based on the idea that, in the picture below, Area(*P*) = Area(big rectangle) – 2Area(*S*).

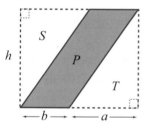

14. a) Use the fact that the diagonals of a kite are perpendicular to prove that the area of the kite is

$$\text{Area of Kite} = \frac{1}{2}\,cd,$$

where *c* and *d* are the lengths of the diagonals.

   b) Explain (only 5 words needed!) why the same formula holds for a rhombus:

$$\text{Area of Rhombus} = \frac{1}{2}\,cd,$$

where *c* and *d* are the lengths of the diagonals.

   c) If □*ABCD* is a square with side length *s* and diagonals of length *d*, use the formula from part b) to conclude that $d = \sqrt{2} \cdot s$.

CHAPTER **6**

Pythagorean Theorem with Applications

The Pythagorean Theorem is the single most useful fact in geometry. It was known in several ancient cultures, but the precise statement and proof are usually attributed to Pythagoras, the Greek leader of a group of philosophers who lived shortly before 500 B.C. The Pythagoreans also helped lay the foundations of geometry by proving that the angles of a triangle sum to 180° and proving theorems about parallel lines and similar triangles.

The Pythagorean Theorem relates the lengths of the three sides of a right triangle. It is a simple idea that turns out to have numerous applications, both practical and conceptual. The Pythagorean Theorem is useful in many geometric measurements, and it is fundamentally important in coordinate geometry and trigonometry.

For these reasons, the Pythagorean Theorem is a key part of all middle school curricula. In the New Elementary Mathematics curriculum it is taught in the 8th grade (NEM 2), but it is sometimes introduced in grade 7.

6.1 Pythagorean Theorem

A **right triangle** is a triangle with two sides that form a right angle. Those two sides are called the **legs** and the side opposite the right angle, which is the longest side, is called the **hypotenuse** of the triangle. The picture below shows a right triangle with legs of length a and b and hypotenuse of length c; this uses the common convention of using the same letter to label a vertex and the length of the opposite side. Recall that in a right triangle, the sum of the two acute angles is 90°.

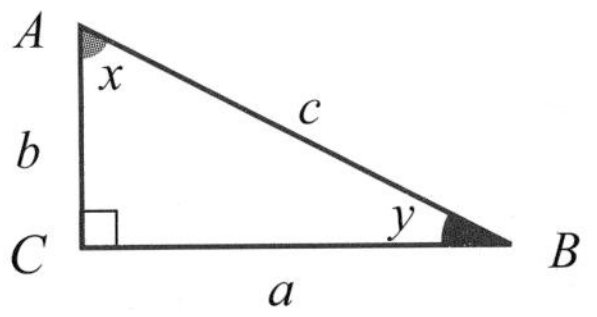

$$x + y + 90° = 180°$$
$$\therefore x + y = 90°.$$

If one knows the lengths of any two sides of a right triangle, it is easy to calculate the length of the third side. The Pythagorean Theorem explains how. The essential point is that there is a

129

simple relation between the *squares* of the lengths — rather than the lengths themselves — of the sides.

PYTHAGOREAN THEOREM. *If a right triangle has legs of lengths a and b and hypotenuse of length c, then* $a^2 + b^2 = c^2$.

Proof. The proof has three parts: a construction, some preliminary observations, and an area calculation.

Construction: Given a right triangle $\triangle ABC$, extend the legs to form segments of length $a + b$ and use those segments to construct a square with sides of length $a + b$ as shown. Mark points $PQRS$ on the sides, dividing each side into a segment of length a and a segment of length b. Then draw the quadrilateral $PQRS$. This creates four triangles (shaded).

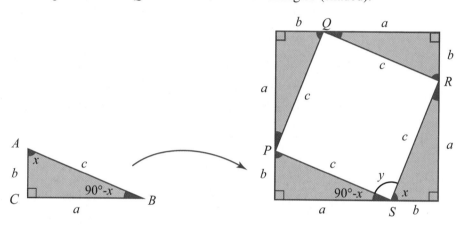

Preliminaries: Each shaded triangle is congruent to the original triangle by SAS. Hence

- each has hypotenuse of length c,

- each has the same acute angles (x and $90° - x$) as the original triangle, and

- the angles at the point S satisfy $\qquad (90° - x) + y + x = 180° \qquad$ ∠s on a line
  $$90° + y = 180°$$
  $$\therefore y = 90°.$$

Similarly, each of the other corners of the center quadrilateral is a right angle. We conclude that *the center quadrilateral is a square.*

Area Calculation: The proof is completed by computing the area of the big square in two different ways. First, since the big square has sides of length $a + b$, its area is

$$\text{Area} = (a + b)(a + b) = a^2 + 2ab + b^2.$$

But the big square is composed of the four shaded triangles, each of area $\frac{1}{2}ab$, and the center square, which has area c^2, so

$$\text{Area} = 4 \cdot \frac{1}{2}ab + c^2 = 2ab + c^2.$$

Equating the above two equations, we obtain

$$a^2 + 2ab + b^2 = 2ab + c^2.$$

Subtracting $2ab$ from both sides gives $a^2 + b^2 = c^2$. $\quad\square$

EXAMPLE 1.1. *Apply the Pythagorean Theorem to find* x, y, z *and the area of rectangle ABCD.*

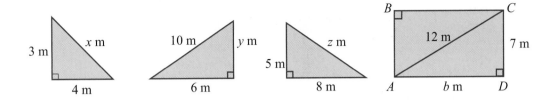

The answers are given by the calculations

$$x^2 = 3^2 + 4^2 \qquad y^2 = 100 - 36 \qquad z^2 = 25 + 64 \qquad b^2 = 144 - 49$$
$$= 25 \qquad\qquad = 64 \qquad\qquad = 89 \qquad\qquad = 95$$
$$x = 5 \qquad\qquad y = 8 \qquad\qquad z = \sqrt{89} \qquad\qquad \text{Area} = 7\sqrt{95}.$$

All of these examples involve taking square roots. In fact, writing the equation $a^2 + b^2 = c^2$ as

$$c = \sqrt{a^2 + b^2}$$

makes clear that square roots will necessarily arise. Thus *students should be familiar with square roots before they are introduced to the Pythagorean Theorem.*

The Pythagorean Theorem is an "if-then" statement: *if* a triangle is a right triangle, *then* the lengths of the sides satisfy $a^2 + b^2 = c^2$. The **converse** of an if-then statement is the statement obtained by interchanging the "if" part and the "then" part. The converse of a true statement may be false, or may be true.

EXERCISE 1.2. *Put a check ($\checkmark$) beside each true statement in the following list.*

Statement	Converse
If a figure is a triangle, then it has 3 sides.	If a figure has 3 sides, then it is a triangle.
If a figure is a square, then it is a rectangle.	If a figure is a rectangle, then it is a square.
If it is a farm machine, then it is a tractor.	If it is a tractor, then it is a farm machine.

With the Pythagorean Theorem we are in luck: both the theorem and its converse are true.

PYTHAGOREAN THEOREM CONVERSE. *If the lengths* a, b, c *of the sides of a triangle are related by* $a^2 + b^2 = c^2$, *then the triangle is a right triangle (with the right angle opposite the side of length c).*

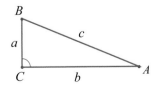

Proof. Given a triangle $\triangle ABC$ with $a^2 + b^2 = c^2$, construct a duplicate triangle as follows.

- Draw a segment $\overline{RP}$ of length b.

- Construct a line L through R perpendicular to $\overline{RP}$.

- Mark point Q on L with $RQ = a$.

- Draw $\overline{PQ}$.

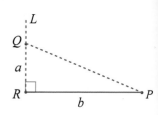

Then $\triangle PQR$ is a right triangle, so $PQ^2 = a^2 + b^2$ by the Pythagorean Theorem. Using the assumption $a^2 + b^2 = c^2$, that becomes $PQ^2 = c^2$, so $PQ = c$. But then $\triangle ABC \cong \triangle PQR$ by SSS. Therefore $\triangle ABC$ must have been a right triangle, with right angle at C.   □

EXAMPLE 1.3. *Many textbooks tell the story that ancient Egyptian surveyors created right angles (to mark the corners of a building or farm field) using a rope triangle with sides 3, 4, and 5 units long. The converse of the Pythagorean Theorem — not the Pythagorean Theorem itself — guarantees that such a triangle is a right triangle.*

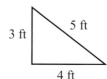

$3^2 + 4^2 = 5^2$,
so this is a right triangle.

Homework Set 21

1. Answer the following problems by drawing a clear picture, drawing the straight-line segment from the beginning point to the end point, and applying the Pythagorean Theorem.

   a) Jim travels 7 miles due north, then goes 3 miles due west, and then 3 miles due south. How far is he from his starting point?

   b) Sue walks 9 city blocks south, 2 blocks east, 3 blocks south, and 7 blocks east. If all blocks are the same length, how far is she from her starting point?

2. Find the lengths of the unknown marked sides a, b, c, d, e and f of the six triangles shown. All measurements are in centimeters.

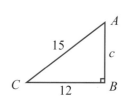

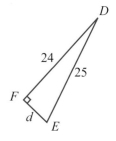

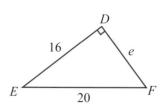

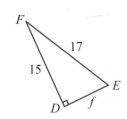

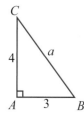

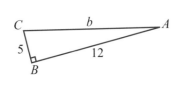

3. A *Pythagorean triple* is a set (a, b, c) of three whole numbers that satisfy $a^2 + b^2 = c^2$. List the Pythagorean triples that appear in the six parts of the previous problem. These will quickly become familiar!

4. The hypotenuse of a right triangle is 20 cm and one leg is 12 cm long. Find the area of the triangle.

5. The sides of a triangle are 6 cm, 13 cm, and 15 cm. Is it a right triangle?

6. Which of the following sets of numbers could be the lengths of the sides of a right triangle? In c), k is some unspecified number.

   a) 3, 4, 5   b) 6, 8, 10   c) $3k, 4k, 5k$

   d) 16, 30, 35   e) 16, 30, 34   f) $\frac{3}{4}, \frac{4}{5}, 1$

7. Determine which of the following triangles are right triangles and name the right angle.

   a) In $\triangle ABC$, $AB = 8$ cm, $BC = 9$ cm, and $AC = 7$ cm.
   b) In $\triangle PQR$, $PQ = 15$ m, $QR = 25$ m, and $PR = 20$ m.
   c) In $\triangle XYZ$, $XY = 36$ in, $YZ = 39$ in, and $XZ = 15$ in.
   d) In $\triangle STU$, $ST = 9$ cm, $TU = 15$ cm, and $SU = 20$ cm.
   e) In $\triangle CDE$, $CD = 8$ km, $DE = 15$ km, and $CE = 17$ km.

8. In the figure, $DC = 6$ cm, $CB = 10$ cm, $AB = 12$ cm, and $AB \parallel DC$. Find h.

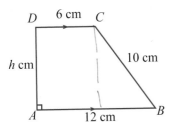

9. The figure below is an isosceles triangle with legs 17 cm, base 16 cm, and height h cm.

   a) Find the value of h.
   b) Find the area of $\triangle ABC$.

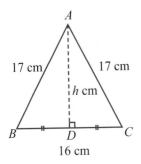

10. A rhombus has sides 10 cm long. If one diagonal is 12 cm long, how long is the other diagonal?

11. A teacher put the following problem on a test:

    "The longest side of a triangle is 17 cm long and one leg is 15 cm long. What is the area of the triangle?"

    a) Explain why this problem, as stated, cannot be answered.

    b) Suppose that the triangle is a right triangle and solve the problem.

12. The picture shows a rectangular box with height 3 in, width 4 in, and length 12 in.

    a) What is the length of $\overline{BE}$?

    b) How long is the diagonal $\overline{BH}$?   *Hint*: $\triangle EBH$ is a right triangle.

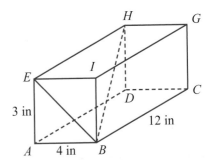

13. President James Garfield discovered a proof of the Pythagorean Theorem based on the picture below. In the picture, the original triangle has been extended to a trapezoid composed of three triangles.

    a) Explain why $\angle x$ is a right angle.

    b) What are the areas of each of the three triangles in terms of a, b and c?

    c) Using the formula for the area of a trapezoid, what is the total area in terms of a and b?

    d) Prove that $a^2 + b^2 = c^2$ by equating your answers to b) and c) and simplifying.

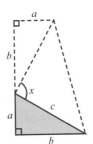

6.2 Square Roots and Pythagorean Triples

Square roots enter the middle school curriculum in two contexts: the quadratic formula and the Pythagorean Theorem. Of these, the Pythagorean Theorem is the easier topic, and is usually covered first. In fact, many grade 6-8 textbooks introduce the Pythagorean Theorem for the sole purpose of providing problems involving square roots. This section provides some guidance for teaching square roots and the Pythagorean Theorem.

The idea of square roots is complicated by the fact that square roots are often irrational. Recall from Chapter 9 of EMT:

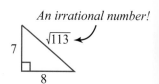

An irrational number!

- A number is **irrational** if it cannot be written as a fraction $\frac{p}{q}$ where p, q are integers. In particular, irrational numbers cannot be written as finite decimals.

- For a whole number N, $\sqrt{N}$ is irrational unless N is a perfect square (i.e., unless N is one of the numbers $0, 1, 4, 9, 16, 25, \dots$).

The square roots that arise in applications of the Pythagorean Theorem are therefore typically irrational numbers.

Thus three ideas are interwoven: square roots, the concept of an irrational number, and the Pythagorean Theorem. For clarity, most curricula follow a teaching sequence that introduces these one at a time:

1. Introduce square roots,

2. Pythagorean Theorem with whole numbers only (Pythagorean Triples),

3. Pythagorean Theorems with irrational square roots, and

4. Applications.

Square Roots

A **square root** of a number x is a number whose square (the result of multiplying the number by itself) is x. Negative numbers have no (real) square roots, zero has a single square root (itself!), and positive numbers have two square roots.

DEFINITION 2.1. *Every non-negative real number x has a unique non-negative square root, called the **principal square root** and denoted $\sqrt{x}$. Altogether, x has two square roots: $\sqrt{x}$ and $-\sqrt{x}$.*

Perhaps confusingly, textbooks, teachers and students all fall into the habit of referring to the principal square root as "the" square root. Thus in common language "the square *root* of 4" is 2, while "the square *roots* of 4" are ±2.

Principal square roots satisfy the properties

$$\sqrt{a}\,\sqrt{b} = \sqrt{ab} \qquad \text{and} \qquad \frac{\sqrt{a}}{\sqrt{b}} = \sqrt{\frac{a}{b}}.$$

These can be used to rewrite products of square roots as a single square root as, for example,

$$\sqrt{3}\sqrt{8} = \sqrt{24} = \sqrt{4 \cdot 6} = \sqrt{4}\sqrt{6} = 2\sqrt{6}.$$

The properties can also be used to rewrite quotients like $4 \div \sqrt{5}$ as fractions times square roots:

$$\frac{4}{\sqrt{5}} = \frac{4}{\sqrt{5}} \cdot \frac{\sqrt{5}}{\sqrt{5}} = \frac{4\sqrt{5}}{5} = \frac{4}{5}\sqrt{5}.$$

This calculation is called *rationalizing the denominator*.

Students sometimes incorrectly believe these are required "simplifications" and that expressions with square roots in the denominator are somehow illegal. From a mathematical point of view, simplifying is unnecessary; writing an answer in a different form does not change its correctness. But often, in the middle steps of a long calculation, simplifying makes the remaining steps easier. For that purpose, students should learn the above ways of rewriting expressions with square roots.

A Common Student Error. It is common for students to mistakenly write

$$\sqrt{100 + 200} \;\text{"="}\; \sqrt{100} + \sqrt{200} \qquad \text{and} \qquad \sqrt{a + b} \;\text{"="}\; \sqrt{a} + \sqrt{b}.$$

These students are applying the simple – but incorrect! — principle

"do something to" $(A + B)$ = "do something to" A + "do something to" B

where the "doing something" is taking the square root. Similar thinking leads to other incorrect simplifications such as "$(x + y)^2 = x^2 + y^2$" and "$\sin(a + b) = \sin a + \sin b$". Teachers should be prepared to spot and correct these misimpressions before they take root in students' thinking. Here are three useful approaches:

- *Give an instructional counterexample.* An **instructional counterexample** is an example presented by a teacher for the purpose of warning students to avoid some potential error (cf. page 11). In this case, the teacher can ask students whether the following are true:

$$\sqrt{1 + 1} \stackrel{?}{=} \sqrt{1} + \sqrt{1} \qquad \sqrt{9 + 16} \stackrel{?}{=} \sqrt{9} + \sqrt{16} \qquad \sqrt{100 + 1} \stackrel{?}{=} \sqrt{100} + \sqrt{1}$$

  and then ask whether $\sqrt{a + b}$ equals $\sqrt{a} + \sqrt{b}$. Instructional counterexamples are most effective when the teacher anticipates the error and delivers the counterexample *before* students have a chance to make the error.

- *Articulate a general philosophy.* The teacher can point out that square roots are defined in terms of multiplication ($\sqrt{100}$ is the number which, *multiplied* by itself, gives 100) and tell students "the square root operation behaves nicely when it sees multiplication, but is bewildered by addition". For example, $\sqrt{ab}$ equals $\sqrt{a}\sqrt{b}$, but there is no nice simplification of $\sqrt{a + b}$.

- *Provide an alternative way forward.* Errors often occur when students are "stuck". For example, a student who is asked to solve

$$8 = \sqrt{1 + x} + 5$$

for x will probably realize that *something* must be done with the square root, but may not know what to do. With growing frustration, this student may think "wouldn't it be nice if $\sqrt{1 + x} = \sqrt{1} + \sqrt{x}$?" and proceed to use this "fact" because nothing else comes to mind. In this case, teachers can demonstrate the method of "put everything but the square root on one side, then square both sides".

Pythagorean Triples

Students' first exercises with the Pythagorean theorem involve only right triangles whose side lengths a, b and c are all whole numbers. As you learned in your previous homework, triples (a, b, c) of whole numbers that satisfy $a^2 + b^2 = c^2$ are called **Pythagorean triples**. In fact, only a handful of Pythagorean triples account for the majority of all examples and problems in textbooks. The seven most common ones are shown below (the dotted one is relatively rare).

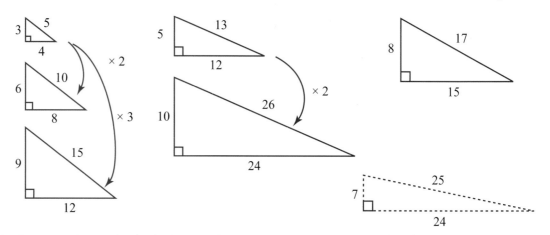

Here is an opportunity for teachers! Teachers who have memorized these seven Pythagorean triples can do many textbook problems instantly in their heads. This impresses students and is valuable for class discussions, for creating quizzes and tests, and for checking students' answers as they work.

In fact, it is enough to memorize only three Pythagorean triples, namely $(3, 4, 5)$, $(5, 12, 13)$, and $(8, 15, 17)$, and learn to spot their multiples. A Pythagorean triple is **primitive** if a, b, and c have no common factor. Each primitive Pythagorean triple gives rise, by multiplying by 2, 3,4, etc. to a series of Pythagorean triples, and most textbook problems are multiples of these three smallest primitive examples. For example, the triples

$$(6, 8, 10) \quad (9, 12, 15), \quad (12, 16, 20) \quad (30, 40, 50) \quad \text{and} \quad (300, 400, 500)$$

are all multiples of $(3,4,5)$ — they all have a ratio of 3:4:5.

EXERCISE 2.2. *Use a Pythagorean triple to (quickly) find the value of x.*

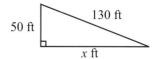

Applications

The Pythagorean Theorem is useful for making indirect measurements. Most middle school textbooks give applications with triangles that can be measured only along two sides because, for example, the other side extends across a river, in the ocean, or straight up in the air. The following example is typical. Read the solution and answer the teacher-knowledge question after the solution.

EXAMPLE 2.3. *A kite is flying vertically above a tree which is* 80 *m from a boy who holds the string. If the string is* 100 *m long, how high is the kite above the ground?*

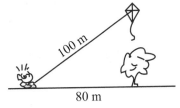

Teacher's Solution:

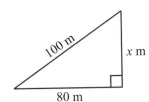

$x^2 + 80^2 = 100^2$ ..... Pythag. Thm.
$x^2 + 6400 = 10000$
$x^2 = 3600$
$\therefore x = 60$.

The kite is 60 m high.

EXERCISE 2.4. *The above problem can be solved easily by mental math. Explain how. (Hint: 1 unit =20 m.)*

Homework Set 22

When the answer is an irrational square root, simplify if possible and express it as a square root. For example, write $2\sqrt{3}$, *not* $\sqrt{12}$ *or* 3.46.

1. *(Calculator)* Of the numbers $\sqrt{10}$, $\sqrt{125}$ and $\sqrt{5625}$, which is rational and which is irrational? Explain your reasoning.

2. One can simplify $\sqrt{18}$ by finding the prime factorization of 18 and noting that $\sqrt{18} = \sqrt{(3 \cdot 3) \cdot 2} = 3\sqrt{2}$. Use this method to simplify the following square roots.

   a) $\sqrt{28}$
   b) $\sqrt{294}$
   c) $\sqrt{1452}$
   d) $\sqrt{1508220}$

3. Answer the following problems by drawing a clear picture, drawing the straight-line segment from the beginning point to the end point, and applying the Pythagorean Theorem.

   a) Sam walks 1 city block north, 2 blocks east, 3 blocks north, and 4 blocks west. If all blocks are the same length, how far is he from his starting point?

   b) Jill walks 3 city blocks south, 1 block west, then 2 blocks north, and then 4 east. If all blocks are the same length, how far is she from her starting point?

4. *(Mental Math)* Do this problem mentally using your knowledge of Pythagorean triples.

   In the triangle shown, find
   a) y if $z = 6$ and $x = 8$,
   b) z if $y = 20$ and $x = 16$,
   c) x if $z = 10$ and $y = 26$.

   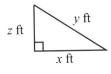

5. *(Mental Math)* Do this problem mentally using your knowledge of Pythagorean triples.

   a) a if $b = 1.2$ and $c = 1.5$,
   b) b if $a = 2.4$ and $c = 2.6$,
   c) c if $a = 2.4$ and $b = 4.5$.

6. Whenever you are given two unequal positive whole numbers, you can name the bigger one m and the smaller one n and compute the three numbers $m^2 - n^2$, $2mn$, and $m^2 + n^2$. This is done systematically in the following table. Complete the table.

m	n	m^2-n^2	$2mn$	m^2+n^2	Pyth. triple?
2	1	3	4	5	√
3	1	8			
3	2			13	
4	1				
4	2				
4	3				
5	1				

7. a) Expand the following expressions: $(x+y)^2$, $(x-y)^2$, $(m^2 + n^2)^2$, and $(m^2 - n^2)^2$.

   b) Given whole numbers m and n, with $m > n$, we can draw a right triangle with one leg of length $a = m^2 - n^2$ and the other of length $b = 2mn$. Use the Pythagorean Theorem and part (a) to prove that the hypotenuse has length $c = m^2 + n^2$.

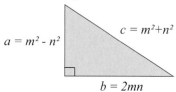

   c) Are the sides of this triangle whole numbers whenever m and n are positive whole numbers?

   d) If you continue the above chart, listing more and more possibilities for m and n, will the numbers $(m^2 - n^2, 2mn, m^2 + n^2)$ be a Pythagorean triple in every case?

8. Give a Teacher's Solution: A window-cleaner has a ladder that is 5 meters long. He places it so that it reaches a windowsill 4 meters from the ground. How far from the wall is the foot of the ladder? (Begin by drawing a diagram.)

9. Give a Teacher's Solution: A ladder leans against the wall and reaches a height of 4.8 m. If the foot of the ladder is 2 m from the wall, find the length of the ladder in meters.

10. Which has the shorter diagonal: the square or the rectangle?

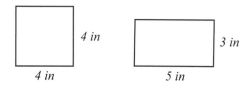

11. Give a Teacher's Solution: Points P and Q are on the opposite sides of a pond. M is a point such that PM and QM can be measured. It is found that $PM = 24$ m,

$QM = 26$ m and $\angle QPM = 90°$. Calculate the distance between P and Q.

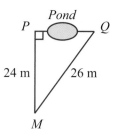

12. (*Mental Math*) Find a, b, c and d mentally. List the *primitive* Pythagorean triples that you use along the way.

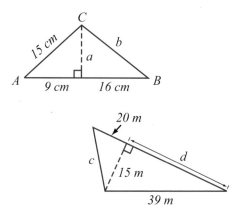

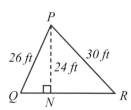

13. Calculate the length QR in $\triangle PQR$.

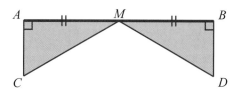

14. A bridge with supports $\overline{MC}$ and $\overline{MD}$ is built across a river. If $AB = 15$ m, $AC = 4$ m, and $AM = MB$, find the length of the support MC.

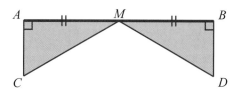

15. This problem teaches students to use algebra to solve a geometry problem. Give a Teacher's Solution. Start by introducing a letter for one of the unknown side lengths.

The shortest side of a right triangle is 10 m. If the difference between the other two sides is 2 m, find the perimeter of the triangle.

16. ❊ Here is a "challenger problem" for students who have solved the routine problems.

A water-plant originally 10 cm above the water surface is blown 50 cm sideways by a strong wind as shown. Find the depth of the pond.

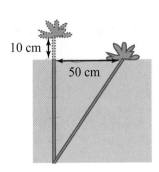

6.3 Special Triangles and Further Applications

Middle school textbooks single out two types of triangles for extra study: isosceles right triangles and 30-60-90 triangles. The side lengths of these "special triangles" are in simple ratios. This leads to "Unknown Side Problems" that can be solved mentally using ratios. Solving such problems gives students a preview of two later topics: similar triangles (the subject of the next chapter) and trigonometry. In this way, trigonometry enters the curriculum earlier than most teachers realize!

THEOREM 3.1 (45-45-90 △). *In an isosceles right triangle, the hypotenuse is* $\sqrt{2}$ *times as long as each leg.*

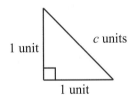

Proof: Take 1 unit = length of one leg.

$$c^2 = 1^2 + 1^2 = 2$$
$$\therefore c = \sqrt{2} \text{ units.}$$

Since $\sqrt{2} = 1.414\ldots$ the hypotenuse is about 1.4 times as long as the other sides. Thus in problems involving isosceles right triangles, one side length is obtained from another by either multiplying or dividing by $\sqrt{2}$. To determine which to do, remember that multiplying by $\sqrt{2}$ makes lengths longer.

EXAMPLE 3.2. *Find the values of x and y in the following figures.*

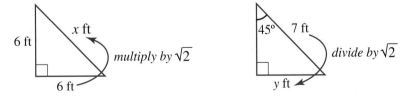

Solution: In the first triangle, two legs of equal length meet at a right angle, so this is an isosceles right triangle. The hypotenuse is therefore $\sqrt{2}$ times as long as each leg, so $x = 6\sqrt{2}$.

The second triangle has interior angles of 90°, 45° and 45°, so is also an isosceles right triangle. Again, the hypotenuse is $\sqrt{2}$ as long as a leg, so

$$y = \frac{7}{\sqrt{2}}.$$

If desired, this can also be written as $y = \dfrac{7}{\sqrt{2}} \cdot \dfrac{\sqrt{2}}{\sqrt{2}} = \dfrac{7\sqrt{2}}{2}$.

EXAMPLE 3.3. *Find the area of a square whose diagonal is 10 cm.*

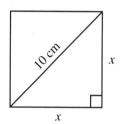

Solution: The lower half of the square is an isosceles right triangle whose legs have length $x = 10/\sqrt{2}$ cm. Squaring gives the area:

$$x^2 = \frac{10}{\sqrt{2}}\text{ cm} \cdot \frac{10}{\sqrt{2}}\text{ cm} = \frac{100}{2}\text{ cm}^2.$$

The area of the square is 50 cm^2.

A second type of "special triangle" occurs frequently: the 30-60-90 triangle.

To *recognize* a 30-60-90 triangle:

Spot a 90° angle and either a 30° or 60° angle (the third angle must then be 60° or 30°).

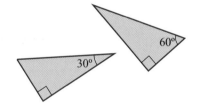

To *create* a 30-60-90 triangle:

Fold an equilateral triangle in half.

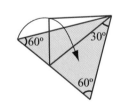

This folding picture illustrates the main idea in the next proof.

THEOREM 3.4 (30–60–90 Triangles). *In a 30–60–90 triangle,*

- *the hypotenuse is twice as long as the short leg;*
- *the other leg is $\sqrt{3}$ times the short leg.*

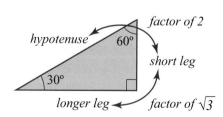

Proof. Starting with a $30-60-90$ triangle, $\triangle ABC$, double the length of the short leg to the point D and draw segment $\overline{AD}$. The shaded and unshaded triangles are then congruent and together they form an equilateral triangle.

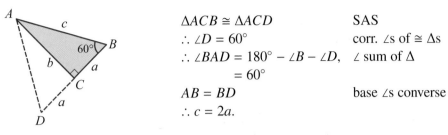

$\triangle ACB \cong \triangle ACD$	SAS
$\therefore \angle D = 60°$	corr. $\angle$s of $\cong$ $\triangle$s
$\therefore \angle BAD = 180° - \angle B - \angle D,$	$\angle$ sum of $\triangle$
$\qquad = 60°$	
$AB = BD$	base $\angle$s converse
$\therefore c = 2a.$	

We can then find b by applying the Pythagorean Theorem to the shaded triangle:

$$
\begin{aligned}
b^2 &= c^2 - a^2 \\
&= 4a^2 - a^2 \qquad \text{since } c = 2a \\
&= 3a^2.
\end{aligned}
$$

Taking the square root gives $b = \sqrt{3}a.$ □

To apply Theorem 3.4, first confirm that you have a 30-60-90 triangle and then relate all lengths to the length of the short leg.

EXAMPLE 3.5. *In the figures below, use mental math to find p, q, and r.*

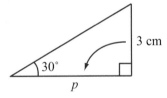

Teacher's Solution:

p is $\sqrt{3}$ times the length of the short leg.
Therefore $p = 3\sqrt{3}$ cm.

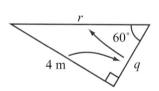

Short leg: $q = \dfrac{4}{\sqrt{3}}$ m.

Hypotenuse: $r = 2q = \dfrac{8}{\sqrt{3}}$ m.

EXAMPLE 3.6. *The diagonal of a rectangle is 8 cm long and makes a 30° angle with one side. What is the area of the rectangle?*

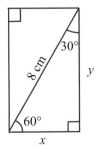

Teacher's Solution:

In the 30-60-90 triangle,

Short leg: $x = 8 \text{ cm} \div 2 = 4 \text{ cm}.$

Longer leg: $y = \sqrt{3}x = 4\sqrt{3} \text{ cm}.$

Area: $xy = 16\sqrt{3} \text{ cm}^2.$

Another Proof of the Pythagorean Theorem

There are many proofs of the Pythagorean Theorem. Students can benefit from comparing and contrasting several proofs. This section presents a second common proof of the Pythagorean Theorem. This "windmill proof" uses a different picture than the proof in Section 6.1, but the logic is very similar.

We begin, as before, with a right triangle with legs of length a and b, labeled so that $b \geq a$. Again we observe that the sum of the acute angles is $90°$.

$$x + y + 90° = 180°$$
$$\therefore x + y = 90°.$$

Windmill Proof. Draw a segment of length b extending the short leg beyond the right angle. Complete the extended portion of that segment to a square with sides of length $b - a$. Extend each side of the square for a distance a to form the "windmill" figure shown in the middle. Label the endpoints of the extended segments A, B, C and D and draw quadrilateral $ABCD$.

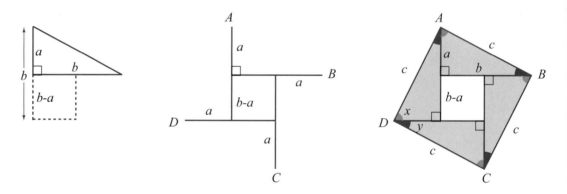

In this figure, each shaded triangle is congruent to the original triangle by SAS (each has a right angle and legs of length a and b). Consequently,

- the four sides of $ABCD$ each have length c, and

- each corner angle of $ABCD$ has measure $x + y = 90°$.

Thus $ABCD$ is a square with sides of length c, so it has area c^2. But then

$$
\begin{aligned}
c^2 &= \text{Area(center } \square \text{)} + 4 \cdot \text{Area(original } \triangle \text{)} \\
&= (a - b)(a - b) + 4 \cdot \frac{1}{2}ab \\
&= a^2 - 2ab + b^2 + 2ab.
\end{aligned}
$$

This simplifies to $c^2 = a^2 + b^2$. □

Notice the similarities with the proof given in Section 6.1. Both use SAS to check that triangles are congruent, both use the fact that the sum of the angles of a triangle is $180°$ to check that angles are right angles, and both involve computing area in two different ways.

Caution. Textbook "proofs" of the Pythagorean Theorem often simply display the square-within-square picture above and do the area calculation. They neglect to show how to start with a right triangle and *build* the figure. They also assume that the center part of the figure is a square, without explanation. Because some of the logic of the proof is left out, students may have questions for the teacher!

The picture below is also common, and confusing. It gives a visual interpretation of the formula $a^2 + b^2 = c^2$: the three squares have areas a^2, b^2 and c^2, so the Pythagorean Theorem says that the total area of the two smaller squares is equal to the area of the largest square. *This picture is not a proof* of the Pythagorean Theorem, nor is it connected with the way that the Pythagorean Theorem is used in applications.

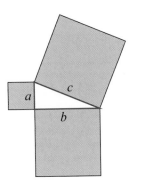

$a^2 + b^2 = c^2.$

Homework Set 23

1. In the figure below, how long is z if $x = 4$? If $y = 7$? If $x + y = 12$?

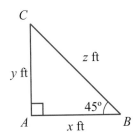

2. Answer the following questions about 30-60-90 triangles with side lengths as shown:

   a) How long is y if $z = 8$? If $z = 12$? If $z = 120$?

   b) How long is x if $z = 4$? If $z = 10\sqrt{3}$? If $z = 14$?

   c) How long is z if $x + 2y - z = 5$?

   d) How long is z if $x + y - z = 15$?

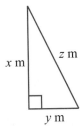

3. The diagonal of a square room is 12 m. Find the perimeter of the room. (Use a calculator and give your answer to the nearest meter.)

4. A lawn is in the shape of an equilateral triangle of side 6 m. Find the area of the lawn. (Use a calculator and give the answer to 3 significant digits.)

5. Suppose that you are given a triangle ABC, with $AB = 7$, $BC = 7\sqrt{3}$, and $AC = 14$. What are the measures of each angle of the triangle?

6. In the figure, $RQ = 6$ ft. Find the following:

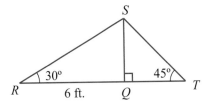

   a) RS.

   b) ST.

   c) QT.

   d) The perimeter of $\triangle RST$.

   e) The area of $\triangle RST$.

7. In the figure, CD = 6 cm, BC = 5 cm, and AC = 12 cm, with a and b marked as shown. Find lengths a and b.

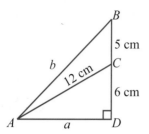

8. In the figure, AD = 1 cm, DC = 4 cm, and BD = 2 cm.

   a) Find the lengths of AB and BC.

   b) Show that $\angle ABC$ is a right angle (quote a theorem).

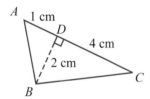

9. Find the length AC in terms of x (measured in m).

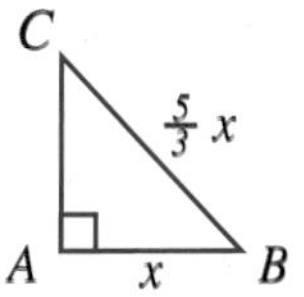

10. In the figure below, PS = 20 cm, QS = 15 cm, QR = 12 cm, and $\angle QSP$ = 90°. Find the area and the perimeter of quadrilateral $PQRS$.

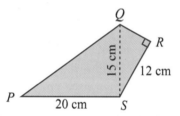

11. Each side of a rhombus is 13 feet long and the diagonal is 24 feet long. Sketch and find the length of the other diagonal.

12. Draw a rectangle KLMN with KL = 6 m and KN = 10 m. Mark a point P on $\overline{LM}$ such that triangle PNK is isosceles with equal sides KP and KN. Find PN.

13. In the figure, EG = 20 cm. Find the lengths

   a) EF,

   b) DE,

   c) FH,

   d) GH.

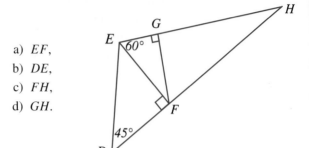

14. The figure shows two right triangles with their right angles aligned. Find (a) length a, and (b) angle x.

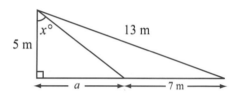

15. a) Draw a segment $\overline{XY}$ of length 12 cm.

    b) Extend this to a parallelogram $XYZW$ with YZ = 13 cm and with diagonal $\overline{XZ}$ perpendicular to $\overline{XY}$.

    c) Find the area of $XYZW$.

16. A hill rises for 100 m at an incline of 45°, then a further 60 m at an incline of 30°. What is its total height h?

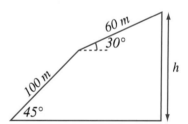

17. At one moment, a plane flying horizontally was a distance 5000 m vertically above a man. Ten seconds later, it was 6000 m from the man. What was the speed of the plane in km/h? Draw a sketch and give your answer to 2 significant digits.

CHAPTER 7

Similarity

The human brain is extraordinarily adept at recognizing when two figures have the same shape, but different size and position. This ability is part of our system of depth perception. As one approaches an object, its apparent size increases, even though its actual size is unchanged. Our brains must continuously compensate for this effect. As a result, even young children easily recognize a shape as "the same" after it has been shifted in position, rotated, and magnified.

same shape, different sizes

This notion of "same shape" is captured by the precise mathematical concept of similarity. Similarity is a powerful and productive concept. It enables architects to design buildings, artists to draw with perspective and astronomers to measure the solar system. It enables us to interpret maps and scale diagrams. It is the fundamental idea behind trigonometry and surveying.

Similarity is defined in terms of ratios and proportions. As a result, the precise definition of similarity is introduced after students have become familiar with ratios, and afterwards the studies of ratios and similarity build on one another. Thus similarity is necessarily a middle school topic.

7.1 Introducing Similarity and Similar Right Triangles

When teaching similarity, part of the teacher's job is to transform the intuitive notion of "same shape" into precise mathematics. This section examines the first steps in that process. The steps involve launching the topic with the precise definition of similar figures, and establishing the first and most useful of the criteria for checking whether triangles are similar.

Instruction begins with the vague definition that *two figures are similar if they have the same shape, but not necessarily the same size*. This assigns a word to a process — recognizing similar figures — that our brains do subconsciously. Visual exercises such as finding matching pairs of similar shapes help to make the process conscious. They give students an intuitive understanding of the meaning of the term "similar figures".

145

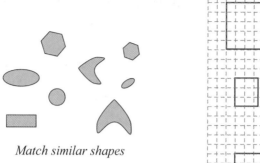

Match similar shapes

change angles
not similar

double one
side length
not similar

double both
side lengths
similar

The next step has students examine angles and side lengths of similar figures. Figures drawn on graph paper are easily scaled. Students can label side lengths, measure the angles, and observe the effects of stretching horizontally and vertically. Graph-paper pictures like those above show that transformations create a figure similar to the original one only if (i) all angles are unchanged, and (ii) all side lengths are multiplied by the same factor.

EXERCISE 1.1. *Similarity is introduced to 7th grade students on pages 371-375 of New Elementary Mathematics 1. Look through those pages. Which of the above two types of activities are used?*

Another approach to similarity begins with the notion of scaling by a specified **scale factor**. For segments, scaling by a factor of k makes the segment k times as long, as shown below. Scaling by factors larger than 1 enlarge the segment and scaling by factors less than 1 shrink the segment. For triangles, scaling by a factor of k makes *every* side longer or shorter by the *same* factor k.

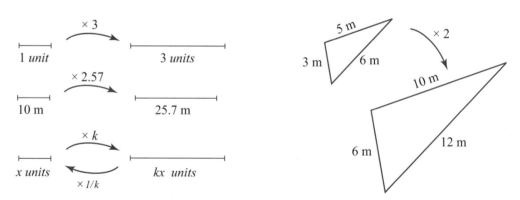

Now look at the two triangles pictured above. Suppose that you were shown these triangles, without the arrow, and asked whether they are related by a scale factor. Could you tell? In fact, there are two ways to check:

1. Pair up sides of the triangles, making three pairs of corresponding sides. Then compare the ratios "length of one side of the big triangle : length of the corresponding side of the small triangle". For the triangles shown, the three ratios are the same:

$$\text{Upper sides: } \frac{10 \text{ cm}}{5 \text{ cm}} = 2, \quad \text{Left sides: } \frac{6 \text{ cm}}{3 \text{ cm}} = 2, \quad \text{Lower-right sides: } \frac{12 \text{ cm}}{6 \text{ cm}} = 2.$$

2. Consider the ratios of corresponding sides *with each triangle*. The side lengths in the small triangle are in a ratio of 5 : 3 : 6; the corresponding side lengths in the large triangle are 10 : 6 : 12. The two ratios are equivalent.

When the sides of two triangles are paired by some correspondence, we say that **corresponding sides are proportional** if there is a number k such that each side of one triangle is k times the length of the corresponding side of the other triangle. The number k is called the *scale factor* or *proportionality constant*.

EXAMPLE 1.2. *For two of these three triangles, corresponding sides are proportional. Which ones?*

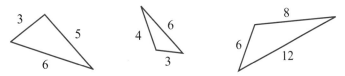

Now comes the key definition of this chapter. Similarity, like congruence, is defined in terms of angle measures and side lengths. But for similarity we are only interested in the ratios of side lengths, not the lengths themselves.

DEFINITION 1.3. *Two triangles are **similar** if, under some correspondence,*

- *Corresponding angles are equal, and*

- *Corresponding sides are proportional.*

According to the definition, congruent triangles are a special type of similar triangles: ones that are proportional with a scale factor of 1.

Teaching Comment. The triangles in Example 1.2 have sides labeled with numbers. What do these numbers mean? Does the label 6 mean 6 cm? 6 feet? 6 miles? Does it mean a length at all? We aren't told! There is a teaching issue behind the disappearing units.

Throughout elementary school, lengths and areas are always written with units: feet, meters, square inches, etc. But after similarity is introduced, units can sometimes be omitted because we are just interested in the *ratios* between lengths. Accordingly, textbook illustrations begin using **implied units**. In the left-hand triangle below, the labels mean that there is *some* unit – "the implied unit" – so that the sides are 3 units, 5 units, and 6 units long. The implied unit might be a meter, an inch, or it might be a unit 12.6 cm long. It doesn't matter; the ratios are

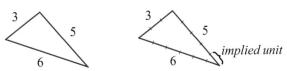

the same regardless of the unit. The use of implied units is a subtle point. Without a teacher's explanation, students may not realize that the numbers written next to segments are lengths, measured using some unmentioned and unwritten unit.

Similar Right Triangles

A right triangle has one 90° angle and two acute angles. If we know the measure of one acute angle, we can find the other by subtracting from 90°.

Now consider two right triangles, like those above, each with an angle of 27°. Then both triangles have angles measuring 27°, 63°, and 90°. Triangles with three pairs of congruent angles are called **equiangular**.

EXERCISE 1.4. *Of the five right triangles below, three are equiangular. Which ones?*

The following theorem is *the* key fact about similarity for right triangles.

THEOREM 1.5. *Equiangular right triangles are similar.*

Proof. Given two equiangular right triangles, construct a congruent copy of the smaller one inside the larger.

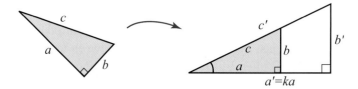

The side length a' is some multiple of the side length a, so we can write $a' = ka$. To complete the proof that the triangles are similar, we must show that the other two sides are related by this same scale factor k, that is, $b' = kb$ and $c' = kc$.

To prove $b' = kb$, we draw the shaded triangle shown on the right and compute its area in two ways. First,

$$\text{Area}(\text{shaded } \Delta) = \frac{1}{2}(\text{base} \times \text{ht}) = \frac{1}{2}ka \cdot b.$$

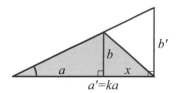

Alternatively, the area of the shaded triangle is the area of the big triangle minus the unshaded area. After tipping your head, the unshaded triangle has base b' and height x, so

$$
\begin{aligned}
\text{Area(shaded } \Delta) \;&=\; \text{Area(big } \Delta) \;-\; \text{Area(unshaded } \Delta) \\
&=\; \frac{1}{2}b' \cdot ka \;-\; \frac{1}{2}b' \cdot x \\
&=\; \frac{1}{2}b'(ka - x) \\
&=\; \frac{1}{2}b'a.
\end{aligned}
$$

Equating these two expressions for Area(shaded Δ) gives $\frac{1}{2}b'a = \frac{1}{2}kab$, which simplifies to

$$b' = kb.$$

Now that we know that $b' = kb$, we can show that $c' = kc$ using these figures:

Compute the area of the triangle below in 2 ways.

c h b a

Area = ½ab,
Area = ½ch.

$\therefore ch = ab$.

Also, compute the area of this triangle in 2 ways.

c' h a kb

Area = ½$a(kb)$,
Area = ½$c'h$.

$\therefore c'h = k(ab)$.

Therefore, $c'h = k(ab) = k(ch)$. Dividing this equation by h gives $c' = kc$. □

Scaling a Triangle

There is a simple geometric construction that takes a triangle and builds a scaled copy of it. The construction is especially easy for right triangles. Then, for general triangles, one can decompose into two right triangles and repeat, as shown in Construction 10.

CONSTRUCTION 9. *Given a right triangle with sides of length a, b and c, and a length a' that is k times as long as a, construct a similar right triangle with one side of length a'.*

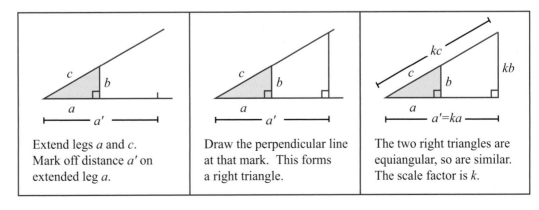

Extend legs a and c. Mark off distance a' on extended leg a.	Draw the perpendicular line at that mark. This forms a right triangle.	The two right triangles are equiangular, so are similar. The scale factor is k.

scale a triangle

CONSTRUCTION 10. *To scale an arbitrary triangle to a specified side-length, decompose the triangle into right triangles and apply the construction above on each right triangle.*

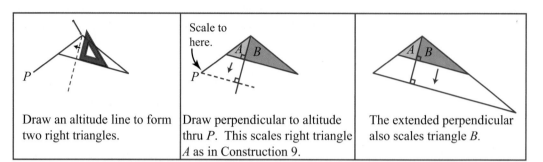

	Scale to here.	
Draw an altitude line to form two right triangles.	Draw perpendicular to altitude thru *P*. This scales right triangle *A* as in Construction 9.	The extended perpendicular also scales triangle *B*.

In the last picture of Construction 10, each half duplicates the picture of Construction 9. It is then easy to see that the scaled triangle is similar to the original. Thus,

---

THEOREM 1.6. *Scaling a triangle:*
- *Doesn't change angles, and*
- *Multiplies all lengths by the same factor k.*

Therefore, the scaled triangle is similar to the original.

Similarity and the Pythagorean Theorem

The next theorem is a famous fact about right triangles, which we will call the "Mother-Daughter Theorem". Once again, we decompose a triangle into two right triangles, but this time the original triangle is itself a right triangle.

THEOREM 1.7 (Mother-Daughter Theorem). *In a right triangle, the altitude to the hypotenuse separates the triangle into two triangles, each similar to the original.*

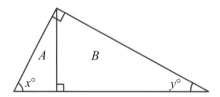

Proof. The picture shows a mother triangle with daughters *A* and *B*. Daughter *A* and the mother both have an acute angle of $x°$, so they are similar. Daughter *B* and the mother both share the complementary acute angle of $y°$, so they are also similar. Thus all three triangles are similar. □

The Mother-Daughter Theorem is the basis for an especially elegant proof of the Pythagorean Theorem.

THEOREM 1.8 (Pythagorean Theorem). *If a right triangle has legs of lengths a and b and hypotenuse of length c, then* $a^2 + b^2 = c^2$.

Given: A right triangle with legs a and b, and hypotenuse c.
To prove: $c^2 = a^2 + b^2$.

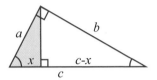

Construction: Draw the altitude to the hypotenuse, separating the hypotenuse into segments of length x and $c - x$.

Proof. • Since the shaded daughter is similar to the mother triangle $\dfrac{a}{x} = \dfrac{c}{a}$, so $a^2 = cx$.

• Since the unshaded daughter is similar to the mother, $\dfrac{b}{c - x} = \dfrac{c}{b}$, so $b^2 = c(c - x)$.

• Adding then gives $a^2 + b^2 = cx + (c^2 - cx) = c^2$. Done! □

Homework Set 24

Problems 1-6 refer to Chapter 14 of NEM1, which is an introduction to similar figures for 7th graders.

1. In NEM 1, answer Problem 1 on page 372.

2. Continuing on pages 372-4, write the answers to Problem 2 and Problem 3abc by drawing the figures directly in your textbook (not to be handed in). Then use graph paper to answer:
   • Problems 3d and 3e.
   • Problems 4a, 4d, and 4f.

   If you do not have graph paper, you can create and print some at www.printfreegraphpaper.com.

3. Continuing on page 375, answer Problem 5a.

4. Continuing on page 376, answer Problem 6b.

5. In Exercise 14.1 of NEM 1 (pages 377-381) answer Problems 3, 5a and 5d, and 7.

6. The lengths of the sides of a hexagon are 8 cm, 10.3 cm, 15 cm, 5.1 cm, 22.5 cm, and 13.2 cm respectively. If the shortest side of a similar hexagon is 1.7 cm, find the longest side of the similar hexagon.

7. Draw a triangle (your choice). Label the vertices A, B and C. Using a compass and a straightedge (but no ruler!), construct a similar triangle $\triangle A'B'C'$ with sides 3 times as long.

8. In the figure below,
   a) Why are the shaded triangles similar?
   b) What is the scale factor?
   c) What is y?
   d) What is the ratio of areas of these triangles?

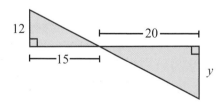

9. A tower casts a shadow 100 feet long. A 9 foot pole is placed upright at the point P so that the tip of its shadow coincides with the tip of the shadow of the tower at point O. Distance OP is measured and found to be 12 feet. How tall is the tower?

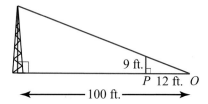

10. A tree casts a shadow 18 m long while a 3 m pole casts a shadow 4 m long. How tall is the tree?

11. The figure shows two nested right triangles. Find x. (First find the scale factor between the smaller and the larger triangles).

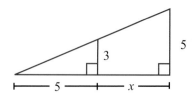

12. In the figure, $BC = 12$, and $CD = 8$.

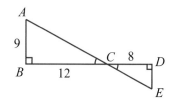

a) Give an "Elementary Proof" that $\triangle ABC \sim \triangle EDC$.

b) Find CE.

13. Find the sides marked with letters. All lengths are given in centimeters.

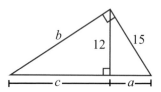

14. In the figure below, $AP = 5$, $PB = 3$, $AQ = 4$, and $QC = a$.

a) Name the triangle similar to $\triangle ABC$.

b) Find a and b.

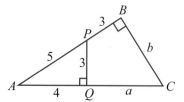

15. For a right triangle, one can apply the area formula using three different base-altitude pairs. Taking b as the base, one gets Area $= \frac{1}{2}ba$. Taking a as the base, one gets Area $= \frac{1}{2}ab$ — the same. Use the Mother-Daughter Theorem (Theorem 1.7) to prove that the third possibility (taking c as the base) also gives the same area.

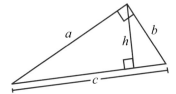

7.2 Similar Triangles

The previous section focused on similar *right* triangles. However, the definition of similarity applies to all triangles: two triangles are similar if there is a correspondence so that:

- corresponding angles are equal, and

- corresponding sides are in proportion.

Altogether this sets six conditions: that 3 pairs of angles have equal measure and that 3 side-ratios are equal. There are three criteria, often called "similarity tests", that are often used to verify that triangles are similar. Each one requires checking only two or three conditions; the remaining conditions are then automatically true. Similarity tests are often introduced in middle school with the modest goal of having students *learn to use* them.

Intuitively, the angles of a triangle determine its shape, but not its size. Here is a simple class activity connecting that intuition with the definition of similar triangles.

EXERCISE 2.1. *Draw a triangle △ABC of your choice. Using a ruler and protractor, measure the angles and draw a second triangle △XYZ with ∠A = ∠X, ∠B = ∠Y and ∠C = ∠Z.*

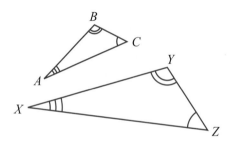

1. Measure all 6 sides in centimeters:

   $AB = $ ___ $BC = $ ___ $AC = $ ___
   $XY = $ ___ $YZ = $ ___ $XZ = $ ___

2. Find the ratios
   $\frac{AB}{XY} = $ ___ $\frac{BC}{YZ} = $ ___ $\frac{AC}{XZ} = $ ___.

3. Are corresponding sides in proportion? ___

4. Is △ABC ~ △XYZ? ___

Exercise 2.1 helps students understand the phrase "corresponding sides are proportional" and introduces the notation ~ for similarity. It also provides evidence that equiangular triangles are automatically similar. The teacher then summarizes the conclusion as a clear statement, and gives it an abbreviation.

If two triangles have three pairs of equal angles, then the triangles are similar. (Abbreviation: **equiangular.**)

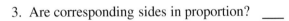

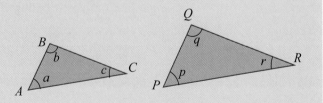

$a = p$, $b = q$, $c = r$,

∴ △ABC ~ △PQR   equiangular.

Students then set about solving problems using this "equiangular" criterion. Teachers can point out the following two hints, which make it easier to recognize and name equiangular triangles.

Hint 1: Any two angles of a triangle determine the third (since the angles total 180°). Consequently, *triangles with two pairs of matching angles are similar*. For this reason, the "equiangular" criterion is sometimes called the "angle-angle" or AA test.

Hint 2: To claim that triangles are similar, one must specify a correspondence – a way of pairing vertices. To spot a correspondence, match vertices with equal angles, or match sides by length: shortest with shortest, longest with longest, and middle with middle.

EXAMPLE 2.2. *Are these triangles similar? If so, state the correspondence.*

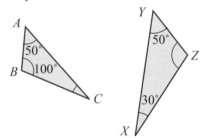

$\angle A = \angle Y = 50°$
$\angle Z = 180° - 30° - 50°$ $\angle$ sum of $\triangle$
    $= 100°$
$\angle B = \angle Z = 100°$
$\therefore \triangle ABC \sim \triangle YZX$ equiangular.

There are two other criteria that guarantee that triangles are similar.

If all 3 sides have the same scale factor, then the triangles are similar.
(Abbreviation: **3 sides proportional.**)

$$\frac{AB}{KL} = \frac{BC}{LM} = \frac{AC}{KM} = \frac{1}{2},$$

$\therefore \triangle ABC \sim \triangle KLM$ 3 sides proportional.

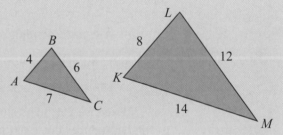

If two pairs of sides have the same scale factor and the included angles are equal, then the triangles are similar.   (Abbreviation: **ratio of 2 sides, incl. $\angle$.**)

$$\frac{AB}{UV} = \frac{AC}{UW} = 2,$$

$\angle A = \angle U = 43°,$

$\therefore \triangle ABC \sim \triangle UVW$ ratio of 2 sides, incl. $\angle$.

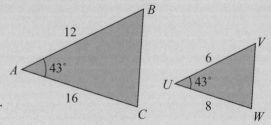

All three similarity criteria are consequences of the fact that a scaled triangle is similar to the original, as stated in Theorem 1.6. To understand why, think of comparing triangles using a two-step process: first scale, then check for congruence. Specifically, consider the triangles R and T in the following illustration. To check whether R and T are similar, we do two steps:

STEP 1.   Scale triangle R by the factor $k = a'/a$, creating a new triangle S with side lengths ka, kb, and kc. Then $ka = a'$, so S and T have at least one pair of equal sides.

STEP 2.   Check whether $S \cong T$. *If so, then the three triangles are similar to each other and hence $R \sim T$.*

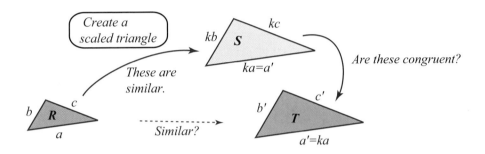

All three similarity tests are now easily proven:

- If triangles R and T are equiangular, then S and T are equiangular and have one pair of sides of the same length. Hence $S \cong T$ by ASA, so the three triangles are similar.

- If all 3 sides of triangles R and T are proportional, then T has sides of length ka, kb and kc. Hence $S \cong T$ by SSS, so the three triangles are similar.

- If 2 corresponding sides of R and T are proportional and the included angles are equal, then S and T have two corresponding sides of equal length and the included angles are equal. Hence $S \cong T$ by SAS, so again the three triangles are similar.

Hint 3: Similar triangles often occur as *triangles within triangles*. Here are three examples. You should be able to recognize these pictures within some of your homework problems.

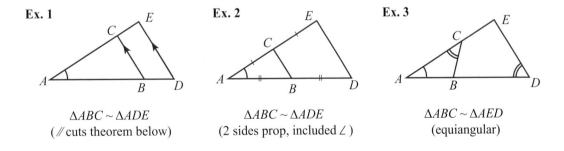

THEOREM 2.3 (Parallel Cuts Theorem). *When parallel lines intersect two crossed lines, the triangles formed are similar.*   (*Abbreviation:* **∥ cuts.**)

In problems, the Parallel Cuts Theorem appears in two separate cases. Recognizing the two figures is a quick way of spotting similar triangles.

Case 1:

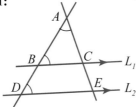

Given: $L_1 \parallel L_2$
To prove: $\triangle ABC \sim \triangle ADE$

$\angle A$	common angle
$\angle B = \angle D$	corr. $\angle$s, $L_1 \parallel L_2$
$\therefore$ $\triangle ABC \sim \triangle ADE$	equiangular.

Case 2:

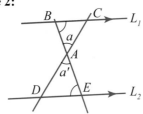

Given: $L_1 \parallel L_2$
To prove: $\triangle ABC \sim \triangle AED$

$a = a'$	opp. $\angle$s
$\angle B = \angle E$	alt. $\angle$s, $L_1 \parallel L_2$
$\therefore$ $\triangle ABC \sim \triangle AED$	equiangular.

Constructions that Use Similarity

Suppose you are given a line, a straightedge and a compass, and a 1-decimeter bar. It is easy to measure off 1 meter along a line: use the bar to make equally-spaced marks on the line. Ten of these 1-decimeter segments are 1 meter long. You can make the marks using the compass (set to the length of the bar). The following construction can be done with straightedge and compass in the same manner.

CONSTRUCTION 11. *Given a segment $\overline{AB}$, mark equally-spaced points $C, D, E \ldots$ along the ray $\overrightarrow{AB}$ so that the distances $AB, BC, CD, \ldots$ are equal.*

EXERCISE 2.4. *Draw a line, mark two points A and B and do Construction 11.*

Next, suppose that you want to mark off a 1 centimeter segment, again using only a compass and straightedge. Thus, the task is to divide the bar into 10 equal parts. This task may seem impossible, but it can be done with a surprisingly simple construction:

CONSTRUCTION 12. *Given a segment and whole number n, divide the segment into n equal parts.*

We illustrate the construction by trisecting a segment $\overline{AZ}$. The same method can be used to divide segments into *n* equal parts for any whole number *n*.

- Pick a point *B* not on the segment $\overline{AZ}$. Draw ray $\overrightarrow{AB}$.

- Mark points *C* and *D* on the ray such that *AB=BC=CD*.

- Draw line $\overline{DZ}$.

- Draw lines parallel to $\overline{DZ}$ through *B* and *C*.
  (The figure shows how to copy ∠*D* to make ∠*B* and ∠*C*.)

- Mark points *X*, *Y* where these lines intersect *AZ*.

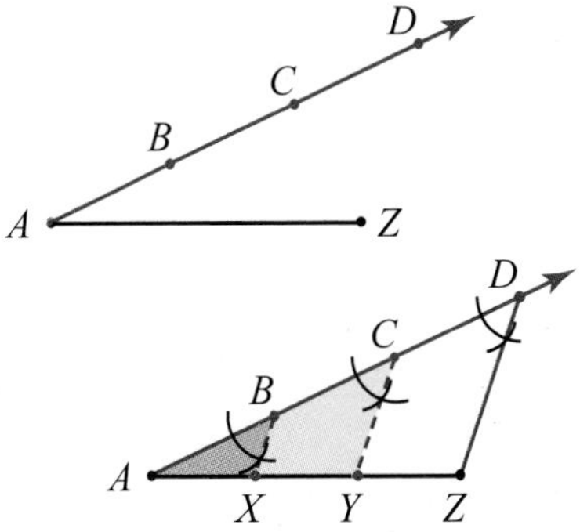

The parallel lines produce three nested triangles. The triangles are similar by the Parallel Cuts Theorem 2.3 and their sides along $\overline{AB}$ have lengths in a ratio of 1 : 2 : 3. Consequently, the side lengths *AX* : *AY* : *AZ* are in the same ratio. Thus *X* and *Y* trisect segment $\overline{AZ}$.

EXERCISE 2.5. *Apply this method to divide the segment AZ in this picture into 5 equal parts. To keep this simple, just sketch the parallel lines in Step 3.*

Homework Set 25

1. For each row, state which triangles, if any, are similar.

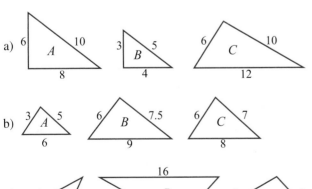

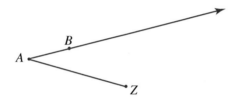

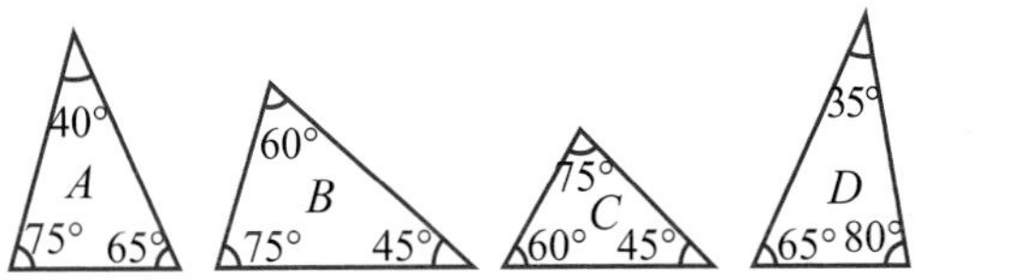

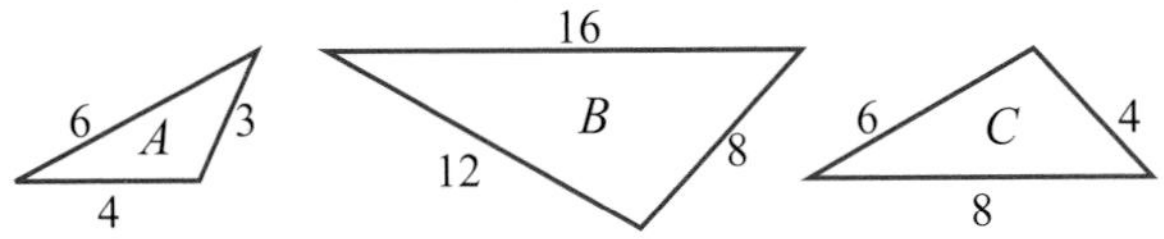

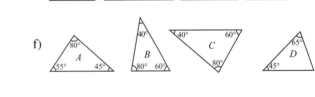

2. For each pair of triangles, state whether the pair is similar or not. If yes, name the correspondence and give reasons.

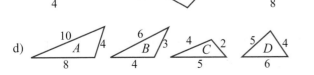

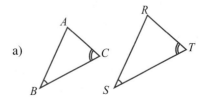

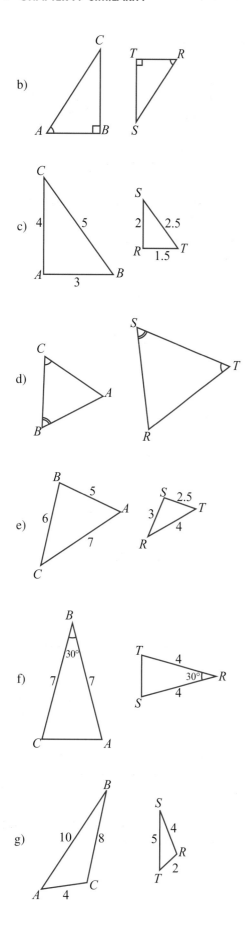

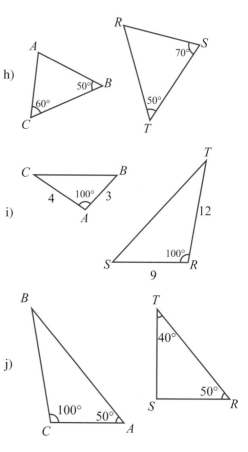

3. For each pair of similar triangles, find the lengths of the sides marked by letters.

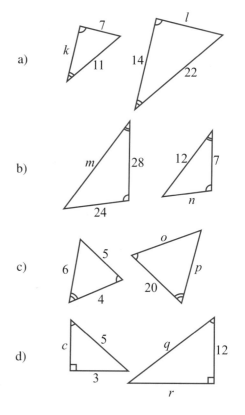

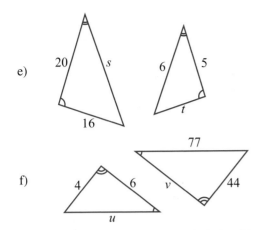

e)

f)

4. For each figure in Problems a–b, find the sides marked with letters.

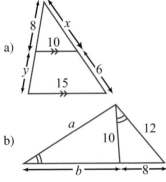

a)

b)

5. Can two triangles be similar if the first contains a 70° angle and the second contains a 115° angle? Explain.

6. Read section 14.3 (pages 386 to 390) of NEM1. Then on pages 390–391 do Problems 2, 3, 6, and 10a (use ruler and compass for this last one).

7. A light shines on a wall. A 12 inch ruler is held parallel to the wall between the light and the wall. If the ruler is 7 feet from the light bulb and 18 feet from the wall, how long is its shadow?

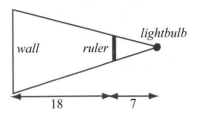

8. In the figure below, $\overline{AB}$ and $\overline{AC}$ are straight lines, $PB = 2$, $QC = 6$, $PQ = 6$, $BC = 9$ and $\angle P = \angle B$.

   a) Prove that $\triangle ABC \sim \triangle APQ$.

   b) Find AP.

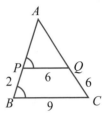

9. In the figure below, $\overline{DB}$ is a straight line, $DC = 32$, and $DB = 40$.

   a) Prove that $\triangle ABC \sim \triangle EDC$.

   b) Find c.

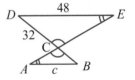

10. Do Exercise 2.5 in the text of this section.

7.3 Coordinate Systems and Slope

The number line and coordinate systems are fundamental tools of mathematics. They enable us to describe geometric figures by numbers and equations. Most important of all, they enable us to think of functions in terms of their graphs.

Developing these conceptual ideas is a major theme of K-8 mathematics. The number line is introduced in kindergarten and repeatedly used and added to as students learn fractions, negative numbers, square roots and irrational numbers. Coordinates and graphing are developed over several years beginning in grade 4 or 5.

This section describes how to use geometric constructions to build a number line and to set up a coordinate system. It continues with a discussion of slope and the graphs of lines. Similar triangles appear repeatedly along the way.

Coordinates on a Line

Any line L can be made into a copy of the number line, as follows: First choose a point 0 on the line (which will be the point zero on the number line), a unit length, and one of the two rays that lie in L with endpoint 0 (to use as the positive direction on the number line).

STEP 1.   Using a compass, mark off unit lengths (in both directions) starting from O. Label these by integers.

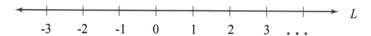

STEP 2.   To locate fractions, use Construction 12 from the previous section to divide the segment from 0 to 1 into n equal segments.

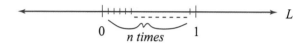

The newly marked points are named $\frac{1}{n}, \frac{2}{n}, \frac{3}{n}$, etc. To find the positive fraction $\frac{a}{n}$, count a fractional units to the right of zero; the multiples of $\frac{1}{n}$ continue past 1 on the number line. For example, taking $n = 3$ locates the points $\frac{1}{3}, \frac{5}{3}, \frac{10}{3}$, etc. In this way the entire set of rational numbers can be constructed, using only a compass and a straightedge.

Some — but not all — irrational numbers can also be constructed in this manner. For example, recall that $\sqrt{2}$ is the length of the hypotenuse of a right isosceles triangle with legs of length 1. The picture shows how to construct such a triangle and use a compass to locate $\sqrt{2}$ on the number line.

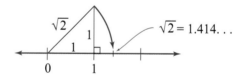

After some thought, you should be able to see how to similarly locate $\sqrt{3}$, $\sqrt{5}$ and some other irrational numbers. Having located $\sqrt{2}$, we can use Construction 12 to partition the segment from 0 to $\sqrt{2}$ into equal parts and thereby locate $\frac{1}{2}\sqrt{2}$ and in fact any fractional multiple $\frac{c}{d}\sqrt{2}$. We can then add to any of the already-determined lengths to locate irrational numbers such as

$$\frac{2}{5} + \frac{12}{7}\sqrt{2}.$$

The ancient Greeks wondered whether *all* numbers could be located using only compass and straightedge. This was an unsolved problem for more than 2000 years. The answer is now known: many irrational numbers, π for example, cannot be constructed with a compass and straightedge alone. Nevertheless, any number can be located on the number line by the process described in the next step.

STEP 3. Every real number has a decimal expansion which can be finite or infinite, as it is for $\pi = 3.14159265\ldots$. In the decimal expansion of π, the first two digits tell us that the number lies on a segment of width $1/10$ (between 3.1 and 3.2); the next digit restricts it to a segment of length $1/100$, etc. Thus the expansion locates the number to any desired accuracy, and the full infinite expansion specifies a single point on the number line.

In summary,

Any line L can be made into a number line by fixing

- a point on L called 0,
- a unit length,
- a positive direction on L.

With this done, each real number corresponds to a point on the line and vice versa.

In books, number lines are almost always drawn horizontally with the positive direction to the right. But the horizontal arrangement is purely a convention. Any line can be made into a number line by the above construction — or by placing a ruler along it.

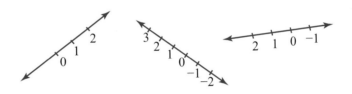

Coordinates on the Plane

In 1637 the French mathematician and philosopher René Descartes had the idea of systematically labeling the points in a plane using two perpendicular number lines. Descartes' idea is one of the most powerful techniques in mathematics. It is used every time we graph an equation. It is based on the following straightedge-and-compass construction. The construction starts with an entirely blank plane and proceeds in four steps.

STEP 1. Choose a line L in the plane. Then choose a point 0 on L, a unit length, and a positive direction, and construct coordinates on L. Call the resulting number line the x-axis. Include an arrow indicating the positive direction.

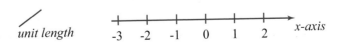

STEP 2.   Construct another line, called the *y*-axis, perpendicular to the *x*-axis through 0. Choose a positive direction on it (again indicated with an arrow) by rotating the positive *x*-axis counterclockwise 90°.

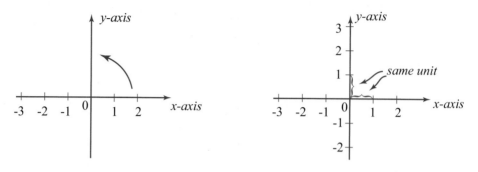

STEP 3.   Construct coordinates on the *y*-axis. Usually, the same unit of length is used for both axes.

STEP 4.   Each point *P* now has an "associated rectangle" found by drawing lines through *P* parallel to the *x*-axis and the *y*-axis. These lines intersect the *x*-axis at a point called the *x*-**coordinate at** *P* and the *y*-axis at a point called the *y*-**coordinate at** *P*.

The numbers *x* and *y* are recorded as an ordered pair of real numbers (x, y) with *x*-coordinate first and the *y*-coordinate second. For the point *P* shown we write $P = (2, 3)$ or more briefly $P(2, 3)$.

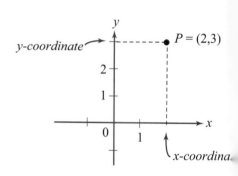

The above 4-step procedure creates a *coordinate system on the plane*. Once a coordinate system is created, every point is specified by an ordered pair, and every ordered pair specifies a point.

Usually the axes are drawn horizontally and vertically.

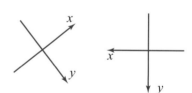

But these choices give equally valid coordinate systems.

Slope of a Line

A coordinate system allows one to describe lines by equations. Lines and equations are related using the definition of the slope of a line. One way to start a discussion of slope is to consider a segment $\overline{PQ}$ that extends from the lower left to the upper right. The corresponding **rise-run triangle** is the right triangle $\triangle PQR$ with PR parallel to the *x*-axis, and RQ parallel to the *y*-axis. Set

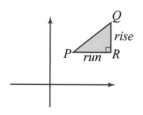

$$\text{slope of } \overline{PQ} = \frac{RQ}{PR} = \frac{\text{rise}}{\text{run}}.$$

Facts about slope are seen by using similar right triangles. In the next two facts, we continue to consider only lines that extend from the lower left to the upper right.

FACT 3.1. *All segments on a given line have the same slope.*

Proof. Pick points P, Q, P' and Q' on a line L. Then

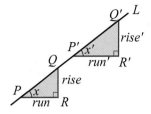

$$x = x' \qquad \text{corr. } \angle s, \ PR \parallel P'R'$$
$$\triangle PQR \sim \triangle P'Q'R' \qquad \text{equiangular.}$$
$$\frac{\text{rise}'}{\text{run}'} = \frac{\text{rise}}{\text{run}} \qquad \text{ratio of corr. sides.}$$

$$\therefore \text{ slope of } \overline{P'Q'} = \text{slope of } \overline{PQ}.$$

Because of Fact 3.1, the slope is a number associated with the line L. It can be computed using any convenient rise-run triangle, always with the same result.

The angle x in the above proof is called the **inclination of** L. The proof of Fact 3.1 shows that lines with the same inclination have the same slope. Conversely, two rise-run triangles with the same slope are similar (because the slope is the ratio of corresponding sides), and therefore have equal inclination angles. Thus:

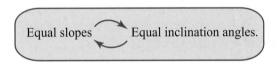

Equal slopes ⟲ Equal inclination angles.

FACT 3.2. *Parallel lines have equal slopes. Lines with equal slopes are parallel.*

The figure shows two rise-run triangles along lines L and L'. Notice that $x = x'$ (why?).

The lines have equal inclination angles, so they have equal slopes.

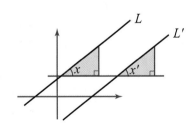

The rise and the run can also be expressed in terms of the coordinates of the chosen points P and Q. When this is done, one sees that some lines have negative slope.

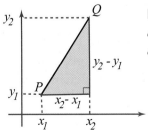

DEFINITION 3.3. *If a line L passes through points $P = (x_1, y_1)$ and $Q = (x_2, y_2)$ with $x_1 \neq x_2$, we define the* run *to be the difference $x_2 - x_1$ and the* rise *to be $y_2 - y_1$ and*

$$\textit{slope of } L = \frac{\textit{rise}}{\textit{run}} = \frac{y_2 - y_1}{x_2 - x_1}.$$

The run and the rise can be negative numbers. When they have opposite signs, the fraction rise/run, which is the slope, is negative and the line is oriented *downward to the right* as in the Example 3.4 below. When the rise and the run have the same sign (either both are positive or both are negative), the slope is positive, and the line is oriented *upward to the right*, as in the previous pictures. In the remaining case, when $y_1 = y_2$, the slope is zero and the line is horizontal. There is no slope number for vertical lines because division by zero is undefined.

EXAMPLE 3.4. *Find the slope of the line L through the points* $(5, 1)$ *and* $(-1, 4)$.

Solution. Taking (x_1, y_1) to be $(5, 1)$ and (x_2, y_2) to be $(-1, 4)$, we find that

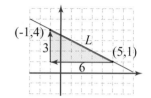

$$\text{slope of } L = \frac{y_2 - y_1}{x_2 - x_1} = \frac{4 - 1}{-1 - 5} = \frac{3}{-6} = -\frac{1}{2}.$$

To understand the signs of the run and the rise, one can think of walking from the first point to the second point along the legs of the rise-run triangle. In the above example, one starts at $(5, 1)$, moves horizontally 6 units in the negative direction, then vertically 3 units in the positive direction to arrive at $(-1, 4)$. Thus, as the arrows indicate, the run is negative and the rise is positive.

Two numbers are called **negative reciprocals** if their product is -1. The negative reciprocal of 3 is $-\frac{1}{3}$, while the negative reciprocal of $\frac{5}{3}$ is $-\frac{3}{5}$ because $-\frac{3}{5} \times \frac{5}{3} = -1$. In general, the negative reciprocal of $\frac{a}{b}$ is $-\frac{b}{a}$.

THEOREM 3.5. *The slopes of perpendicular lines are negative reciprocals. Lines whose slopes are negative reciprocals are perpendicular.*

Proof. If lines L and M are perpendicular, draw a vertical line to the right of their point of intersection, creating a right triangle (shaded). The horizontal line through the point of intersection is the altitude to the hypotenuse and so splits the shaded triangle into two daughter triangles. The daughters are similar to each other by Theorem 1.7 (look at the picture sideways). Hence

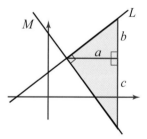

$$\frac{b}{a} = \frac{a}{c} \qquad \text{ratio of corr. sides.}$$

The daughter triangles are rise-run triangles for lines L and M. Using the above fact, we have

$$\text{slope of } L = \frac{b}{a} = \frac{a}{c}$$

and, paying attention to signs,

$$\text{slope of } M = -\frac{c}{a}.$$

Thus the slopes are negative reciprocals.

With a little thought, one can see that these steps are reversible: if the slopes are negative reciprocals, the daughter triangles are similar, and therefore the lines are perpendicular. □

Equations of Lines: A Teaching Sequence

linear equation

An equation whose graph is a line is called a **linear equation**. The equation of a line can be determined by knowing

- the slope and a point on the line, or
- the slope and the y-intercept, or
- two points on the line.

Beginning algebra courses cover all three, one after another, starting from the definition of slope. Usually, students start with problems where the slope and one point are given. The equation of the line is found in two simple steps: write down the definition of slope, then multiply both sides by the denominator.

EXAMPLE 3.6. *Find the equation of the line with slope 7 passing through the point* $P = (3, 4)$.

How to find the point-slope form

Solution. Pick a point Q on the line. We will not be explicit about which point we have chosen; instead we will write the coordinates of Q as simply (x, y). By the definition of slope,

$$7 = \text{slope of } \overline{PQ} = \frac{y - 4}{x - 3}.$$

Multiplying both sides by $(x - 3)$ gives

$$y - 4 = 7(x - 3).$$

This equation holds for every point (x, y) on the desired line, so is an equation for the line.

The same procedure applies with all the numbers replaced by letters. The result is called the **point-slope form** of a linear equation. It says that the equation of the line with slope m passing through a given point with coordinates (x_1, x_2) is

$$y - y_1 = m(x - x_1).$$

Students can solve problems like Example 3.6 by memorizing the point-slope form and replacing m, x_1 and y_1 by the numbers specified in the problem — no thinking is needed. But the point-slope form is not the starting point. Teachers begin by serving up easy problems like Example 3.6 and helping students get started. Students then do dozens of problems until the procedure used to solve Example 3.6 becomes routine. Practicing the procedure is easier than memorizing, and reveals how the equation of a line emerges from the definition of slope.

The point-slope form can be rewritten to become an equation of the type "y = something", which makes it easier to read and easier to graph. For the equation of Example 3.6, one can "solve for y" by adding 4 to both sides, applying the distributive property, and collecting terms. The steps for the general case, on the right below, are exactly the same.

$$
\begin{aligned}
y - 4 &= 7(x - 3) \\
y &= (7x - 21) + 4 \\
y &= 7x - 17.
\end{aligned}
\qquad\qquad
\begin{aligned}
y - y_1 &= m(x - x_1) \\
y &= mx - mx_1 + y_1 \\
y &= mx + \underbrace{(y_1 - mx_1)}_{b} \\
y &= mx + b.
\end{aligned}
$$

One advantage of the form $y = mx + b$ is that both m and b have simple geometric interpretations. The number m is still the slope. To interpret b, notice that the line with this equation intersects the y-axis at the point $(0, y)$ where $y = m \cdot 0 + b = b$, that is, at the point $(0, b)$. Consequently, the number b is called the *y-intercept* and the equation $y = mx + b$ is called the **slope-intercept form** of the equation of a line.

Finally, to determine the equation of a line using two points, first calculate the slope using the two points, and then use the point-slope procedure described above.

Homework Set 26

This homework set has three strands. Problems 2–6 examine how the Primary Mathematics textbooks develop graphing ideas, beginning with pictograms in grade 2 and ending on the verge of defining slope in grade 5. Problems 7–12 involve slope, and the remaining problems are map-scale problems.

1. Draw a number line and, without using a calculator, indicate the approximate location of the following numbers:

$$\tfrac{5}{3} \qquad 0.8 \qquad 2.04 \qquad -1.2 \qquad -\tfrac{31}{15}$$

2. (*Study the Textbook!*) Look over pages 58-63 of Primary Math 3B, answering the questions mentally. There are three basic ways to represent data or relationships:

   a) As table of values.

   b) As a bar graph or line graph.

   c) As an equation, like $y = 3x + 5$.

   Which is taught first in the Primary Math curriculum, graphs or equations? Most curricula follow this order.

3. Page 59 of Primary Math 3B introduces bar graphs to students. Previously, in second grade, students worked with pictograms like the one shown on page 58. Compare the pictogram on page 58 with the bar graph on page 59. List four specific differences between these graphs.

4. How does the bar graph on page 61 of Primary Math 3B differ from the others on pages 58-63?

5. (*Study the Textbook!*) Read pages 51-53 in Primary Math 5B. We have moved from bar graphs to line graphs. Notice that:

   • The horizontal axis evolves to be a number line. The idea of graphing in the coordinate plane is being developed.

   • Most of the questions on pages 52 and 53 ask about changes in the height of the graph. These are really questions about slope.

   Copy the graph from Problem 1 on page 52. Then draw the two rise-run triangles that students should focus on to answer questions 1(a) and 1(b).

6. (*Study the Textbook!*) Page 53 gives the first example of a linear graph. Read it carefully and answer the questions

mentally. Then write *three* aspects of this linear graph problem that make it especially easy for students to understand.

7. Show that the points $A(0, 0)$, $B(2, 1)$, $C(1, 3)$ and $D(-2, 4)$ are the vertices of a trapezoid (graph the points and calculate slopes).

8. Find the number z so that the line joining $A(z, 4)$ and $B(2, 3)$ is parallel to the line joining $C(-5, 3)$ and $D(1, 1)$.

9. For the points $A(1, 7)$, $B(4, 5)$ and $C(3, 2)$:

   a) Find the slope of $\overline{BC}$.

   b) Find the point at which the line through A parallel to $\overline{BC}$ cuts the y-axis.

10. The vertices of a quadrilateral are the points $R(1, 4)$, $S(3, 2)$, $T(4, 6)$, $V(2, 8)$. Is the quadrilateral a parallelogram? Explain why or why not.

11. If the line containing points $(-8, m)$ and $(2, 1)$ is parallel to the line containing $(11, -1)$ and $(7, m + 1)$, what must be the value of m?

12. What values of k will make the line containing points $(k, 3)$ and $(-2, 1)$ perpendicular to the line through $(5, k)$ and $(1, 0)$?

13. In the homework for the previous section, you did some of the "map scaling" problems on page 390 of NEM1. Now do one more: write a Teacher's Solution to Problem 4 on page 390.

14. Do Problem 6 at the bottom of page 399 of NEM1.

15. A floor plan for a house has a scale of 1 cm: 1.6 m.

   a) If a room is 3 cm by 4.8 cm on the floor plan, how large is the actual room?

   b) If the house is 18 m wide, how wide is it in the floor plan?

16. A model of the Statue of Liberty is 9 cm tall (including the pedestal and raised arm), while the actual statue is 300 feet tall. Give a Teacher's Solution to the following two questions. Be sure to include the units at each step.

a) If the top of Liberty's head is 7.8 cm high on the model, how high is her head on the actual statue?

b) If the granite pedestal is 90 feet high, how high should it be on the model?

17. On a map with a scale of 1 cm to 8 miles, what is the distance between two villages if they are:

a) 24 miles apart,

b) 83 miles apart,

c) 18 miles apart,

d) 1600 miles apart?

7.4 Similar Right Triangles and Trigonometry

Similarity is especially easy for right triangles. As we saw in Section 7.1 (Theorem 1.5), two right triangles with equal acute angles are similar.

For example, the two right triangles below both have angles of 34°, so they are similar. Said differently, any two right triangles that contain an angle of 34° are related by some scale factor k. If we know that scale factor, then we can use measurements in the first triangle to deduce measurements in the second triangle.

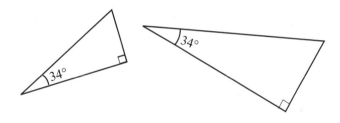

This simple observation is the key to three important topics that are introduced in middle school and which continue to be important throughout high school mathematics, namely:

- the slope of a line,

- indirect measurement, and

- trigonometry.

We have already discussed slope. This section describes the other two topics at a level appropriate for middle school teaching.

Indirect Measurement

Indirect measurement refers to ways of measuring an object without actually holding a ruler up against it. Indirect measurement is frequently needed because direct measurement with a ruler is inconvenient (as in finding the height of a tree) or impossible (as with finding the diameter of the moon). Think about it: how do astronomers measure the diameter of the moon?

Similar triangles are extremely useful for indirect measurements. The following exercise shows the idea. It is a typical middle school problem on indirect measurement.

EXERCISE 4.1. *Kristen finds a spot where, when she puts her head to the ground and looks at a nearby building, the top of the building lines up with the top of the school flagpole. If the flagpole is 10 meters tall and Kristen is 20 meters from the flagpole and 100 meters from the building, how tall is the building?*

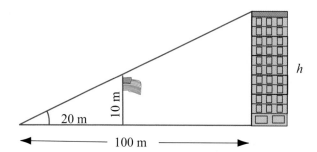

Such problems are solved in two steps. The first step is identifying the similar triangles and explaining why they are similar. In this problem we have two equiangular right triangles.

The second step is to find the unknown measurement by equating ratios. There are several distinct ways to do this. All are of roughly equal difficulty, and all three are useful.

Method 1	Find the scale factor. Use it to rescale.	$k = \dfrac{\text{base of big } \Delta}{\text{base of small } \Delta} = \dfrac{100}{20} = 5.$ $h = 5 \times 10 \text{ m} = 50 \text{ m}.$
Method 2	Equate ratios of corresponding sides. Solve for unknown.	Ratio of bases = Ratio of heights. $\dfrac{100 \text{ m}}{20 \text{ m}} = \dfrac{h}{10 \text{ m}} \implies h = 50 \text{ m}.$
Method 3	Equate ratios within each triangle. Solve for the unknown.	Ratio within small Δ = Ratio within big Δ. $\dfrac{\text{ht.}}{\text{base}} = \dfrac{10 \text{ m}}{20 \text{ m}} = \dfrac{h}{100 \text{ m}} \implies h = 50 \text{ m}.$

Trigonometry

Trigonometry is essentially a simplification of Method 3 above. Given a right triangle with acute angle θ, we can unambiguously label the sides: the longest side is the hypotenuse, the leg opposite the angle θ is the *opposite*, and the leg which is next to the angle θ is the *adjacent*. In Method 3 we consider the ratios between two of the three sides.

There are three such ratios. Each ratio depends on the angle θ *and nothing else*. Indeed, any two right triangles that contain an angle congruent to θ are similar (because equiangular triangles are similar!), so the ratios of their corresponding sides are equal. We give the three ratios names.

DEFINITION 4.2. *For each angle* θ, *set*

$$\sin\theta = \frac{opp}{hyp},$$

$$\cos\theta = \frac{adj}{hyp},$$

$$\tan\theta = \frac{opp}{adj}.$$

Here sin, cos *and* tan *are abbreviations for* sine, cosine *and* tangent.

Trigonometry starts with the observation that if we compile a table of these three numbers for each acute angle θ — or program a calculator to find these ratios — then we can use that information to quickly solve indirect measurement problems. The principle is that if we know one acute angle and the length of one side, then we can determine all lengths in a right triangle.

EXAMPLE 4.3. *Sam has another way to measure the height of Kristen's building (see Exercise 4.1). He stands 80 meters from the building. By careful measurement, he finds that the angle of elevation (the angle between the ground and the top of the building) is* $32°$.

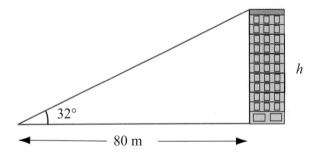

To calculate the height h of the building, Sam writes

$$\frac{h}{80} = \frac{\text{opp}}{\text{adj}} = \tan 32°,$$

and uses a calculator to find $\tan 32° = 0.624$. The height of the building is therefore $h = 80 \cdot 0.624 = 50$ meters. Easy – and no flagpole is needed!

In many middle school curricula, students are introduced to trigonometry in a unit which defines sine, cosine and tangent as in Definition 4.2 and then gives applications, including problems requiring indirect measurement. In high school, the curriculum returns to trigonometry, and begins the subject over again from the beginning.

The second time through, students learn the most important identity in trigonometry:

$$\sin^2 \theta + \cos^2 \theta = 1.$$

And no wonder: it is just the Pythagorean Theorem in a slightly different form!

By definition:
$\sin \theta = a$
$\cos \theta = b.$

Pythagorean Theorem:
$a^2 + b^2 = 1$
$(\sin \theta)^2 + (\cos \theta)^2 = 1.$

High school curricula start with this identity and use it to derive many other identities, including the trigonometric formulas for the sums and differences of angles.

Homework Set 27

These homework problems are applications of the definitions of sin, cos and tan. For each, draw a sketch *and* use a calculator *to find the sine, cosine or tangent of the given angles.*

1. An antenna mast is supported by four wires attached to points on the ground, each 57 m away from the foot of the mast. If each wire makes an angle of 32° with the horizontal, find the height of the mast.

2. To find the width of a river, a boy places a wooden stake at a point A on one side directly opposite an object B on the opposite bank. From A, he walks 50 m along the bank to a point C. He observes that $\angle ACB$ is 34°. Find the width of the river.

3. A ladder leans against a wall, touching a window sill, and makes an angle of 62° with the ground. Find the height of the window sill above the ground, and the length of the ladder if the foot of the ladder is 3 m from the foot of the wall.

4. A 4 m plank rests on a wall making a 42° angle with the wall and extending 1.2 m beyond the wall as shown. Find

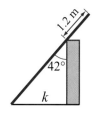

a) the height of the wall, and

b) the distance k from the plank to the wall.

5. A tree is h m high. The angle of elevation of its top from a point P on the ground is 23°. From another point Q, 10 m from P and in line with P and with the foot of the tree, the angle of elevation is 32°. Find h.

6. The lower edge of a window of a house is 15 m above ground level. The angles of elevation of the top and bottom of the window are 27.4° and 23.25° respectively from a point K on level ground. Find the height of the window.

7. Two men stand at points A and B in line with a point F at the foot of a building. A is 50 m from F and F is directly under point T at the top of the building. The angle of elevation $\angle FAT$ is 30° and the angle of elevation $\angle FBT$ is 40°. How far apart are the two men?

8. A building 75 m tall stands on level ground, 54 m from a taller building. The angle of elevation from the top of the shorter building to the top of the taller building is 32.92°. How high is the taller building?

9. During a total eclipse, the moon passes in front of the sun. Remarkably, at the moment of totality the moon almost exactly covers the sun. The moon has a diameter of about 2200 miles and its distance from earth is about 240,000 miles. The sun is 93,000,000 miles away from the earth. What is the approximate diameter of the sun?

CHAPTER 8

Area Concepts and Circles

Area is a surprisingly complicated topic. Instruction on area usually begins in grade 2 and is extended every year through grade 8 (nor is that the end: area is also a major theme of calculus). Chapter 5 told the beginning of this story. There we saw how young children learn to measure area by counting unit squares, how that leads to understanding the properties of area, and how those properties lead to formulas for the area of triangles and parallelograms. We now continue the story by looking at the aspects of area studied in grades 6 – 8.

We begin by converting between different area units and comparing the areas of similar figures. Both lead to useful new ways of thinking about area. The corresponding ideas about volume are developed and used extensively in the next chapter.

Finding the perimeter and area of a circle involves an issue not previously faced: what do length and area mean for curved figures? This mathematical question requires calculus to address properly. But school curricula contain clever explanations that keep the discussion at middle school level while remaining faithful to the mathematical reasoning. The explanations and the mathematics are described in Sections 8.2 and 8.3.

Section 8.4 moves out of the perfect world of geometry. Actual physical measurements are not exact, and students must learn to deal with approximations and levels of accuracy. Our discussion of these issues includes student- and teacher-level knowledge.

8.1 Converting Area Units and Scaling

This section examines two related topics. We first think about how a given area measurement can be rewritten in terms of a different unit. For example, if a desktop has an area of 1800 square inches, what is its area in square feet? The second topic is in some sense the reverse: what happens to area measurements when we scale a region and measure it using the same unit of area?

The metric system is designed to make conversions between units very simple. All units of length are related to the basic unit — the meter — by powers of ten; three such units are shown below, at their actual size:

$$1 \text{ cm} = 10 \text{ mm}$$
$$1 \text{ dm} = 10 \text{ cm}$$
$$1 \text{ m} = 10 \text{ dm} = 100 \text{ cm}$$
$$1 \text{ km} = 1000 \text{ meters.}$$

×10   ×10

1mm   1cm   1 dm

As in Chapter 1, one can convert a metric length measurement from one unit into another by shifting the decimal point. For example, 724 cm = 7.24 m and 2760 m = 2.76 km.

For each length unit there is a corresponding unit square, and hence a corresponding unit of area. Thus the metric units of area are 1 mm^2, 1 cm^2, 1 dm^2, 1 m^2, 1 km^2, and one more is described at the end of this section. Metric area units are related by powers of 10, so conversions between them is done by shifting the decimal point, but *not by the number of places indicated by the prefixes*. In fact, a common mistake is to assume that area units are related by the same factor as length units.

EXERCISE 1.1. *Correct Rajesh's errors:* "$1 \ m^2 = 100 \ cm^2$" *and* "$1 \ cm^2 = 10 \ mm^2$".

Teachers can proactively help students avoid this error by asking them to draw actual-size pictures of area units. Unit squares with areas 1 mm^2, 1 cm^2, 1 dm^2 are shown below.

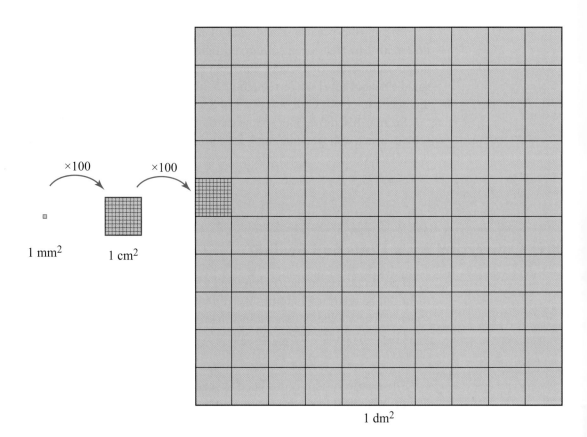

×100   ×100

1 mm^2 1 cm^2

1 dm^2

Rectangular array pictures make clear that when one unit of length is 10 times another, the corresponding unit square has $10 \times 10 = 100$ times the area. Conversion of area units is done with the *square* of the conversion factor used for the corresponding length units.

> If one length unit is k times another, then the corresponding area units are related by a factor of k^2.

The convention of writing 1 square unit as 1 unit^2 makes conversions easy. Recall that a length measurement like 5.2 cm is a *quantity* — a number times a unit. To multiply quantities, one multiplies the numbers, and separately multiplies the units. Everything works out very neatly when we write unit $\times$ unit as unit^2. For example,

$$
\begin{aligned}
1 \text{ m}^2 = (1 \text{ m})^2 &= (100 \text{ cm})^2 \\
&= 100 \text{ cm} \times 100 \text{ cm} \\
&= 100 \times 100 \text{ cm} \times \text{cm} \\
&= 10{,}000 \text{ cm}^2.
\end{aligned}
$$

and

$$
1 \text{ ft}^2 = (12 \text{ in})^2 = 12 \text{ in} \times 12 \text{ in} = 144 \text{ in}^2.
$$

The key to these conversions is to *use parentheses carefully* and to go one step at time:

> a) Using parentheses, write the area unit in the form (length unit)^2.
>
> b) Replace the part inside parentheses by a different length unit.
>
> c) Multiply quantities.

After some practice, students will see that the notation actually tells them what to do!

EXAMPLE 1.2. *a)* $2.56 \, km^2 =$ _____ m^2.

b) $3.2 \, ft^2 =$ _____ in^2.

Teacher's Solution: a)
$$
\begin{aligned}
2.56 \text{ km}^2 = 2.56 \times (1 \text{ km})^2 &= 2.56 \times (1000 \text{ m})^2 \\
&= 2.56 \times (1{,}000{,}000) \text{ m}^2 \\
&= 2{,}560{,}000 \text{ m}^2.
\end{aligned}
$$

b)
$$
\begin{aligned}
3.2 \text{ ft}^2 = 3.2 \times (1 \text{ ft})^2 &= 3.2 \times (12 \text{ in})^2 \\
&= 3.2 \times 12 \times 12 \text{ in}^2 \\
&= 460.8 \text{ in}^2.
\end{aligned}
$$

There is one more common metric unit of area: the hectare. The hectare is needed because the ratio between one meter and one kilometer is large — a factor of 1000. As a result there is a huge gap in the corresponding area units: 1 square kilometer is $(1000)^2 = 1,000,000$ square meters. To fill the gap, an intermediate unit of area is used. One **hectare** is the area of a 100 m by 100 m square or $10,000$ square meters — about the size of two football fields. While we use acres, outside the U.S. land area is measured in hectares.

EXERCISE 1.3. *A farmer's field is* $48,300 \ m^2$. *How many square kilometers is this? How many hectares is it? Of these three area units, which do you think farmers would find the most useful for expressing the size of their fields?*

How Scaling Affects Area

Recall that if two polygons are similar there is a number, called the scale factor k, so that each length measurement in the second polygon is k times the corresponding length in the first polygon. How are the areas of similar polygons related? To answer, we consider several examples: first rectangles, then triangles, then general polygons.

EXAMPLE 1.4. *Rectangle A is similar to Rectangle B, with lengths of corresponding sides in a ratio of* 1 : 3. *What is the ratio of their areas?*

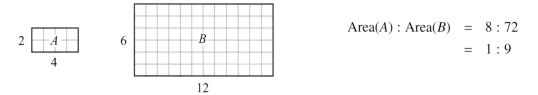

$$\text{Area}(A) : \text{Area}(B) = 8 : 72$$
$$= 1 : 9$$

In the above example, the scale factor is 3 and the second rectangle has 9 times the area of the first. In general, when similar rectangles P and Q are related by a scale factor of k, their areas are related by a factor of k^2:

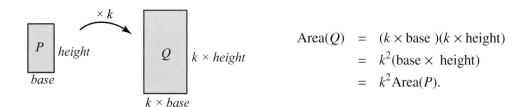

$$\text{Area}(Q) = (k \times \text{base})(k \times \text{height})$$
$$= k^2(\text{base} \times \text{height})$$
$$= k^2 \text{Area}(P).$$

The same fact is true for triangles.

THEOREM 1.5. *If similar triangles S and T are related by a scale factor of k, their areas are related by a factor of* k^2.

Proof. In the first triangle S, choose the longest side as the base, draw the altitude to that side and label it by its length h. In the second triangle T, draw and label the corresponding base-altitude pair, as shown. The bases are then related by a factor of k, but it is not immediately clear how the heights h and h' are related.

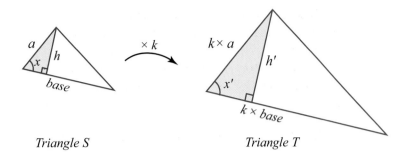

Triangle S   *Triangle T*

Because S and T are similar triangles, the angles labeled x and x' are equal. Hence, the shaded triangles are similar to each other (they are equiangular). Since the length of side a is multiplied by k, the height h is multiplied by the same factor, so $h' = kh$. We can then compute areas:

$$\begin{aligned} \text{Area}(T) &= \frac{1}{2}(k \times \text{base}) \cdot kh \\ &= k^2 \times \frac{1}{2}\text{base} \cdot h \\ &= k^2\,\text{Area}(S). \end{aligned}$$

□

The same reasoning applies to similar polygons: subdivide one polygonal region into triangles and draw the corresponding subdivision of the other.

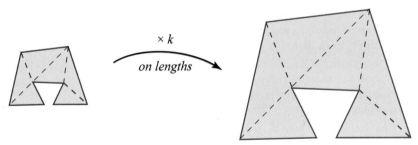

Then

Polygons related by scale factor k $\Rightarrow$ Lengths in corresp. triangles related by factor k

$\Rightarrow$ Areas of corresp. triangles related by factor k^2

$\Rightarrow$ Areas of polygons related by factor k^2.

Thus we arrive at the main fact of this section:

AREA SCALING PRINCIPLE.

If two figures are similar and are related by a scale factor of k, then their areas are related by a factor of k^2.

EXERCISE 1.6. *Figures A and B are similar. If the area of A is 3 cm², what is the area of B?*

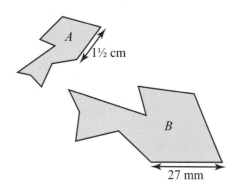

$1\frac{1}{2}$ cm = 15 mm.

Length scale factor: $\dfrac{27 \text{ mm}}{15 \text{ mm}} = \dfrac{9}{5} = 1.8$.

Area scale factor: $(1.8)^2 = 3.24$.

$$\therefore \text{Area}(B) = 3.24 \times \text{Area}(A)$$
$$= 3.24 \times 3 \text{ cm}^2$$
$$= 9.72 \text{ cm}^2.$$

Homework Set 28

1. (*Study the Textbook!*) Pages 331 and 332 of NEM1 are a review of area for 7th graders. The review starts with the definition of square centimeter and deduces the formula Base × Height for the area of a rectangle. But the text skips over a tricky point. What is this missing point?

2. Continue reading NEM1 through page 336. Do Problems 1, 3, 4, 5, 7 and 8 on the pages 336-338.

3. Read Worked Example 3, pages 335-336 of NEM1. Then go to the bottom of page 338 and use the same format to answer Problem 17 parts a), b), c), d), g), j), and k).

   These use the metric units of area: square millimeter (mm²), square centimeter (cm²), square meter (m²), square kilometer (km²), and the *hectare*, which is the metric version of an acre:

   hectare: 1 ha = 100 m × 100 m = 10,000 m².

4. What is the area of a rectangle (in cm²) with width 17 mm and length 15 dm?

5. One of the diagonals of a rhombus is 6 m long and its area is 0.000024 km².

   a) What is the area in square meters?

   b) How long is the other diagonal? (See Problem 11, page 128.)

   c) How long are the *sides* of the rhombus?

6. (*Calculator*) An *acre* is defined to be 43,560 square feet. How many acres are in a square mile? Write a Teacher's Solution which displays how you solved this problem.

7. What is the effect on the area of a rectangle if its base is doubled and its height is left unchanged? If its base and height are both doubled? If its base is doubled and its height is cut in half? Make sketches to illustrate your answers.

8. The perimeters of two similar triangles are 12 ft and 45 ft. The area of the smaller triangle is 64 ft². What is the area of the larger triangle?

9. In the figure below, $\overline{AE}$ and $\overline{DB}$ are lines, $CD = 2$ cm, $DE = 5$ cm, and $AB = 9$ cm.

   a) Name a pair of similar triangles in the figure below.

   b) What is the ratio $BC : CD$?

   c) If the area of $\triangle ABC$ is 30 cm², what is the area of $\triangle CDE$?

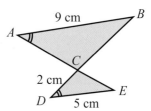

10. The figure shows two parallel lines separated by 9 cm. Furthermore, $AB = 8$ cm, $BC = 10$ cm, and $CD = 5$ cm. What is the total area of the shaded region?

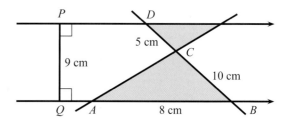

11. In the figure, $\overline{AB} \parallel \overline{DC}$, $AC = 2$ cm, and $CE = 6$ cm. Find the area of the shaded figure.

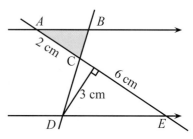

8.2 Circles and Pi

Extending the concepts of length and area to circles is one of the most interesting steps in the K-8 geometry curriculum. For the first time, students must think about measuring lengths along paths that are not straight lines, and think about measuring the area of regions that are bounded by curved paths. Because the ideas are new, teachers need to begin with very simple examples that highlight the concepts, and then shift to developing students' problem-solving skills.

All discussions of circles revolve around a few basic terms. To avoid confusion, it is important that all students understand the precise definitions. Most importantly, recall that a circle is not just a "round shape"; the word refers to a precisely-defined figure:

DEFINITION 2.1. *Choose a point P in the plane and a distance R. The* **circle** *with center P and radius R is the set of all points in the plane that are distance R from the point P.*

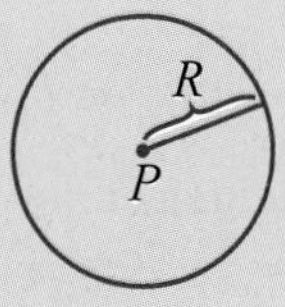

Discussions about circles involve line segments of three types:

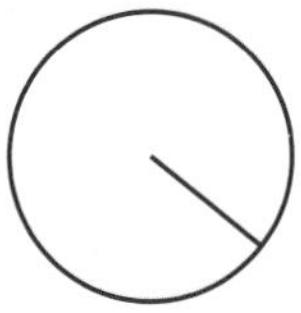

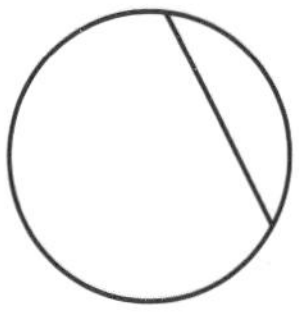

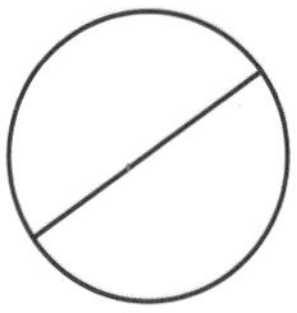

A *radius* is a segment with one endpoint at the center and the other on the circle.

A *chord* is a segment with both endpoints on the circle.

A *diameter* is a chord passing through the center of the circle.

The length of the diameter is also called the *diameter* of the circle. Thus the words "radius" and "diameter" have two meanings, one referring to a segment, and the other to a length. Both teachers and students should be clear and consistent when using these terms.

EXERCISE 2.2. *a) Is the center a part of a circle?*
b) How can you locate the center of a circular piece of paper by folding?
(See page 24 of Primary Math 6B.)

Now comes an important advance: measuring the "perimeter" of a circle. The length around a circle is called it circumference.

circumference

DEFINITION 2.3 (School Definition). *The* circumference *of a circle is the length around the circle.*

Previously, students always measured lengths along straight lines using rulers, and found perimeters by adding the lengths of straight segments. Now, for the first time, students consider the length of a *curved* path. Rulers are not designed to accurately measure the length of a curve — try it and see! Thus, from the students' perspective, the school definition uses the word "length" with a new, expanded meaning. The expanded meaning is made clear by giving students experience measuring the distance around curves and curved objects. They can measure with a string or a wire, with a flexible tape measure, or by rolling a circular object on a flat surface and measuring the distance rolled with a ruler.

Of course, distances can be measured with various units. When measuring circles, a natural choice is to use the diameter as a unit.

The circumference is about ____ *times the diameter.*

definition of π

There are two distinct mathematical points here. First, the number

$$\frac{\text{Circumference}}{\text{Diameter}}$$

obtained by dividing the circumference by the diameter *is the same for all circles*. This specific number is so important that it is given its own name: π (the Greek letter "pi").

> Circumference $= \pi \times$ Diameter.
>
> $\pi \approx 3.14$ or $\dfrac{22}{7}$.

Finding the value of π is the second mathematical point. Measurements show that π is slightly larger than 3, and there are methods to calculate it very precisely (see the end of Section 8.3). The Primary Math books use the approximation $\pi \approx 3.14$ in some problems and $\pi \approx \frac{22}{7}$ in other problems; this variety helps build students' proficiency calculating with both decimals and fractions.

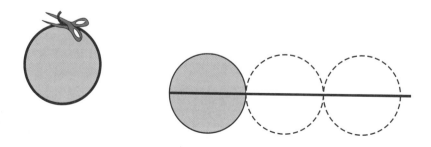

Sectors

Here are three more terms associated with circles:

central angle
arc
sector

- A *central angle* is an angle whose vertex is at the center of the circle.

- An *arc* is the part of a circle spans some central angle.

- A *sector* is the portion of a disk that lies inside a central angle.

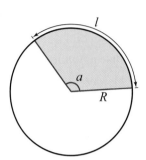

There are three measurements associated with a sector:

(i) the radius R,

(ii) the central angle a, and

(iii) the length l of the subtended arc.

Any two of these determine the third. The key to solving problems about these measurements is to *determine what fraction of the whole circle is represented by an arc or sector.*

EXAMPLE 2.4. *Find the perimeter of sector OPQ. (Take $\pi = 3.14$.)*

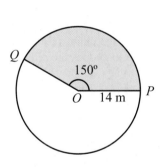

Fraction of circle : $\dfrac{150°}{360°} = \dfrac{15}{36} = \dfrac{5}{12}$.

The length of arc PQ is that fraction of the circumference $2\pi r$:

$$\text{Arc length} = \frac{5}{12} \times 2(3.14)\,14 \approx 36.6 \text{ m}.$$

Therefore

$$\text{Perimeter of sector } OPQ = (36.6 + 14 + 14) \text{ m} = 64.6 \text{ m}.$$

EXAMPLE 2.5. *An arc of a circle has the same length as the radius of the circle. What is the measure of the central angle that it spans?*

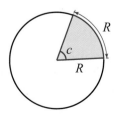

If the radius is R then the circumference is $2\pi R$. As a fraction of the circumference, this arc is

$$\frac{R}{2\pi R} \text{ circle } = \frac{1}{2\pi} \text{ circle.}$$

Therefore

$$a = \frac{1}{2\pi} \cdot 360° \approx 57.3°.$$

High school students learn that this angle is called one *radian*.

Homework Set 29

1. The following numbers can be used as approximations of π. How accurate are they? For each, express the relative error as a percent (significant to 1%). Recall that relative error is the fraction (error)÷(true value).

    a) 3   b) 3.14   c) 22/7   d) 3.1416   e) $\sqrt{10}$.

2. (*Study the Textbook!*) Work through pages 22-29 of Primary Math 6B, reading the text and answering all the problems (write the answers in your textbook).

    a) Make a list of the geometry terms (vocabulary words) that are introduced in these pages.

    b) Many of these problems take π to be either 3.14 or 22/7. Is there any problem here that *doesn't* do that?

3. Do all 6 problems on page 30 of Primary Math 6B.

4. A piece of wire 16 cm long is wound around a circular pipe with a radius of 20 cm. What central angle does the wire subtend? (The wire may wrap around more, or less, than shown in this picture). Express your answer in degrees.

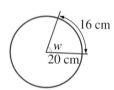

5. (*Study the Textbook!*) These ideas are revisited at the seventh grade level in NEM1 pages 339-341, along with the formula πR^2 for the area of a circle (which we will discuss in the next section).

    a) Read page 339. How is π defined here? Give your answer in words, not as a formula.

    b) In Exercise 12.2, do Problems 1e, 2b, and 3b, 4c, and 5a. Note that every problem is different! One cannot solve these by just memorizing formulas.

    c) If you ignore decimal points, many of the numbers in these problems are multiples of 7 (e.g., 28, 21, 154). Why did the authors choose multiples of 7?

6. Continuing in NEM1, read Worked Example 6 on page 341. Give Teacher's Solutions to Problems 7, 9, 10, and 11 on page 342.

7. A machine part is made by bending a metal strip into a circular arc according to the design below. How many such parts can be made from a metal strip 2 meters long?

8. A flower is drawn inside a circle of radius 10 cm. The flower is made of arcs of radius 10 cm. Find the total perimeter of the flower.

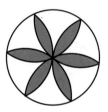

9. a) The circumference of a circle is 15 inches. To increase the circumference to 18 inches, how much longer must we make the radius?

    b) If the radius of a circle is increased by 2 units, how much does the circumference change? *Hint:* Let r and C stand for the original radius and circumference. Then $C = 2\pi r$ and the new circumference is $C_{new} = 2\pi(r + 2) = \ldots$.

    c) Suppose that a wire is stretched tightly around the Earth along the equator. (Assume that the Earth is a circle along the equator with a circumference of 40,000 km.) Approximately how much would the length of the wire have to be increased so that it was everywhere 1 meter above the surface?

10. (*Calculator*) The earth travels in an orbit which is nearly a circular path with the sun at the center and a radius of 93,000,000 miles. If the earth makes one orbit in 365 days, what is its approximate speed in miles per hour?

8.3 Area of Circles and Sectors

Elementary school students learn to find the area for polygonal regions, first by counting unit squares, then by using formulas and the area properties. Then, sometime in grades 5-7, they are introduced to the problem of finding the area of a circle. At that point there are two teaching issues to be addressed:

- What does "area" mean for curved regions?

- What is the exact formula (if one exists!) for that area?

Both questions have especially simple answers for circular regions.

The illustration below shows one intuitive way to introduce the concept of area for curved regions. The idea of "painting regions" makes clear that every region has *some* area. But it does not provide a way to calculate areas.

unit square

If it takes 1 can of paint to paint the unit square, how many cans are needed to paint this region?

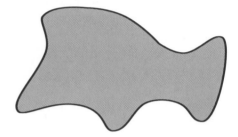

To actually calculate area, we have two tools: the method of "filling with unit squares" and the area properties. Page 31 of Primary Math 6B shows how to estimate the area of a quarter-circle by covering it with square units. The same method works for any curved region: overlay the region with 1 cm squares and count the squares that are more than half inside the region, as in the first picture below. We can obtain a better estimate by subdividing each square centimeter into four equal smaller squares, each with an area of $\frac{1}{4}$ cm^2, as in the right-hand picture below. An even finer grid, with 1 mm squares for example, gives even better estimates, but requires enormously more work and is still not exact.

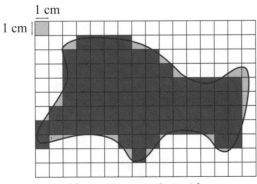

82 squares mostly inside.
Area ≈ 82 cm^2.

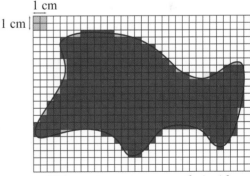

335 quarter-squares mostly inside.
Area ≈ 335 × $\frac{1}{4}$ = 83.75 cm^2.

For circles, there is a simpler approach. Without ever considering unit squares, one can use the area properties and some clever pictures to obtain the exact formula for the area of a circle.

Area of a Circle

Pizza Method: Given a circle of radius R, slice it into sectors and rearrange the sectors as shown. The resulting region has the same area as the circle, and very nearly fills a rectangle (shown in black) with height R and with base equal to half the circumference of the circle. Thus the area of the circle is approximately $\pi R \times R$.

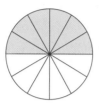 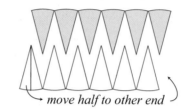 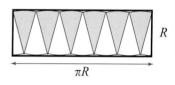

move half to other end

Further thinking is needed because the rearranged slices do not *exactly* form a rectangle — the top and bottom are not straight lines! However, notice that:

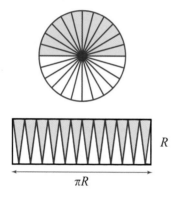

- Using thinner slices creates a figure, still with the same area as the circle, that is even closer to the shape of the black rectangle.

- Now *imagine* repeating this again and again with ever thinner slices, creating figures ever closer to the black rectangle.

We conclude that the circle has *exactly* the same area as the rectangle.

For any circle, Area $= \pi \times$ Radius $\times$ Radius.

Braided Rug Method: Imagine a circular rug with radius R made of concentric strands of yarn. Cutting the rug from the edge to the center and straightening the strands creates a triangular rug with the same area as the original.

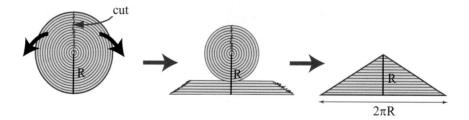

The triangle has height R. Its base is the circumference of the rug, which is $2\pi R$. Therefore,

$$\begin{aligned} \text{Area of Circle} \ &= \ \text{Area of Triangle} \\ &= \ \frac{1}{2} \cdot R \cdot 2\pi R \\ &= \ \pi R^2. \end{aligned}$$

The first = sign requires an explanation because the straightened rug is not a perfect triangle — the ends of the strands create step-like edges. But by imagining rugs made from thinner and thinner strands, one sees the straightened rug becoming exactly the shape of the triangle. One concludes that the circle and the triangle have exactly the same area, and that area is πr^2.

Polygon Method: Given a circle of radius R, draw an inscribed regular n-gon. The polygon can be decomposed into n congruent triangles as shown. When n is a large number, the area of the circle is very nearly the area of the polygon. Thus

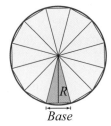

$$\begin{aligned} \text{Area of Circle} \ &\approx \ (\text{Number of triangles}) \times (\text{Area of each}) \\ &= \ n \times \frac{1}{2} \, \text{Base} \times \text{Height}. \end{aligned}$$

But whenever n is a large number,

$$\text{Height} \approx R \qquad\qquad \text{Base} \approx \frac{\text{Circumference}}{n}.$$

Because the circumference is $2\pi R$, this gives

$$\begin{aligned} \text{Area of Circle} \ &= \ \cancel{n} \times \frac{1}{2} \times \frac{2\pi R}{\cancel{n}} \times R \\ &= \ \pi R^2. \end{aligned}$$

As in the previous methods, one picture is not enough: one must imagine doing this for polygons with more and more sides, and notice that in all three places where the $\approx$ symbol is used, the approximation becomes more and more exact.

The Polygon and Pizza methods are essentially the same. The Polygon Method avoids the cutting and rearranging, but it requires a better understanding of elementary algebra. Consequently, the Pizza Method is used in most textbooks for grades 5-7, and the Polygon Method is the preferred method in high school textbooks.

EXERCISE 3.1. *Read Chapter 2 of Primary Math 6B. Which of the above methods is used?*

Types of "π Problems"

In the Primary Math books, you will encounter problems whose directions ask students to handle the number π in three different ways to solve problems.

1. "Answer in terms of π": keep π as a symbol throughout the calculation and express the answer as a multiple of π.

2. "Take $\pi = 3.14$": keep π as a symbol as long as possible, then replace by 3.14 and use decimals.

3. "Take $\pi = \dfrac{22}{7}$": use fractions throughout and simplify fractions along the way.

The three types of problems serve different purposes. The first actually provides practice for algebra: students are doing calculations involving a symbol, just as in algebra. The second provides practice with decimals, and the third provides practice with fractions.

Furthermore, many Primary Mathematics problems are compatible with the suggested values of π. Problems that ask students to use a particular value of π are often designed so that *the solution is especially simple when the suggested value is used.* In particular, in "$\frac{22}{7}$" problems, look for cancelations of factors of 7.

EXAMPLE 3.2. *Find the area of the semicircle. Take $\pi = \frac{22}{7}$.*

Area $= \frac{1}{2}\,\pi r^2$

Mixed fractions and decimals: $\quad \dfrac{1}{2} \cdot \dfrac{22}{7} \cdot (3.5)^2 = $ mess!

All fractions: $\quad \dfrac{1}{\cancel{2}} \cdot \dfrac{\cancel{22}^{11}}{\cancel{7}} \cdot \dfrac{\cancel{7}}{2} \cdot \dfrac{7}{2} = \dfrac{77}{4}$ easy!

Area of Sectors

The area of a sector is found by first answering the question: the sector is what fraction of the whole circle?

EXAMPLE 3.3. *Find the area of the shaded region. Use $\pi = \frac{22}{7}$.*

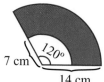

7 cm 120° 14 cm

Teacher's Solution:

Fraction of circle: $\dfrac{120°}{360°} = \dfrac{1}{3}$.

Area of the entire large disk − Area of the entire small disk:

$$
\begin{aligned}
\pi \cdot 14^2 - \pi \cdot 7^2 &= \frac{22}{\cancel{7}}\,(1\cancel{4}^{2} \cdot 14 - \cancel{7} \cdot 7) \qquad \text{cancel 7's before multiplying!}\\
&= 22\,(14 \cdot 2 - 7)\\
&= 22 \cdot 21.
\end{aligned}
$$

Area of shaded region: $\dfrac{1}{3} \cdot 22 \cdot 21 = \dfrac{22 \cdot \cancel{3} \cdot 7}{\cancel{3}} = 22 \cdot 7 = 154.$

The shaded region has area 154 cm^2.

Calculating π

In school mathematics, π is taken as given: it is a specific number whose decimal expansion is approximately 3.14 and more precisely is

$$3.14159265\ldots$$

As textbooks often mention, mathematicians have proved that π is an irrational number. Thus the exact value of π cannot be written as a fraction, and the decimal expansion of π is neither terminating or repeating. Nevertheless, mathematicians can calculate π to great precision — to billions of decimal places. Obviously, this is not done by measuring bicycle wheels. How is it done?

There are many algorithms for calculating π. Some are very efficient, meaning that a relatively small number of computations are needed to find many decimal places of π. But none is elementary enough for K-8 mathematics. The algorithm described next is at the high school level.

First observe that π is the area of a circle of radius 1. We can therefore find π by calculating the area of a quarter circle and multiplying by 4, exactly as is done on page 31 in Primary Math 6B. There the area of a quarter circle was found by superimposing a 10×10 grid and counting squares. We will repeat with a 50×50 grid. The number of squares is then too large to count by hand. But we can still write the number of squares inside the quarter circle as a formula.

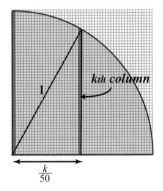

The grid has 50 columns. The portion of each column that lies inside the circle is very nearly a rectangle. The idea is to add up the areas of those thin rectangles.

Notice that:

- Each column has width $\frac{1}{50}$.

- The base of the kth column is distance $k \times \frac{1}{50} = \frac{k}{50}$ from the origin (k steps each of size $\frac{1}{50}$).

The kth column is shown in the picture as the darker shaded column. By the Pythagorean Theorem the height of that column is

$$\text{height} = \sqrt{1 - \left(\dfrac{k}{50}\right)^2}.$$

Multiplying by the width $1/50$ gives the area of the kth column. We can then add the areas of the first column ($k = 1$), the second column ($k = 2$), up to the last column ($k = 50$). The resulting formula is

$$\pi = 4 \times \text{area of quarter circle} \approx 4 \sum_{k=1}^{50} \dfrac{1}{50} \sqrt{1 - \dfrac{k^2}{50^2}}.$$

This calculation can be done on a graphing calculator or a computer. The result is $\pi \approx 3.098$, not a very good approximation. However, we can repeat with a 500×500 grid and then with a 5000×5000 grid; the formula is the same except that each occurrence of the number 50 is replaced first by 500, then by 5000. The results are tabulated below; the blue digits are correct.

Grid size	Approximation to π
50	3.098
500	3.137
5000	3.1412

Even larger grid sizes give more and more correct digits for π.

Using calculus, one can derive many other formulas for calculating π to any desired accuracy. An especially simple one is

$$\pi = 4\left(1 - \frac{1}{3} + \frac{1}{5} - \frac{1}{7} + \frac{1}{9} - \frac{1}{11} - \cdots\right).$$

Homework Set 30

1. (*Study the Textbook!*) Primary Math 6B covers circumference and area of circles on pages 22-37. About how many class days is that? To get a rough count, count the number of arrows referring the students to Exercises in Workbook 6B and add a few because homework may not be assigned every day.

2. Do all the problems on page 37 of Primary Math 6B. The students have been prepared to tackle some challenging problems!

3. If the diameter of a circle is doubled, how does its area change? Explain your answer in one sentence.

4. Find the ratio of the radii of two circles if the ratio of their areas is 4 : 9.

5. Find the radius of a circle whose area is equal to the sum of the areas of two circles of radii 5 cm and 12 cm.

6. Do Problem 9 on page 345 of NEM1. Which has larger area: the shaded or unshaded region?

7. A circle has radius 1 unit. What percent of its area lies outside the circle with the same center and a) radius $\frac{1}{2}$ unit? b) radius $\frac{3}{4}$ unit?

8. Jessica used her calculator to find the area of a disk of radius 12 in. She first found that $\pi \cdot 12 = 37.7$, then squared

this number and wrote Area $= 1421$ in^2. What was Jessica's error?

The grade 6 material on areas and perimeter is reviewed and extended on pages 339-348 of NEM1.

9. Do Problems 3a, 5b, and 6a on page 342 of NEM1.

10. Some grade 6-7 area problems involve introducing and solving for an unknown. On page 343 of NEM1, Worked Example 8 presents such a problem. Read it carefully, and give similar Teacher's Solutions to Problems 13, 14, 15, and 16 on pages 345-346.

11. Do Problems 17 and 18 on page 346.

Every good curriculum includes challenging exercises for students who finish early—exercises that also help teachers! In NEM1, the starred problems on pages 346-347 and the "Challenger" problems on 348-349 are such exercises.

12. ✳ Do Problems 19-21 on page 346.

13. ✳ Give Teacher's Solutions to Problems 22, 23 and 24 on page 347 (Hint for 24: use your answer to Problem 17 on the previous page.)

14. ✳✳ If you finish early, try *Challenger Problems* 1, 2, 3, and 5 on pages 348-349 of NEM1.

8.4 Approximation and Accuracy

This section discusses some aspects of measurement that arise in almost all practical applications of mathematics. In their middle and high school science courses, students learn about approximation and accuracy, about the importance of one's choice of units, and about how accuracy is affected by calculations. Most elementary curricula include work on some of these topics, often in the context of "data analysis". But from the moment children first begin measuring, they are confronted with issues of how to approximate and which units to use. They need their teacher's guidance.

Recall that elementary mathematics involves two basic models. The set model involves discrete objects and whole numbers only. The measurement model involves some version of the number line and any number, including fractions and irrational numbers, that may arise. In practice, there is a fundamental difference between these models, as can be seen from the following classroom exercise.

EXERCISE 4.1.

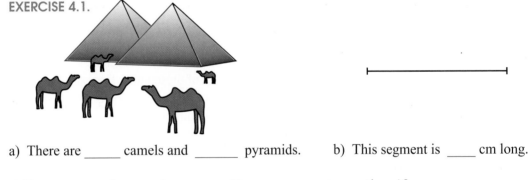

a) There are _____ camels and _____ pyramids.   b) This segment is ____ cm long.

c) Does everyone in your class agree with your answers to question a)? ___
d) Does everyone agree with your answer to b)? ___

Discrepancies in measuring lengths are not simply due to carelessness. For part b) in Exercise 4.1, some students will measure to the nearest centimeter and find that the segment is 4 ± 0.5 cm. Others will measure to the nearest millimeter and obtain 3.9 ± 0.1 cm. Neither measurement is exact.

With a finely-etched ruler and a magnifying glass, you might be able to determine that the segment is 3.86 ± 0.01 cm. But you can never measure its *exact* length.

Measurements of area are similarly inexact. One way to measure the area of an irregular region is to superimpose a grid and count the number of grid squares in the region. The following pictures show an example, first using a 1 cm grid, then using a $\frac{1}{2}$ cm grid.

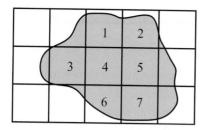

Area ≈ 7 squares = 7 cm²

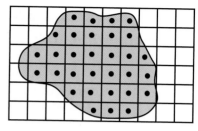

Area ≈ 31 squares = 31× .25 cm²
= 7.75 cm²

Again, finer grids will give more precise measurements, but no such measurement is exact. The same issue arises whenever we measure volume, weight, temperature, speed — in fact with all measurements except those that are necessarily whole numbers.

> All physical measurements are approximations.

Choice of Units

When you measure length, you can choose to measure in inches, feet, or miles. For metric units there is a similar choice between centimeters, meters, and kilometers. In theory, any length measurement can be expressed in any of these units. For example, you can express the distance from New York to London in inches, or you can express your shoe size in miles. But a poor choice of unit makes the measurement difficult to understand.

There is no specific rule determining what unit is appropriate for a given measurement. But a general rule is to choose units so that *the number of measured units is between 1 and 1000.*

EXERCISE 4.2. *Each of the five measurements listed is expressed in several equivalent ways. Circle the ones that use an appropriate unit.*

Weight of school girl	41,000 g	41 kg	0.041 tons
Length of pencil	15 cm	0.15 m	0.00015 km
Capacity of a car gas tank	52,000 mℓ	52 ℓ	
Area of a lake	34,000,000,000 cm²	3,400,000 m²	3.4 km²
Length of a desk	135 cm	1.35 m	0.000135 km

EXERCISE 4.3. *Write the metric unit that is appropriate for the stated measurement:*

a) Weight of a cat ____

c) Capacity of a baby food jar ____

b) Height of a building ____

d) Weight of a coin ____

Most elementary curricula include exercises that ask students to choose appropriate units. The choices are clear if students have acquired a sense of the size of the various units. Thus such exercises are diagnostic — they help teachers evaluate the strengths and weakness of students' understanding. If students have difficulty answering problems like Exercise 4.3, the teacher should consider additional hands-on measurement activities, making sure that these involve units of each size.

Accuracy

The *accuracy* of a measurement is how close it is to the true value. Usually, the true value is not known, so the accuracy must be determined by some method independent of the actual measurement. This can be tricky! It requires analyzing the device used to make the measurement. For example, if a bathroom scale says that a woman weighs 136.2 pounds, is that her actual weight to the nearest tenth of a pound? Nearest half pound? The answer depends on the quality of the scale and can only be determined by testing the scale by weighing other objects of known weight.

precision

A related notion is precision, which indicates the extent to which multiple measurements agree with each other. Precision is not the same as accuracy. The woman's scale, for example, might repeatedly read 136.2 pounds yet still be 5 pounds over her true weight; it is then precise but not accurate. Precision, unlike accuracy, can be determined by measuring the same quantity many times.

Accuracy also depends on the care and skill of the person making the measurements and can be affected by extraneous and unanticipated factors. In a middle school science class, for example, a student's careful reading of a balance scale might be affected by the fact that he is not wearing his glasses or by the fact that, at the crucial moment, his lab partner pours water over his head.

People can be misled by measurements when their accuracy is not reported. A visitor to a small natural history museum wondered about the age of a dinosaur skeleton. Finding no one else, she asked the janitor, and was told the dinosaur was 80 million and 7 years old.

"How can you be so accurate?" she asked.

"Easy," replied the janitor, "I've worked here for 7 years, and when I came they told me the dinosaur was 80 million years old".

Such confusions are less likely to occur when the accuracy of measurements is honestly reported.

> To avoid misinterpretation, all statements about physical measurements should indicate the level of accuracy.

There are four common ways to state the accuracy of a measurement:

1. As a range or interval.
2. As a relative error.
3. Using significant digits.
4. For statistical measurements, giving the margin of error.

Students encounter all four of these in school mathematics. We will describe them one at a time and comment on their utility.

A range or interval can be specified by giving its lower and upper endpoints, or by giving its midpoint and half-width. For example:

- The tree is between 40 and 50 feet tall.

- At the beginning of the experiment, the rat weighed 156 ± 3 grams.

Both statements indicate that a measurement has been made and, after taking into account the accuracy of the measurement, one is sure that the true measure lies within the stated range. Stating a range is the simplest and most easily understood way to communicate the accuracy of a measurement.

relative error

When a measurement has been taken, and the maximum possible error is known, the **relative error** is the fraction

$$\text{Relative error} = \frac{\text{maximum possible error}}{\text{measured value}}.$$

The relative error is usually expressed as a percent.

EXAMPLE 4.4. *At takeoff, a fully loaded passenger airplane has a gross weight of* $185,200\pm400$ *pounds. For this measurement,*

$$\textit{Relative error} = \frac{400}{185,200} = \frac{4}{1852} = 0.002 = 0.2\%.$$

Example 4.4 indicates why one would want to express accuracy in terms of relative errors. When weighing some objects — yourself for example — an error of 400 pounds is unacceptable. But when weighing an airplane, an error of 400 pounds is insignificant; in this case the error is considerably less than 1% of the weight. In a great many practical situations, the relative error is the most appropriate and intuitive way to judge the accuracy of a measurement.

In science and engineering, the accuracy of measurements is often given using the convention of *significant figures*. With this convention, the accuracy of a measurement can be inferred from the reported measurement itself.

significant digits

Given a measurement written in decimal form (e.g., 45.28 meters), identify the digits that are known with confidence (these are called the **significant digits**) and a last digit that is an estimate. Use the last digit to round off the significant digits, then delete it and all other non-significant digits. Finally, report the resulting number with the correct place value positioning (this may require putting in zeros in the positions of some of the deleted digits).

EXAMPLE 4.5. *a) A laboratory scale gives a weight of 32.584 grams with the digits 3, 2, and 5 known confidently and the last two digits uncertain. One then reports the weight as 32.6 grams. The reader can then infer that the weight has been accurately measured to the nearest 1/10 gram.*

b) The age of a Tyrannosaur fossil is said to be 80,000,007 years, but the measuring technique has an accuracy of only ±3 million years. Using the convention of significant figures, the age should be reported as 80,000,000 years.

Laboratory experiments often require doing a series of calculations with measured quantities, and it is standard practice to keep track of the accuracy at each step. The method of significant figures greatly simplifies this process; the accuracy is built into the way the measurements are written so that the calculations themselves keep track of the accuracies. The simplicity makes the method well-suited for high school science classes. In preparation, the method is taught in middle school, often in conjunction with teaching scientific notation. Looking back further, one can see how students' understanding of accuracy depends on having acquired a firm understanding of place value in the early grades.

margin of error   Statistical measurements are usually stated along with a **margin of error**. Polling results, for example, might report "48% of voters will vote for candidate X" and then add "the margin of error in this poll is 3%". Many people might interpret this to mean that candidate X will get between 45% and 51% of the vote. What it actually means is that there is a certain high probability (usually taken as a 95% chance) that candidate X will get between 45% and 51%. Furthermore, there are always two implicit caveats: the reported margin of error assumes that the pollster's mathematical model is correct and that the sample used is truly random.

Computing statistical margins of error is complicated and is certainly beyond middle school mathematics. But middle and even elementary school students read and hear reports about statistical measurements in books, in newspapers, on the web, and on the radio. To properly interpret these, students should understand the key point of the previous paragraph: the margin of error specifies an interval in which the true value *probably* lies, but there remains a chance that the true value lies outside that interval.

The next step is to express matching in terms of the vertices of the triangle. To proceed, we need (i)

Calculating with Error Statements

Most measurements are not taken in isolation. Usually one must make several measurements, and from them calculate the desired quantity. For example, to find the volume of a box one must measure its width, breadth, and height, and then multiply these together. If the accuracy of each measurement is known, one can find the accuracy of the final quantity. However, the procedure is not as straightforward as one might think, as the following "teaching example" shows.

EXAMPLE 4.6. *A rectangular house lot measures* 150 ± 2 *feet by* 200 ± 3 *feet. What is its area?*

Ryan's answer: The lot is approximately $150 \cdot 200 = 30,000$ ft^2. The error is at most 2×3 ft^2, so the area is $30,000 \pm 6$ ft^2.

Ryan's reasoning is not correct. Here are several ways that a teacher can guide Ryan.

1. *Ask Ryan to calculate the smallest and largest possible area:*

   - smallest possible area: $148 \cdot 197 = 29,156$ ft^2.

   - largest possible area: $152 \cdot 203 = 30,856$ ft^2.

The first number is roughly 850 less than $30,000$, and the second is roughly 850 more than $30,000$. Rounding the error up, we can state that the lot is $30,000 \pm 900$ ft^2.

2. *Use the distributive property.* Ryan will wonder: why is the error so large? Why isn't it just 2×3 ft^2? To see what Ryan has missed, think about multiplying using the distributive property:

$$
\begin{aligned}
(150 \pm 2)(200 \pm 3) &= 150 \cdot 200 \pm 150 \cdot 3 \pm 2 \cdot 200 \pm 2 \cdot 3 \\
&= 30,000 \pm (450 + 400) \pm 6.
\end{aligned}
$$

The ± 6 at the end is actually just a tiny part of the possible error. The main part of the error is the middle two terms — which Ryan neglected to calculate.

3. *Draw a picture.* The picture shows three rectangles: a center 200×150 foot rectangle, an inner white rectangle depicting the smallest possible region and an outer rectangle depicting the largest possible region. The picture makes clear why Ryan's 2×3 ft^2 is just a small part of the actual uncertainty in the area. It also gives a visual presentation of why the distributive property is relevant.

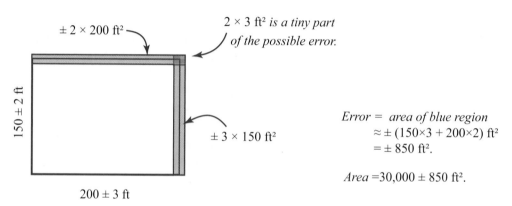

$\pm 2 \times 200$ ft^2

2×3 ft^2 *is a tiny part of the possible error.*

150 ± 2 ft

$\pm 3 \times 150$ ft^2

200 ± 3 ft

Error = *area of blue region*
$\approx \pm (150 \times 3 + 200 \times 2)$ ft^2
$= \pm 850$ ft^2.

Area $= 30,000 \pm 850$ ft^2.

Homework Set 31

1. Identify a suitable unit for each of the following measurements. Your choices are: mm, cm, m, km, cm^2, m^2, km^2, g, and kg.

   a) the weight of a person.

   b) the length of a classroom blackboard.

   c) the width of a sheet of paper.

   d) the area of Manhattan island.

   e) the distance from Los Angeles to San Francisco.

   f) the weight of an envelope.

   g) the width of a pencil.

   h) the area of a laptop computer screen.

2. By law, an "extra large" egg weighs between $2\frac{1}{4}$ and $2\frac{1}{2}$ oz. What is the weight of a dozen extra large eggs (excluding the carton)?

3. A rectangular room has a width of 12 feet ± 3 inches and a breadth of 16 feet ± 3 inches. What is its area in square feet?

4. An irrigated cornfield is circular with a radius of 85 ± 3 meters.

   a) What is its area?

   b) What is the relative error in your calculated area?

CHAPTER 9

Volume and Surface Area

Just as area is the number of unit squares needed to cover a region, the volume of a solid is the number of unit cubes needed to fill the solid. Of course, most solids – a rock for example – cannot actually be filled with unit cubes. This makes volume more difficult to understand than length and area. Consequently, volume is studied later in the school curriculum.

In this chapter we introduce volume, relate it to capacity and weight, and derive formulas for calculating the volume of common solids. All three topics are standard parts of any curriculum.

The second theme of this chapter is the metric system. Earlier chapters showed how students are introduced to metric units for length, capacity, weight and area. We now include units of volume and review the entire metric system, emphasizing how the metric system is easy to learn, easy to use, and easy to teach.

9.1 Introducing Volume

Volume measurements come in three different forms: liquid, solid, and air/space. Each has unique features that make it easy or hard to measure.

1. The volume of a **Liquid** is easily measured — use a measuring cup.

2. The volume of a **Solid** is easily measured for rectangular solids, but volume is not intuitive or easy to measure for irregular solids.

3. The volume of **Air/Space** is neither intuitive nor easily measured.

All three forms of volume are important for school science and are part of all curricula.

The Primary Mathematics curriculum begins with the most easily-understood form of volume: the volume of liquids and the capacity of containers. Students do the activities described in Section 1.3 and, within days, begin solving problems that use the basic units of liquid volume (liter, milliliter, cup, pint, quart and gallon).

The volume of solids is approached differently. The teaching sequence begins by introducing unit cubes. For each unit of length, a **unit cube** is any cube whose sides are 1 unit long. The corresponding unit of volume, called a **cubic unit** , is defined as the volume of a unit cube.

The teaching sequence for rectangular solids then follows exactly the same steps used to develop area. Students first count unit cubes and then find the volume of rectangular solids by multiplication. Finally, in grade 6, the volume of rectangular solids is related to capacity.

An Elementary Curriculum Sequence

Section 1.3 described the K-3 curriculum sequence for capacity and volume (see page 15). We now continue tracing that curriculum sequence, starting at grade 4.

cuboid

Grade 4 — Volume of Cuboids.   A *cuboid* is a rectangular solid built from unit cubes. The volume of a cuboid is the number of cubes needed to build it. Students initially find volumes by counting cubes, first with unit cubes of unspecified size, and then in terms of cubic centimeters (1 cm^3) and cubic meters (1 m^3).

The discussion quickly leads students to the key observation: *the volume of a cuboid can be found by multiplication.* There is no need to count every cube! The pictured boy is obviously pleased with his insight. But the insight is not a spark of genius; it is natural because earlier teaching laid the groundwork. Cuboids are three-dimensional rectangular arrays, and students saw rectangular arrays when they learned multiplication and again when they learned about area.

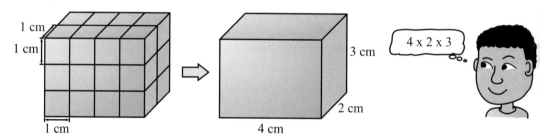

Volume of a Cuboid = Length × Width × Height.

The picture above also indicates a transition in the way students think about volume. Originally, solids are collections of cubes, and volumes are found by counting. But students soon understand that the volume of a solid is the number of cubes needed to fill the solid—whether or not it is actually possible to fill with cubes.

Children work with liquid capacity in grades 2 and 3. In grade 4, the units of capacity (liters and milliliters) are linked to units of solid volume (cubic centimeters). The link is made on page 97 of Primary Math 4B with a single picture:

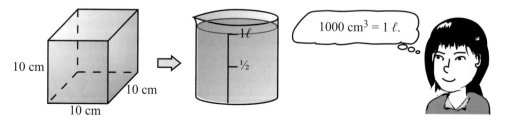

The picture illustrates the exact definition of a liter: a liter is the capacity of a cube that measures 10 centimeters on each side, or 1000 cubic centimeters. Accordingly, one cubic centimeter is 1/1000th of a liter, which is called 1 milliliter.

DEFINITION 1.1. *1 liter is 1000 cubic centimeters and 1 mℓ is 1 cubic centimeter.*

$$1 \; \ell \quad = \quad 1000 \; cm^3$$

$$\Big) \div 1000$$

$$1 \; m\ell \quad = \quad 1 \; cm^3 \; \leftarrow$$

Grades 5 and 6 — Indirect Measurement.   Solids with irregular shapes — rocks, potatoes, people — cannot be filled with unit cubes or assembled from cuboids. Yet such solids still have volume. The volume can be measured using a brilliantly simple idea: when a rock is placed into a tank of water, the water level rises and

$$\text{Vol(Water \& Rock)} \; = \; \text{Vol(Water)} \; + \; \text{Vol(Rock)}.$$

Thus the volume of the rock is the difference

$$\text{Vol(Water \& Rock)} - \text{Vol(Water)},$$

which is often called the "volume displaced by the rock".

EXERCISE 1.2. *Study Page 83 of Primary Math 5B. Notice that the graduated cylinder is marked in milliliters, but the answer is to be in cubic centimeters. In which grade did students learn to convert between milliliters and cubic centimeters?*

The idea of displaced volume is developed in a series of problems in the grade 5 and 6 Primary Math books. These "tank problems" are some of the most marvelous problems in any elementary mathematics curriculum!

EXERCISE 1.3. *Carefully read and solve the first problem on page 84 of Primary Math 5B. Note the format of the "Teacher's Solution".*

Tank problems make it obvious that every solid has *some* specific volume, even if the volume cannot be found by a formula. They also give students practice at multi-step measurement problems, problems that provide excellent preparation for middle and high school science.

Homework Set 32

Problems 1-5 refer to pages 90 – 99 *of Primary Math 4B, where 4th grade students are introduced to volume. If you do not have have access to these pages, start with Problem 6 below.*

1. (*Study the Textbook!*)   Read pages 90–93 of Primary Math 4B. Page 93 shows the reasoning that gives the volume formula for cuboids. Write one sentence describing the point of the picture at the bottom of page 93.

2. Continue, reading pages 94-96 and writing the answers to all questions in your copy of the text. Then, for parts B, C, and D of Problem 6 on page 96, write clear answers that show how to do the multiplication mentally (remember, to multiply by 5, take half the number and multiply by 10).

3. (*Study the Textbook!*)   The first problem on page 97 presents the definition of 1 liter and 1 milliliter, which is extremely important!

   a) Write down the three facts relating $1\,\ell, 1\,m\ell$ and $1\,cm^3$ that appear in this problem.

   b) Write answers for the remaining problems on page 97.

4. Do all of the problems on page 98 and write the answers as a list (write only the 7 answers, separated by commas).

5. Similarly list the answers to all problems on page 99.

6. (*Study the Textbook!*) Open Primary Math 5B and read page 81.

   a) Instead of giving the lengths of 3 edges and asking for the volume of a cuboid, what do these problems do?

   b) Which problem on these pages introduces the idea that the volume of a cuboid is (Area of base) × height?

7. The problems on the next page (page 82) reinforce the idea that the volume of a cuboid is the area of the base times the height.

   a) Carefully read and answer Problems 4, 5 and 6.

   b) What new idea is taught in Problem 5?

   c) The problems on this page introduce the idea of measuring volume using water, which is used in the next section. They also introduce the idea of converting between different units of volume — which ones?

8. (*Study the Textbook!*) Page 83 introduces "Archimedes's principle": the idea that one can measure the volume of an irregular-shaped object by placing it in water and measuring how much water is displaced. Examine this page carefully (note what the "student helper" says) and answer the questions indicated by the green boxes.

9. Next, on page 84, solve Problems 1 and 2 in your textbook. Then, on your homework sheet, answer all problems on page 85.

10. Finally, skip ahead to pages 88-89 and do Review Problems 25, 26, and 28. Notice how Problem 26 uses the principle that the volume of water does not change when it is moved to another container.

11. The four solids below are formed from rectangular solids. Find the volume of each, making your method clear.

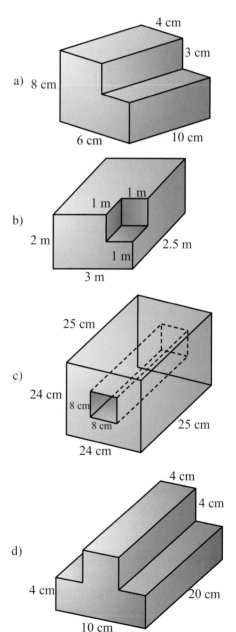

9.2 Metric Volume

Elementary school students study five types of physical measurement: length, weight, capacity, area and volume. The metric units for these five types of measurements are related. All units are defined in a simple manner from one basic unit: the meter. The result is a consistent system that makes conversion between volume, capacity, and weight very easy. Understanding this consistency is an eye-opening experience for students — a revelation that will make dealing with measurements much easier for the rest of their lives.

The chart below shows the metric and the customary units for liquid volume. The metric system has just two units of capacity, related by a factor of 1000. The second column lists the ten units commonly used in American kitchens and recipes. When arranged this way, one sees that these units are related by powers of 2 (except for the first one). But this is a lot of units!

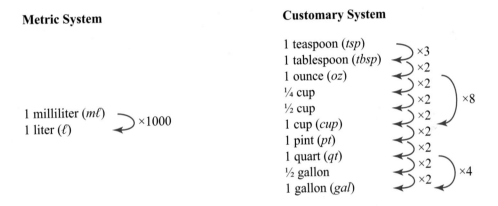

Metric System

1 milliliter (*ml*)
1 liter (*l*) ⟩ ×1000

Customary System

1 teaspoon (*tsp*)
1 tablespoon (*tbsp*) ×3
1 ounce (*oz*) ×2
¼ cup ×2
½ cup ×2   ⟩ ×8
1 cup (*cup*) ×2
1 pint (*pt*) ×2
1 quart (*qt*) ×2
½ gallon ×2   ⟩ ×4
1 gallon (*gal*) ×2

Here is an exercise that shows the advantages of a well-designed system of units.

EXERCISE 2.1. *Complete the following expressions.*

a) 3.82 *l* = _____ m*l* and 1300 m*l* = _____ *l*.

b) 1 cup = _____ tsps.

c) 37 cups = __ gal + __ qts + __ pts + __ cups

d) 1 cubic foot = _____ quarts (use the fact that 1 gallon is 231 cubic inches).

The metric system was designed to be a coherent system of measurement units. The designers (French scientists of the 1790s) began by fixing a unit of length. Any convenient length would have worked. But to lend their choice an air of scientific respectability, they had surveyors determine the distance from the north pole to the equator; one 10 millionth of this distance was taken to be the fundamental unit of length: the meter.

The metric system was then constructed using two basic principles:

- Units of length are constructed from the meter by repeatedly multiplying or dividing by 10. The units are systematically named by combining the word "meter" with an appropriate prefix.

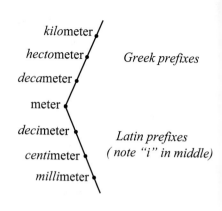

Greek prefixes

Latin prefixes (note "i" in middle)

- Each unit of length determines, in order, a unit of area, volume, capacity, and weight by this scheme:

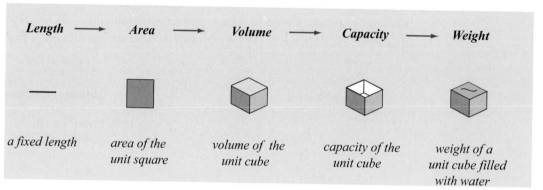

Length ⟶	Area ⟶	Volume ⟶	Capacity ⟶	Weight
a fixed length	area of the unit square	volume of the unit cube	capacity of the unit cube	weight of a unit cube filled with water

Notice that the unit of weight is defined as the weight of a unit volume of the most common of all liquids — water.

Two such sequences define most of the metric units encountered in elementary school. One sequence is pictured below. It starts with 1 cm and builds a cubic centimeter. The corresponding unit of capacity is a milliliter and of the unit of weight is a gram. These units are small: a cubic centimeter is smaller than a thimble, and a penny weighs 2.5 grams.

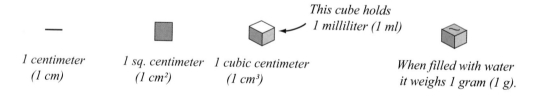

This cube holds 1 milliliter (1 ml)

1 centimeter (1 cm)   *1 sq. centimeter (1 cm²)*   *1 cubic centimeter (1 cm³)*

When filled with water it weighs 1 gram (1 g).

A set of medium-sized units is created in the same way starting with the unit of length 10 times as long: 1 decimeter. This time the sequence builds a cubic decimeter, and uses it to define a liter and a kilogram. Liters and kilograms are practical units useful for describing everyday objects. A standard 1-liter bottle of water, which is excellent for classroom demonstrations, contains 1000 cm³ and weighs 1 kilogram.

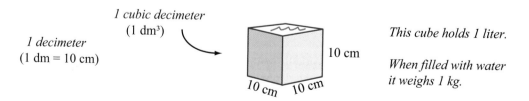

1 cubic decimeter (1 dm³)

1 decimeter (1 dm = 10 cm)

10 cm
10 cm 10 cm

This cube holds 1 liter.

When filled with water it weighs 1 kg.

A third set of units is used less commonly. Starting with a meter, one gets a large unit of volume: 1 cubic meter. A cubic meter of water contains 1000 ℓ and weighs 1 metric ton.

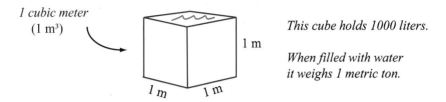

The units of capacity and weight are summarized in the following definitions.

DEFINITION 2.2. *A* **liter** *is defined to be one cubic decimeter. It contains 1000* **milliliters**.

$$1 \, m\ell \;=\; 1 \, cm^3$$

$$1 \, \ell \;=\; 1 \, dm^3 \;=\; 1000 \, cm^3. \quad \overset{)\times 1000}{}$$

DEFINITION 2.3. *A* **gram** *is the weight of 1 milliliter of water, a* **kilogram** *is the weight of 1 liter of water, and a (metric)* **ton** *is the weight of 1 m^3 of water.*

$$1 \, g \;=\; weight \; of \; 1 \, m\ell \; or \; 1 \, cm^3 \; of \; water$$

$$\overset{)\times 1000}{}$$

$$1 \, kg \;=\; weight \; of \; 1 \, \ell \; or \; 1 \, dm^3 \; of \; water$$

$$\overset{)\times 1000}{}$$

$$1 \, ton \;=\; weight \; of \; 1000 \, \ell \; or \; 1 \, m^3 \; of \; water.$$

EXERCISE 2.4. *a)* 32 ℓ = _____ cm^3 and 5.06 cm^3 = _____ ℓ.

b) 0.35 *kg is how many grams? How many liters of water is 0.35 kg? How many milliliters?*

Conversion by Substitution

As in Section 8.1, we can convert measurements expressed in cm^2 into mm^2 by writing 1 cm = 10 mm and then squaring:

$$1 \, cm^2 = (1 \, cm)^2 = (10 \, mm)^2 = 10 \times 10 \times mm \times mm = 100 \, mm^2.$$

The same process applies to volume units, but this time you *cube*,

$$1 \text{ cm}^3 = (1 \text{ cm})^3 = (10 \text{ mm})^3$$
$$= 10 \text{ mm} \times 10 \text{ mm} \times 10 \text{ mm}$$
$$= 10 \times 10 \times 10 \text{ mm} \times \text{mm} \times \text{mm}$$
$$= 1000 \text{ mm}^3.$$

The method is described in the box below. The key is to use parentheses carefully and let the notation $\text{unit}^3 = \text{unit} \times \text{unit} \times \text{unit}$ guide you.

---

a) Write the unit in the form $(\text{length unit})^3$.

b) Replace the unit inside parentheses by a different length unit.

c) Separately multiply numbers and units.

The same procedure works for all conversions, metric or not. With a little practice, students learn to convert quickly by shifting the decimal point, skipping the intermediate steps.

EXAMPLE 2.5. *Write 0.034 m^3 in terms of cubic centimeters.*

$$\textbf{Solution}: \quad 0.034 \text{ m}^3 = 0.034 \times (1 \text{ m})^3 = 0.034 \times (100 \text{ cm})^3$$
$$= 0.034 \times \underbrace{(100 \times 100 \times 100)}_{\text{shift } right \text{ 6 decimal places}} \text{ cm}^3$$
$$= 34,000 \text{ cm}^3.$$

If you are confused about which direction to shift the decimal place, just notice: multiplying by $100 \times 100 \times 100$ makes a number much *larger*.

One can convert from a unit to a larger unit in exactly the same way. As in the next example, factors of $\frac{1}{10}$ appear. Each factor of $\frac{1}{10}$ shifts the decimal point one place to the left.

EXAMPLE 2.6. *Write 6750 dm^3 in terms of cubic meters.*

$$\textbf{Solution}: \quad 6750 \text{ dm}^3 = 6750 \times (1 \text{ dm})^3 = 6750 \times \left(\frac{1}{10} \text{ m}\right)^3$$
$$= 6750 \times \underbrace{\left(\frac{1}{10} \times \frac{1}{10} \times \frac{1}{10}\right)}_{\text{shift } left \text{ 3 decimal places}} \text{ m}^3$$
$$= 6.75 \text{ m}^3.$$

The Metric System in a Nutshell

The table on the next page summarizes all of the common units in the metric system. The rows follow the sequence described in the blue box on page 198 in this section. The columns show the conversion factors between units of the same type.

Metric Conversion Factors

Length	Area	Volume	Capacity	Weight
1 km	*1 km²*	*1 km³*		
⟩ ×1000	⟩ ×1,000,000	⟩ ×1,000,000,000		
1 m	*1 m²*	*1 m³*		*1 ton*
⟩ ×10	⟩ ×100	⟩ ×1000		⟩ ×1000
1 dm	*1 dm²*	*1 dm³*	*1 ℓ*	*1 kg*
⟩ ×10	⟩ ×100	⟩ ×1000	⟩ ×1000	⟩ ×1000
1 cm	*1 cm²*	*1 cm³*	*1 mℓ*	*1 g*
⟩ ×10	⟩ ×100	⟩ ×1000		
1 mm	*1 mm²*	*1 mm³*		

Homework Set 33

1. Do the following area and volume conversions. Use the method of Examples 2.5 and 2.6 in this section:
   a) 2867 mm^2 = _____ dm^2.
   b) 0.32 m^3 = _____ cm^3.
   c) $58,300 \text{ mm}^3$ = _____ m^3.

2. Convert by shifting decimal places:
   a) Length: 0.732 m = _____ cm.
   b) Weight: 2867 g = _____ kg.
   c) Liquid volume: $7.4 \ \ell$ = _____ $\text{m}\ell$.

3. When converting area units, the place value shift is twice what it is for the corresponding length units. Convert:
   a) 1200 cm = _____ m.
   b) 1200 cm^2 = _____ m^2.
   c) 2.6 cm^2 = _____ mm^2.
   d) 0.000237 km^2 = _____ m^2.

4. Similarly, for volume units, the place value shift is three times what it is for the corresponding length units. Convert:
   a) $25,000 \text{ cm}$ = _____ m,
      $25,000 \text{ cm}^3$ = _____ m^3.
   b) 8 dm^3 = _____ cm^3.
   c) 1032 mm^3 = _____ cm^3.

5. a) 12 dm^3 = _____ ℓ.
   b) 2300 cm^3 = _____ ℓ.
   c) 5 m^3 = _____ ℓ.

6. Density is introduced in Section 13.2 (pages 359–360) of NEM1. Read those pages and answer the following questions.
   a) Write down the definition of density.
   b) What is the density of water in grams per cubic centimeter? If something is more dense than water, than its density is (choose one): more than 1, less than 1.

   c) By substituting into the definition of density, answer problems 1a and 2a on page 360 of NEM1.
   d) Give a Teacher's Solution to Problem 5 on page 361 (follow the format of the example at the bottom of page 359).
   e) Give a similar solution to Problem 6. Express the weight in kilograms.

7. Because units of time are not related by powers of 10, conversions involving time require more than shifting decimal points:
   a) 1 day = _____ sec.
   b) Speed: $10 \frac{\text{m}}{\text{sec}}$ = _____ $\frac{\text{km}}{\text{sec}}$ = _____ $\frac{\text{km}}{\text{hour}}$.
   c) Flow rate: $9 \frac{\text{m}\ell}{\text{sec}}$ = _____ $\frac{\ell}{\text{sec}}$ = _____ $\frac{\ell}{\text{min}}$.

8. Primary Math 6B revisits Archimedes' Principle and develops it further. The questions often involve rates; water is drained or poured into a container at so many liters per minute.
   a) Do Problems 1-9 on pages 54-58 in Primary Math 6B.
   b) Continuing, do all 5 problems on page 59.
   c) Then do all problems on page 60. Aren't these fantastic problems?

9. ✳ (*Calculator*) The speed of light is approximately 300,000 km/sec.
   a) About how many miles per second is that? (1 mile = 1.6 km.)
   b) How many times around the earth can light travel in one second? Begin by drawing a sketch of the earth and noting that the distance from the equator to the north pole is 10 million meters.
   c) How many miles does light travel in a year (365.25 days)? This enormous unit of distance is called a light-year.

9.3 Prisms and Cylinders

The last measurement topic in the elementary mathematics curriculum is the volume of the common non-rectangular solids: prisms, cylinders, cones, and spheres. This is a middle school topic because it requires students to be already adept at using the volume properties to find the volumes of rectangular solids, including solids-with-holes. Most treatments of the topic begin with a review of the prerequisite skills, as is done in the 7th grade NEM1 book.

EXERCISE 3.1. *Volume formulas for which solids are described in Chapter 13 of NEM1?*

A **prism** is a solid with two "end" faces (called its *bases*) that are congruent *n*-gons lying in parallel planes, and whose remaining *n* faces (called **lateral faces**) are all parallelograms. Two adjacent lateral faces meet along a **lateral edge**. The **height** of a prism is the length of a segment between the two base planes that is perpendicular to both.

A **right prism** is a prism whose lateral edges are perpendicular to the base planes; the lateral faces are then rectangles. Prisms are named by specifying whether they are right or oblique and then naming the shape of their base.

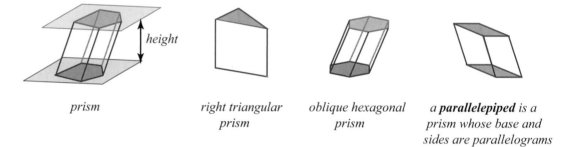

| *prism* | *right triangular prism* | *oblique hexagonal prism* | *a **parallelepiped** is a prism whose base and sides are parallelograms* |

One can also consider solids, such as cylinders and "general cylinders", whose bases are not necessarily polygons. To give a definition, one mimics the definition of prism, eliminating any mention of "lateral edges" because generalized cylinders needn't have edges.

A **general cylinder** is specified by two parallel planes, a region *B* in one of the planes and a line *L* that intersects both planes. The general cylinder is the union of all of the segments that are parallel to *L*, lie between the two planes, and have one endpoint in *B*.

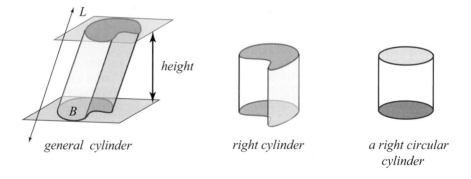

| *general cylinder* | *right cylinder* | *a right circular cylinder* |

The term "right circular cylinder" is shortened to just **cylinder** in most elementary school contexts. We will do the same in this textbook.

Volume of Prisms

The teaching sequence for the volume of cylinders starts by modifying a formula students are already comfortable with: the formula "length × width × height" for the volume of a cuboid. Since "length × width" is the area of the base of the cuboid, the volume formula can be written more simply as "*(Area of base) × height*". Written in this form, the formula gives the volume not just for cuboids, but also for unions of cuboids, and therefore for right prisms and cylinders by the following reasoning:

1) For right rectangular prism:

Volume = (length × width) × height
= (Area of Base) × height.

2) For unions of right rectangular prisms with the same height:

Volume = sum of volumes
= sum of (Area of base) × heights
= (Total Area of Base) × height.

3) Any right general cylinder can be filled with columns, and so is a union of right rectangular prisms:

For any right general cylinder:

Volume = (Area of base) × height.

Of course, prisms and cylinders can be rotated and viewed from different directions. In particular, the bases don't have to be horizontal. Problems that present prisms and cylinders in various alignments help students use the above formula flexibly.

EXAMPLE 3.2. *The picture shows a trough whose ends are trapezoids. Find a) the volume of the trough in cubic centimeters, and b) the capacity of the trough in liters.*

Teacher's Solution: The trough is a prism whose base is the front trapezoid with height 20 cm and base lengths 30 cm and 50 cm.

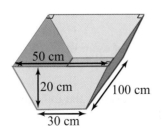

a) Area of base: $\frac{1}{2}(30 + 50) \times 20$ cm^2
   $= 800$ cm^2.

   Volume of trough: (Area of base) × height
   $= 800 \times 100$
   $= 80,000$ cm^3. (8 with 4 zeros)

b) 1 liter $= 1000$ cm^3
   ∴ The trough holds 80 liters.

To find the volume of oblique cylinders, one should change viewpoints. There are two ways to think about constructing prisms and cylinders. One can think of building them by assembling columns, as in picture 3) on the previous page. Alternatively, one can think of building them in layers, like the floors of a skyscraper. The second viewpoint shows what happens to volume as we "tilt" a cylinder, as in the following classroom demonstration.

Start with a region in the plane.

Cut slices of carboard in that shape.

Pile the slices to make a right cylinder.

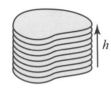
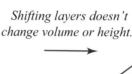
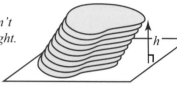

Shifting layers doesn't change volume or height.

Volume = (Area of base)× height.   *Volume is still (Area of base)× height.*

Thus the volume of an oblique prism is also the product of the base area and the height — provided one interprets "height" to mean the perpendicular distance between the base planes, as explained at the beginning of this section. Warning about this formula: a common student error is to use the length of a lateral edge as the "height".

For any general cylinder, including oblique cylinders,

$$\text{Volume} = (\text{Area of base}) \times \text{height},$$

where "height" is the length of the altitude.

volume of a cylinder

The volume formula is very simple for circular cylinders:

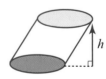

For any circular cylinder,
Volume = (Area of base)× height
= $\pi r^2 h$.

right cylinder   *oblique cylinder*

EXAMPLE 3.3. *For the right cylinder shown, find a) its volume, and b) its surface area.*

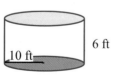

a) Area of base $= \pi r^2$
$= 100\pi$ ft^2.

Volume of cylinder $= (\text{Area of base}) \times \text{height}$
$= 600\pi$ ft^3.

b) The surface of the cylinder consists of three pieces: the top and the bottom, which are disks, and a single curved side. The side can be cut and rolled out to form a rectangle with base length equal to the circumference of the circle:

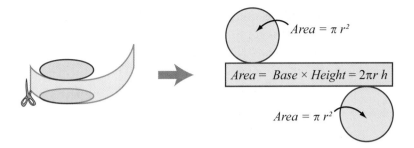

The **Surface area of the cylinder** is the total area of these three pieces. Therefore,

$$
\begin{aligned}
\text{Surface Area} \quad &= \quad \text{Area(Top)} + \text{Area(Bottom)} + \text{Area(Curved Side)} \\
&= \quad \pi r^2 + \pi r^2 + 2\pi rh \\
&= \quad 100\pi + 100\pi + 2\pi \times 10 \times 6.
\end{aligned}
$$

The total surface area is $320\,\pi$ square feet.

Volume Properties

The methods one uses to find volumes (e.g., cutting solids into pieces and rearranging the parts) are the three-dimensional versions of the methods used to find areas. With area, we saw how all the processes we used were repeated applications of a few intuitive facts, which we called the area properties. The basic properties of volume, listed below, are analogous to those of area. The analogy is the basis for teaching volume formulas: volume is studied after area, and facts about volume are taught as extensions of students' understanding of area.

VOLUME PROPERTIES. To each solid S there is an associated real number $\text{Vol}(S)$, called the **volume of S**, with the following properties:

1. $\text{Vol}(S) \geq 0$ for every solid S.

2. Congruent solids have equal volume.

3. If a solid S is the union of two non-overlapping solids A and B, then

$$\text{Vol}(S) = \text{Vol}(A) + \text{Vol}(B).$$

4. The volume of a right rectangular prism is the product of its dimensions:

$$\text{Vol}(S) = \text{Length} \times \text{Width} \times \text{Height}.$$

The "pile of pancakes" picture on the previous page, in which one visualizes solids as made in layers, is useful in other contexts. We will finish this section by casting it as a precise fact about volume called the "Slice Principle". The Slice Principle can be regarded as a fifth volume property.

cross-section

To state the Slice Principle, we first replace the cheese slices by the mathematical notion of a "cross-section".

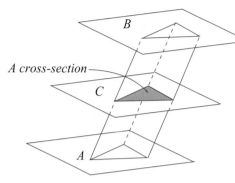

Definition: When a solid lies between parallel planes A and B, each plane C parallel to both A and B intersects the solid in a *cross-section* or *slice*.

Slice Principle. If solids S and T lie between parallel planes A and B and if all of their cross-sections have equal area, then

$$\text{Vol}(S) = \text{Vol}(T).$$

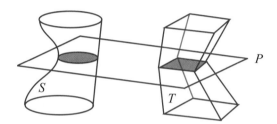

Notice that the slices can have different shapes; all that is required is that the slices at every level have the same *area*.

One can see why this principle is true by imagining that S and T are made out of tiny bricks. If two cross-sections have equal area, then there are equal numbers of bricks at that level; if that is true at every level, then the total number of bricks is the same for both solids. One can also note that, layer by layer, one can rearrange the bricks of the first solid to construct the second solid *without changing the number of bricks*.

Cavalieri's principle

We will use the Slice Principle for cones and spheres in the next two sections. In school textbooks, the Slice Principle is called "Cavalieri's Principle" after Bonaventura Cavalieri, who was a student of Galileo.

Homework Set 34

1. (*Study the textbook!*) Give Teacher's Solutions to all 4 tank problems on page 61 of Primary Math 6B. Your solutions should look like those on page 58 of Primary Math 6B. Notice that, in these solutions, each step begins with an announcement of *what will be calculated* (e.g., "Volume of tank"); then the calculation is done.

2. Fill in the chart at the right.

	base area	height	volume of prism
(a)	11 cm²	8 cm	
(b)	6 m²	21 m	
(c)		19 m	95 m³
(d)	16 cm²		64 cm³

In Problems 3-8, find the volume of the prism shown.

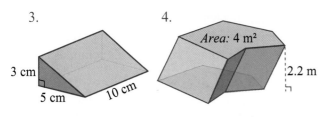

3.

4.

Area: 4 m²

3 cm

5 cm   10 cm

2.2 m

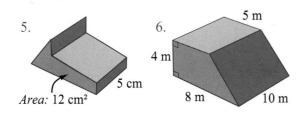

5.

6.

5 m

4 m

5 cm

Area: 12 cm²

8 m   10 m

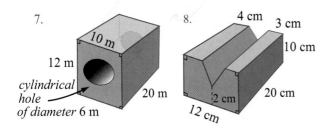

7.

8.

4 cm   3 cm

10 m

12 m

10 cm

cylindrical
hole
of diameter 6 m

20 m

2 cm   20 cm

12 cm

9. The cross-section of a steel beam (an "I-beam") is shown
below. All angles are right angles, and the cross-section
is symmetric both horizontally and vertically. If the beam
is 3 m long,

   a) Find its volume in cm³.

   b) Find its volume in dm³.

   c) If it is made of steel with a density of 7.75 g/cm³,
   find its weight in kilograms.

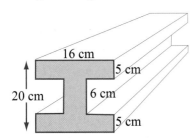

16 cm

5 cm

20 cm

6 cm

5 cm

10. a) For a right prism, are all of the lateral edges the same
   length? Are they for an oblique prism?

   b) For a right prism, is the length of a lateral edge equal
   to the height? Is it for an oblique prism?

11. What is the total surface area of a cube whose volume is
27 cm³?

12. (*Calculator*) Taking $\pi = 3.14$, find the volume of

   a) A cylinder of radius 5 cm and height 20 cm.

   b) A cylinder of diameter 6 cm and height 6 cm.

13. (*Calculator*) A cylindrical water storage tank has a base
diameter of 10 m and contains 219.8 m³ of water. Find
the depth of the water. (Take $\pi = 3.14$.)

14. A cylinder with a base radius of 5 cm contains water with
a depth of 9 cm. When
a stone is immersed in the
water, the depth of the
water increases to 10.5 cm
deep, completely covering
the stone. What is the volume of the stone? Write
your answer in terms of π.

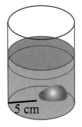

5 cm

15. *Draw a picture and give a Teacher's Solution to the following problem (in the last step, take $\pi = 3.14$ and use a
calculator):*

   A solid metal cube 8 cm on each side is melted and recast
   into a solid cylinder with radius 10 cm. What is the height
   of the cylinder?

16. A solid circular cylinder has a circumference of 44 cm
and a height of 10 cm. Find:

   a) The radius (Take $\pi = \frac{22}{7}$).

   b) The volume of the cylinder.

   c) The surface area of the curved surface of the cylinder.

   d) The total surface area (including top and bottom).

17. Do Problem 4 on page 364 of NEM1.

*The final three problems illustrate some practical appli-
cations. Use a calculator for these.*

18. Do Problem 4 on page 360 of NEM1.

19. ✳ Do Problem 19 on page 366 of NEM1.

20. ✳ One Calorie (1 Cal) is the amount of energy required
to raise the temperature of 1 kg of water by 1° C.

   a) If you drink 500 m*ℓ* of cold water at 7° C, how many
   Calories do you use in heating it to body temperature
   (37° C)?

   b) A cylindrical pot 18 cm in diameter is filled with
   cold water to a depth of 8 cm and placed on a stove.
   If the initial temperature of the water is 12° C, how
   many Calories are required to heat it to 84° C? Use
   a calculator and take $\pi = 3.14$.

9.4 Pyramids and Cones

In Chapters 5 and 8 we studied how the area of a region changes when it is scaled or skewed. We begin this section by restating the scaling and skewing principles for area and extending them to volume. We then use the principles to find volume formulas for pyramids and cones.

Scaling and Skewing

The Scaling Principle.   The Scaling Principle states that if a planar region is scaled by factors a and b in two perpendicular directions, then its area is multiplied by a factor of $a \times b$. Many of the basic area formulas we have previously studied — and a few new ones — can be derived from this principle.

In each of the pictures below, we begin with a unit-size figure and stretch it by a factor of a horizontally and a factor of b vertically.

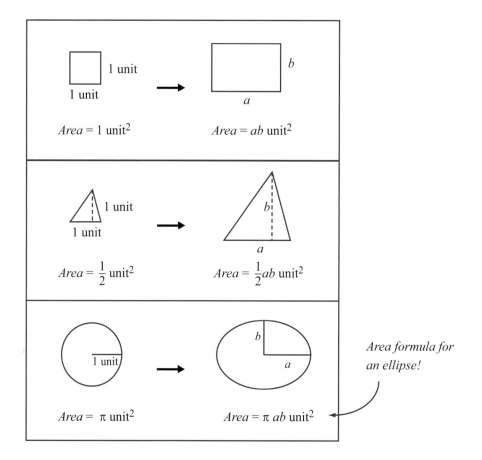

There is an analogous scaling principle for volume: If a solid is scaled by factors of a, b and c in three perpendicular directions, then its volume is multiplied by a factor of abc.

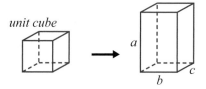

The idea is really quite simple. This boy understands that doubling the height of a glass (without changing the diameter), doubles its capacity. In our daily life, we often apply the scaling principle at this intuitive level.

The Skewing Principle. Skewing or tilting a planar region doesn't change its area.

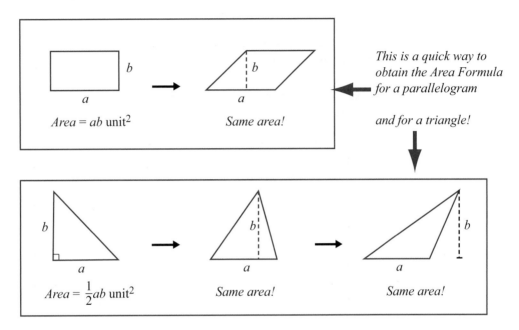

Area = ab unit² → *Same area!*

This is a quick way to obtain the Area Formula for a parallelogram

and for a triangle!

$Area = \frac{1}{2}ab$ unit² → *Same area!* → *Same area!*

We've already seen the analogous skewing principle for solids: we used it in the previous section to obtain the formula for the volume of an oblique cylinder. We will use it again below.

Pyramids and Cones

pyramid

If we compress one base of a prism to a point, we obtain a *pyramid* with that point as its vertex. The base of a pyramid is a polygon and the other faces, called *lateral faces*, are triangles. The edges between two lateral sides are called *slant edges* and their length is the *slant height* of the pyramid. A *regular pyramid* is one whose base is a regular polygon and whose slant edges have equal length.

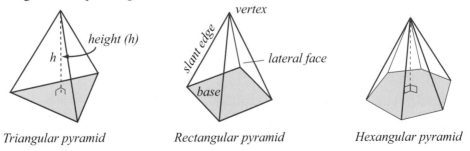

Triangular pyramid   *Rectangular pyramid*   *Hexangular pyramid*

Similarly compressing one base of a general cylinder to a point creates a solid called a *general cone*. Alternatively, we can describe a general cone by fixing a region *B* (the base) in a plane and a point V (the vertex) not on that plane. The **general cone with base B and vertex V** is the union of all line segments $\overline{VP}$ for points P in B.

The *height* of a pyramid or cone is the perpendicular distance from the vertex to the base plane. As with cylinders, the base need not be horizontal and the "height" need not be vertical. The naming scheme for pyramid and cones is the same as for prisms and cylinders.

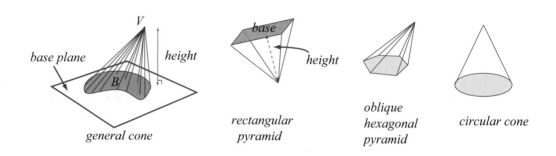

general cone   *rectangular pyramid*   *oblique hexagonal pyramid*   *circular cone*

EXERCISE 4.1. *State a definition for "right circular cone" — this is the solid commonly called a "cone" in ordinary English. Can you define a "right triangular pyramid"?*

Volume Formulas for Pyramids and Cones

The following teaching sequence shows how the Scaling and Skewing Principles lead easily to a formula for the volume of pyramids and cones. The first step is to observe that there is at least *one* pyramid whose volume we can calculate. We can then apply the Scaling and Skewing Principles to find the volumes of increasingly general pyramids.

1. A cube is the union of 6 identical square pyramids.

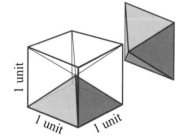

2. Hence a square pyramid with the dimensions shown has

$$\text{Volume} = \frac{1}{6} \text{ unit}^3.$$

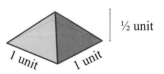

3. Doubling the height doubles the volume:

$$\text{Volume} = \frac{1}{3} \text{ unit}^3.$$

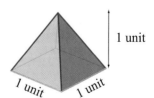

4. Scaling by factors of ℓ, w, and h gives

$$\text{Volume} \;=\; \frac{1}{3}\,\ell wh.$$

$$=\; \frac{1}{3}\,(\text{Base area}) \times h.$$

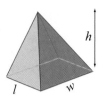

5. Skewing doesn't change the volume

$$\text{Volume} = \frac{1}{3}\,(\text{Base area}) \times h.$$

6. Finally, adopting the "column viewpoint", one sees that *any* pyramid or cone is a union of thin oblique square pyramids.

height

> *For a pyramid or general cone:*
>
> $Volume = \frac{1}{3}$ *(Base area)* × height.

Teaching Comment.   Textbooks and teacher guides often describe the following activity to introduce the formula for the volume of a cone:

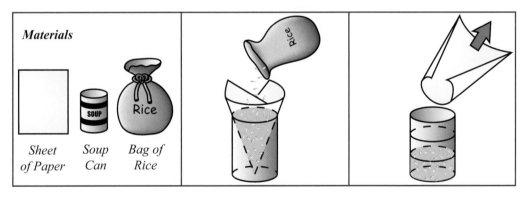

Materials
Sheet of Paper   *Soup Can*   *Bag of Rice*

Rice experiments can show students that the volume of a cone is *approximately* $\frac{1}{3}$ the volume of the cylinder with the same base radius and height. While it is a nice way to launch the topic, teachers should make clear that *the experiment is not a proof*. In contrast, the teaching sequence outlined above shows that the factor of $\frac{1}{3}$ is exact and is arrived at by geometric reasoning, not experiments. In fact, the reasoning is not difficult, and no one has to sweep up the floor afterwards.

EXAMPLE 4.2. *For a circular cone with radius R and height h,*

$$\textit{Volume of the cone} \;=\; \frac{1}{3}\,\pi R^2 h.$$

EXAMPLE 4.3. *The slant height of a circular cone is 10 cm and its base diameter is 12 cm. Find*

  a) its volume, and

  b) its curved surface area.

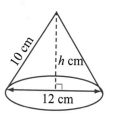

Solution: a) The base has radius 6 cm. By the Pythagorean Theorem

$$h^2 = 10^2 - 6^2 = 100 - 36 = 64,$$

so $h = 8$. (Quicker method: spot the 6-8-10 Pythagorean triple.)

$$\text{Volume of the cone} = \frac{1}{3}(\text{Base area}) \times h$$
$$= \frac{1}{3} \times \pi \times 6^2 \times 8 \ \ \text{cm}^3$$
$$\approx 302 \ \ \text{cm}^3.$$

surface area
of a cone

For part b) we will use the general fact that if we cut the curved side of a circular cone and flatten it out, we obtain a sector (see Problem 9 in the homework set). The area of the sector is found by thinking of it as some fraction of the area of a full circle.

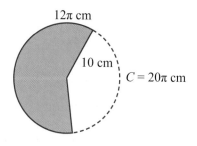

b) The circumference of the base is $\pi \times \text{diam} = 12\pi$ cm.

When cut and flattened, the curved side is a sector with radius 10 cm and arc-length 12π cm.

The circle with this radius has circumference 20π.

The sector is $\dfrac{12\pi}{20\pi} = \dfrac{3}{5}$ of a circle.

Therefore the lateral surface area is $\frac{3}{5} \times \pi(10)^2 = 60\pi$ cm^2. The total surface area of the cone also includes the area of the base, which is $\pi \cdot 6^2 = 36\pi$ cm^2. Thus the total surface area is 96π cm^2.

EXAMPLE 4.4. *The radius of the base of a right cone is 9 cm and its volume is 324π cm^3. Find its height.*

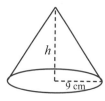

Since the volume of a cone is given by the formula $A = \frac{1}{3}\pi r^2 h$, we can solve for h in the equation

$$324\pi = \frac{1}{3}\pi \times 9^2 \times h$$

to get $h = 12$ cm.

Homework Set 35

1. Use the Scaling Principle to answer the following.

   a) The volume of a cube is 17 in³. If each side is doubled in length, what is the volume of the enlarged cube?

   b) If the radius of a spherical balloon is tripled, its volume becomes _____ times as great.

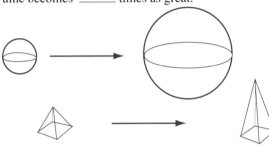

   c) Two pyramids have bases with the same area, but the second is 1.7 times as tall. If the first has a volume of 120 cm³, what is the volume of the second?

2. A pyramid has a square base 5 m on each side. If its volume is 200 m³, what is its height?

3. The base of a cone is a disk with diameter 10 cm. Its slant height is 12 cm. What is the volume of the cone?

4. Find the volumes of the pyramids. *Hint:* In figure b), the base is an equilateral triangle; begin by drawing a separate picture to find the area of the base.

   a)
   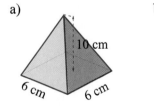

   b)
   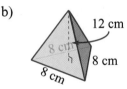

5. A right pyramid has slant edges 9 cm long and a square base with sides 6 cm long.

   a) Find the height of the pyramid.
   b) Find the volume of the pyramid.

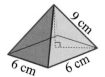

   Hint: Sketch, then use the Pythagorean Theorem twice.

6. A cubical tank (see top of next column) measures 2 m on each side. A solid pyramid of height 2 m and square base with side length 1.5 m is placed in the empty tank. The tank is filled with water, and then the pyramid is removed. What is the height h of the water remaining in the tank?

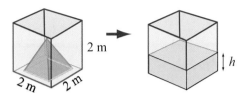

7. An aluminum pyramid with a rectangular base 4 cm by 9 cm is melted and recast into a square pyramid of the same height. How long are the sides of the resulting square pyramid? *Hint: Call the height h and the side of the square base x and compare the volume formulas before and after. It is not necessary to know the height!*

8. The machine part shown is made of two identical cones joined along their bases. What is its volume? Express your answer as a multiply of π.

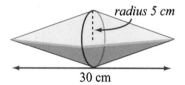

The next two problems show how a teacher might lead students to "discover" a useful formula; the formula expresses the area of the curved surface of a right circular cone in terms of the radius and the slant height.

9. (*Classroom Activity*) Using your compass and protractor and a full sheet of paper, draw a section with radius 12 cm and central angle 130°. Cut it out and tape it together to form a cone (without base). What is the surface area of the cone you have created?

10. (*Classroom Activity*) In the picture below, a paper cone is cut along the segment from A to V and the curved surface is laid flat on the table to form the shaded region S on the right.

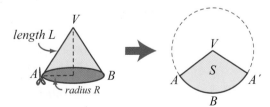

   a) What is the name of the shape of S?
   b) What is the length VA?
   c) How long is the arc from A to A' through B?
   d) What is the circumference of the dotted circle?

e) What fraction of a full circle is region S?

f) What is the area of S?

g) Give a clear statement of the formula for the area of the curved surface in terms of the radius R of the base and the slant height.

9.5 Spheres

The formulas for the volume and the surface area of a sphere are the culmination of the K-8 measurement curriculum. These are amazing formulas! They are subtle, yet are simple to learn and to use, and they have important applications in science. This section shows how these formulas can be explained in terms of elementary mathematics.

The three-dimensional analog of a circle is a sphere. A sphere is determined by specifying a center point and a radius; the definition is then word-for-word the same as the definition of a circle except one now thinks about points in three dimensions.

> **DEFINITION 5.1.** *Fix a point O in space and a distance R. A **sphere** with center O and radius R is the set of all points in (3-dimensional) space that are distance R from the point O.*

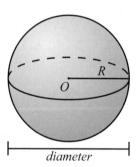

Any segment with one endpoint at the center and the other endpoint on the sphere is also called a *radius* of the sphere. A segment passing through the center with both endpoints on the sphere is called *a diameter*. The length of all such segments is the same (twice the radius) and this length is called *the diameter* of the sphere.

A sphere together with its interior is called a **solid sphere** or **ball**; the boundary surface of a ball is a sphere. Teachers can refer to a floating soap bubble as an example of a sphere and a marble as an example of a solid sphere. Examples help students see that one measures and calculates the *volume* of a solid sphere and the *surface area* of a sphere.

Teaching Comment. Textbooks often fail to distinguish spheres from solid spheres; the word "sphere" is used to refer to both, as we did in the first sentence of this section. Teachers and students also commonly neglect this distinction in classroom language. But students should know the correct terminology, and at all times teachers should be sure that every student knows which type of spherical object, a solid or a surface, is being discussed.

Most of the spherical objects we encounter are impenetrable; one cannot pass a ruler through the center and directly measure the radius or diameter. In this case, the diameter can only be measured *indirectly*, by measuring some length equal to the diameter, or making several measurements that we can use to calculate the diameter. The pictures below show two ways to indirectly measure the diameter of a basketball.

Place books on opposite sides.
Measure the gap between them.

Measure the circumference.
Divide by π.

The right-hand picture refers to the "circumference" of a sphere. To understand how the word circumference applies to spheres, one should think about the intersections of planes and spheres.

How Planes Slice Spheres

Many of the straightedge-and-compass constructions described in Chapter 2 have analogs for figures in three dimensions. Here, for example, is an analog for Construction 5 on page 52:

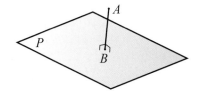

CONSTRUCTION 13. *Given a plane P and a point A not on P, there is one (and only one) point B on P so that line AB is perpendicular to P.*

The line *AB* is called the *perpendicular to P through A*. Among all the points in the plane *P*, this point *B* is the closest to *A*. Accordingly, the length *AB* is called the *distance from A to the plane P*. One of the homework problems for this section will guide you through the details of this construction.

The intersection of a plane and a sphere can consist of no points, one point, or many points. When the intersection is a single point, the plane is called a **tangent plane** to the sphere. Theorem 5.2 below shows that whenever the intersection is more than one point, it is a circle. In the special case when the plane passes through the center of the sphere, the intersection is called an **equator** and the resulting half-spheres are called **hemispheres**. The **circumference of a sphere** is the circumference of an equator.

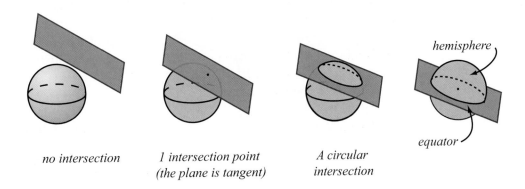

no intersection

1 intersection point
(the plane is tangent)

A circular
intersection

hemisphere

equator

Classroom discussions should distinguish hemispheres, which are 2-dimensional curved surfaces, from solid hemispheres. Half an orange, for example, is a solid hemisphere, not a hemisphere. Also notice that the surface of a solid hemisphere is not a hemisphere — it's a hemisphere together with a disk (this disk is called the *base* of the solid hemisphere).

Whack!

Two solid hemispheres

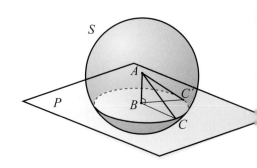

THEOREM 5.2. *If the intersection of a plane P and a sphere S contains more than one point, it is a circle whose center lies on the line through the center of S perpendicular to P.*

Given: Plane P, sphere S with center A.

Construction: Draw $\overleftrightarrow{AB}$ perpendicular to P with B on P.

To prove: Any two points C, C' in $P \cap S$ are equidistant from B.
            Therefore the intersection is a circle with center B.

Proof.	$\angle ABC = \angle ABC' = 90°$	$\overline{AB} \perp P$
	$AB = AB$	common side
	$AC = AC'$	radii of S.
	$\triangle ABC \cong \triangle ABC'$	RHL
$\therefore$	$BC = BC'$	corr. sides of $\cong \triangle$s.

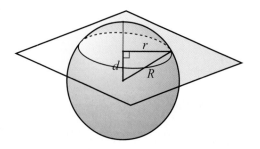

Whenever a sphere and a plane intersect, the Pythagorean Theorem gives a formula for the radius of the intersection circle. If the sphere has radius R and the distance from the plane to the center of the sphere is d, then the radius r of the intersection satisfies $r^2 + d^2 = R^2$, so

$$r = \sqrt{R^2 - d^2}.$$

As you will see, this is a useful observation.

Volume of a Solid Sphere

The formula for the volume of a sphere was one of the triumphs of ancient Greek mathematics. It was discovered by Archimedes around 200 B.C.. Archimedes expressed his formula as a ratio, which he communicated using the imagery below.

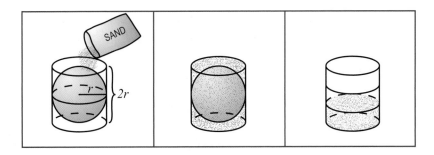

The pictures show sand occupying $\frac{1}{3}$ of the volume of the cylinder, and the sphere occupies the rest. The picture illustrates Archimedes' assertion that *the volume of a sphere is $\frac{2}{3}$ of the volume of the cylinder with the same diameter and height*, regardless of the radius of the sphere. Archimedes asserted — and proved — that this ratio is *exactly* $\frac{2}{3}$, regardless of the radius of the sphere.

Noting the dimensions of the cylinder, Archimedes' assertion gives

$$
\begin{aligned}
\text{Volume of the solid sphere} \quad &= \quad \frac{2}{3} \cdot (\text{Volume of the cylinder}) \\
&= \quad \frac{2}{3} \cdot (\text{Area of the base}) \cdot (\text{height}) \\
&= \quad \frac{2}{3} \cdot (\pi r^2) \cdot (2r) \\
&= \quad \frac{4}{3} \pi r^3.
\end{aligned}
$$

Archimedes discovered this formula by geometric reasoning, not by experiment. He did not measure sand. His clever idea was to compare the volume of a sphere (or hemisphere) to the volumes of a cone and a cylinder.

The proof is remarkably simple. We will give a version using the three solids shown below: a solid hemisphere, a right circular cylinder, and a right circular cone, all with radius R and height R. Align these solids so that the bases of the hemisphere and the cylinder and the vertex of the cone lie in a plane.

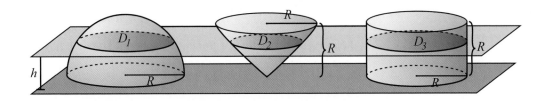

Recall that, by the Slice Principle, two solids have the same volume if each of their cross-sections have equal area. Consider a typical slice at some height h above the base plane, as shown. The cross-section consists of the three disks D_1, D_2, D_3, with different radii. Let's calculate the radius and area of each cross-sectional disk, starting with solid hemisphere.

- By the Pythagorean Theorem, the cross-section D_1 of the hemisphere has radius $r = \sqrt{R^2 - h^2}$. Therefore

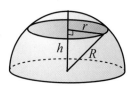

$$\text{Area}(D_1) = \pi r^2 = \pi R^2 - \pi h^2.$$

- The side-view of the cone is a triangle with 45° sides. Consequently, the cross-section at height h has radius h. Therefore

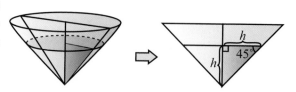

$$\text{Area}(D_2) = \pi h^2.$$

- The cross-section of the cylinder is a disk of radius R, so

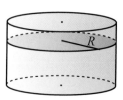

$$\text{Area}(D_3) = \pi R^2.$$

When combined, the three formulas above show that the total area of the first two cross-sections is exactly the area of the third cross-section:

$$\text{Area}(D_1) + \text{Area}(D_2) = (\pi R^2 - \pi h^2) + \pi h^2 = \pi R^2 = \text{Area}(D_3).$$

Because the areas of the c for every height h, we can apply the Slice Principle to conclude that

(Volume of Solid Hemisphere) + (Volume of Cone) = (Volume of Cylinder).

This is one form of Archimedes' formula. To put it in more familiar form, subtract the volume of the cone from both sides and use the volume formulas for the cone and cylinder:

$$\begin{aligned} \text{Volume of Solid Hemisphere} \;&=\; \text{(Volume of Cylinder)} - \text{(Volume of Cone)} \\ &=\; \pi R^3 - \frac{1}{3}\pi R^3 \\ &=\; \frac{2}{3}\pi R^3. \end{aligned}$$

Doubling then gives the volume of the entire sphere. Thus we have proved:

For a sphere of radius R,

$$\text{Volume of Sphere} = \frac{4}{3}\pi R^3.$$

Surface Area of a Sphere

One can use the formulas for the volume of a solid sphere ($\frac{4}{3}\pi R^3$) and a general cone ($\frac{1}{3}$ (Base area)(height)) to reason out a formula that gives the surface area of a sphere. Begin by drawing a sphere of radius R.

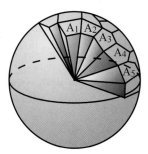

Cover the sphere with regions $A_1, A_2, A_3, \ldots$.
For each region, draw a "cone" with vertex at the center of the sphere.

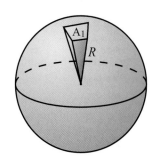

The volume of the "cone" with base A_1 is approximately

$$\text{Volume of cone} \approx \frac{1}{3} \cdot (\text{Area } A_1) \cdot R.$$

The volume of the sphere is the sum of the volumes of these "cones":

$$\frac{4}{3}\pi R^3 \quad \approx \quad \frac{1}{3} \cdot (\text{Area } A_1 + \text{Area } A_2 + \cdots) \cdot R$$

The right-hand side is only an approximation because the bases of these cone-like solids are slightly curved and R is not the exact height. But if we partition the sphere into smaller regions, the bases become flatter and the approximation becomes better. Now imagine repeating the process over and over with smaller and smaller regions, obtaining ever better approximations to the volume of a sphere, *all given by the above formula*. In the end, we conclude that

$$\frac{4}{3}\pi R^3 \quad = \quad \frac{1}{3} \cdot (\text{Surface area of sphere}) \cdot R.$$

Multiplying both sides by 3 and dividing by R, we get:

For a sphere of radius R,

$$\text{Surface Area of Sphere } = 4\pi R^2.$$

Notice that the volume formula for a sphere has a factor of R^3, while the surface area formula has a factor of R^2. The powers of R can be determined by thinking about units. For example, if the radius of a sphere is measured in inches, then the volume and surface area both come out in terms of the appropriate units:

$$\text{Volume} = \frac{4}{3}\pi\,(R\text{ in})^3 = \frac{4}{3}\pi R^3\text{ in}^3,$$

$$\text{Surface Area} = 4\pi\,(R\text{ in})^2 = 4\pi R^2\text{ in}^2.$$

In both cases the power of R is the same power that appears in the unit.

It is common for students to apply volume and surface area formulas with the wrong power of R (e.g., taking the surface area to be $4\pi R^3$). Errors can be averted by showing students how the units — *which should be included in all calculations* — automatically guide one to the the the correct power of R.

Homework Set 36

1. A spherical tank has radius 4 m. How many liters of water can it contain?

2. A hemispherical bowl with diameter 12 cm, full of water, is emptied into an empty cylindrical jug, also with diameter 12 cm. If the jug is then $\frac{2}{3}$ full, find the height of the jug. (After having read this section carefully, you should be able to answer this question *without doing any calculations.*)

3. The radius of a solid sphere is twice the radius of a second solid sphere. What is the ratio of a) their volumes, b) their surface areas?

4. The figure shows a sphere and a solid cylinder with the same diameter and same height. What is the ratio of their surface areas? (Include the top and bottom of the cylinder.)

5. The earth's radius is roughly four times the radius of the moon.

   a) What is the ratio of their volumes?

   b) What is the ratio of their surface areas?

   c) About a quarter of the earth's surface is land. The moon's surface is all land. Fill in the blanks: The earth's volume is about _____ times the moon's volume but the earth has only about _____ times as much land area as the moon.

6. *(Calculator)* Give a Teacher's Solution to the following tank problem. Begin with a sketch.

A graduated cylinder with a diameter of 4 cm contains water to a level of 10 cm. When a spherical steel ball bearing is dropped in, the water level rises to 10.8 cm.

   a) What is the volume of the ball bearing?

   b) What is the diameter of the ball bearing?

7. *(Calculator)* The meter was originally defined as one 10 millionth of the distance from the equator to the north pole. Using this information,

   a) What is the circumference of the earth in kilometers?

   b) What is the radius of the earth?

   c) What is the surface area of the earth in km^2? Express your answer in scientific notation.

   d) What is the volume of the earth in km^3?

8. *(Calculator)* Based on the strength of the earth's gravity, physicists have accurately calculated the mass of the earth to be 5.98×10^{24} kg. Using this information and your answer to Problem 7d, what is the average density of the earth?

$$\text{Average Density} = \frac{\text{Mass of Earth}}{\text{Volume of Earth}} = ?$$

Use scientific notation and give your answer in grams per cubic centimeter. Show clearly how you converted between units.

9. A conical region is removed from a hemispherical solid, as shown. Find the volume of the resulting solid. (Use $\frac{22}{7}$ for π.)

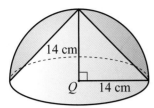

10. The figure below shows a solid spherical shell. Find the volume and surface area of the solid. (Use $\frac{22}{7}$ for π.)

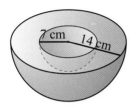

11. The solid below consists of a solid hemisphere and a solid cone. Find its surface area and its volume. Use $\frac{22}{7}$ for π.

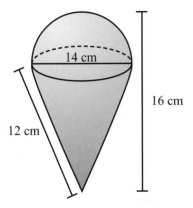

12. ❋ Look over the format we used in Section 2.5 to write down geometric constructions. Then read the statement of Construction 13 in this section. In this problem you will explain how to do Construction 13 using the format of Section 2.5.

To give you a running start, the first four steps are listed below. Copy steps a) - d) onto your paper. Draw sketches showing these steps, and add more steps until done.

  a) Draw two non-parallel lines L_1 and L_2 in plane P.

  b) In the plane Q_1 that contains L_1 and point A, do Construction 5 on page 52 (of this textbook) to obtain a point C on L_1 with $\overline{AC} \perp L_1$.

  c) In the plane P, do Construction 4 on page 52 to obtain a line M_1 in P through C with $M_1 \perp L_1$.

  d) Let R_1 be the plane containing lines $\overline{AC}$ and M_1. Note that $R_1 \perp P$.

  e) ... what's next?

13. ❋ A tank, shaped like a hemispherical bowl with radius 2 m, is filled with water to a height of 1 m. How many liters of water does the tank contain? Give your answer to the nearest liter.

Hint: The answer is *not* half the volume of the hemisphere. Use the slice principle!

CHAPTER 10

Data Displays, Probability and Statistics

Most K-8 curricula include work on "data analysis". This work involves three strands. The first focuses on ways of summarizing and presenting data. In elementary school the emphasis is on methods of organizing and displaying data in tables, bar charts, pie charts, and other displays (students also encounter these while studying science and social science). Later, in middle and high school, students learn the algorithms that give the commonly-used measures of center (mean and median) and dispersion (range, quartiles and standard deviation).

The second strand is probability. This topic usually begins in middle school, building on students' knowledge of fractions and ratios. Even the most basic probability is a subtle mix of intuitive ideas, precise mathematics, and confusing vocabulary. A knowledgable teacher is needed to guide students through the mix.

Finally, middle school students are introduced to statistics in an elementary form commonly called "experimental probability". Experimental probability is a two-step process: one uses data from a survey or experiment to build a probability model, and then uses the model to make inferences or conclusions. Usually, experimental probability is the only aspect of statistics that students see before high school.

10.1 Data Displays

Data display exercises are ubiquitous in K-8 mathematics curricula. Year after year, students organize data into tables and draw charts. This is familiar ground to most teachers and the conceptual level is low, so our descriptions can be brief. Thus this section reviews the various types of tables and charts, but focuses on the structure of the curriculum. We make four main points: (1) data presentation needn't take more than a couple of weeks per school year; (2) bar charts are part of a multi-year curriculum sequence that leads to graphing functions; (3) children learn to interpret tables and charts first, then they learn how to create their own, and (4) teachers must choose data-gathering activities judiciously.

Data come in two types: categorical and numerical. **Categorical data** consist of observed values in discrete groups or categories, for example, yes/no, man/woman/child, or "home state". **Numerical data** consist of values that are real numbers, such as measurements of height or weight. Some data, such as the ages of a group of children, can be regarded as either categorical or numerical.

You may notice that these two types of data correspond exactly to the set and measurement models used by teachers to explain arithmetic. Students begin in kindergarten using set models and categorical data, but as the grades progress they increasingly use measurement models and numerical data. In each grade, work with data is designed to reinforce the arithmetic and geometry skills learned in that grade.

In grades K-3 students learn to organize data by making tally tables, frequency tables and frequency charts as shown below. The **frequency** of a category is the number of data points in that category; the middle picture below shows how frequencies are tabulated. As is evident, these activities are straightforward. They merit only a small amount of class time.

3	7	7	6	7
8	6	5	8	7
6	4	6	10	9
8	7	6	7	8
6	7	8	8	7
5	9	7	6	7
5	5	4	8	6
7	6	8	8	9
5	7	8	6	5
6	7	7	6	7

Score	Tally	Frequency
3	/	1
4	///	3
5	𝍸	5
6	𝍸 𝍸 //	12
7	𝍸 𝍸 𝍸	15
8	𝍸 ////	9
9	////	4
10	/	1

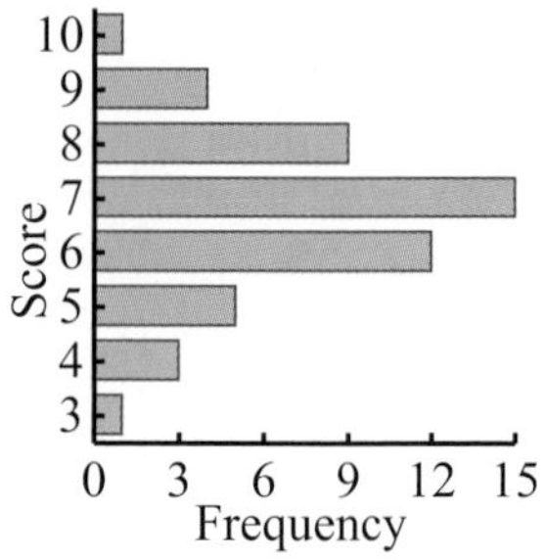
Score
10
9
8
7
6
5
4
3
0
3
6
9
12
15
Frequency

A Curriculum Sequence

The Primary Math curriculum devotes a short time each year — less than two weeks — to data displays. The textbooks are arranged so that this topic occurs near the end of the school year when students are looking forward to summer vacation. The lessons become incrementally more sophisticated each year, as the following teaching sequence shows.

Grade 1: Pictograms.

The number of fish caught by each boy.

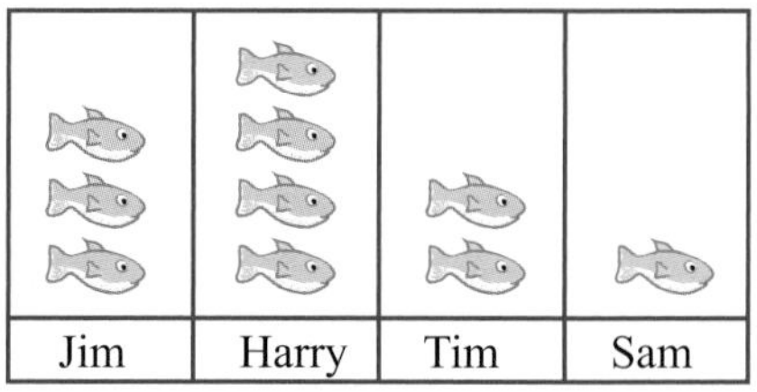
Jim
Harry
Tim
Sam

Grade 2: Abstract pictograms with labels.

The number of stickers four girls have.

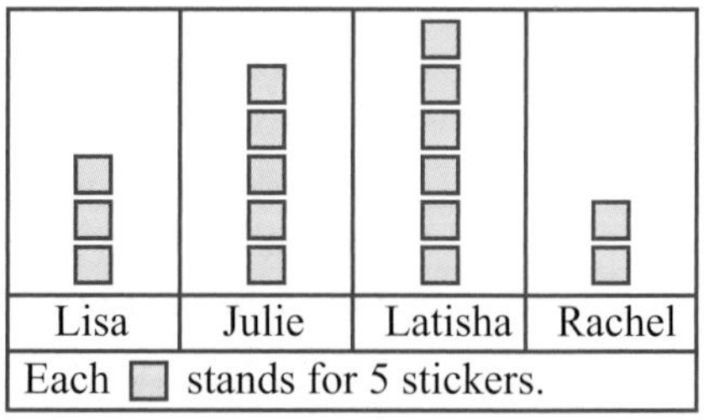
Lisa
Julie
Latisha
Rachel
Each ☐ stands for 5 stickers.

Pictograms can be drawn in either rows or columns (students should learn to interpret both). Note how the pictograms on this page include a title, labels, and information to interpret the length of the rows. It is vital that students appreciate that *pictograms and other data displays are meaningless unless properly labeled.*

Deborah's Savings

April	■ ■ ■
May	■ ■
June	■ ■ ■ ■ ■
July	■ ■ ■ ■
Each ■ *stands for $5.*	

Grade 2: *The pictogram shows Deborah's savings for 4 months.*

(a) Deborah saved $25 in _____.
(b) She saved _____ more in June than in April.
(c) Her total savings in these 4 months was _____.

Grades 3 & 4: Bar charts.

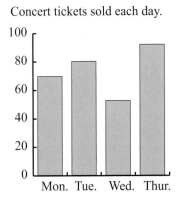

Concert tickets sold each day.

Pictograms evolve into bar charts. Grade 3 students interpret simple bar charts and make bar charts from tables of data. These activities are repeated in grade 4 with bar charts involving large numbers and various choices of units.

Grade 5: Line graphs.

Date	7/22	7/23	7/24	7/25	7/26
Depth (ft.)	20.8	21.4	19.9	19.1	18.7

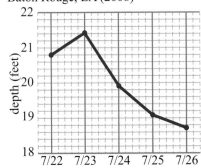

Mississippi River depth at
Baton Rouge, LA (2008)

Notice that the data determines points (not bars) and determines only 5 points on this graph. The segments joining those points give a good guess about the water level in the intervening times. Line graphs are an obvious extension of bar charts and, at the same time, set the stage for graphing linear functions.

Grade 6 & 7: Graphs of linear equations (beginning with lines through the origin).

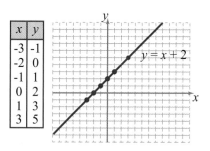

Students now make a transition to continuous data (x can be any real number) by choosing a few values of x, making a table, plotting points, and noting that the points form a line. The lessons emphasize that the graph is a better representation than the table because it shows the values of y for all x.

Grade 7 & 8: Graphs of quadratic and other equations.

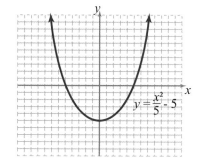

Pie Charts

Pie charts display categorical data as parts of a whole. They are usually introduced in fifth or sixth grade at the time when students are learning about angles and the area formula for circles.

A pie chart is a circle divided into sectors, one for each category. The angle of each sector is determined by the relative frequency of the corresponding item (the **relative frequency** is the frequency of the item divided by the total frequency of all items). To build a pie chart from a set of data, students (i) make a table of relative frequencies, (ii) convert relative frequencies into angles, and (iii) draw the chart.

EXAMPLE 1.1. *When Mr. Tenebruso asked his fifth grade class which subject they liked most, 13 said Mathematics, 7 said Science, 3 said Language Arts, and 1 said Social Studies.*

There are 24 students altogether.

Mathematics: $\dfrac{13}{24} \times 360° = 195°$.

Science: $\dfrac{7}{24} \times 360° = 105°$.

Language Arts: $\dfrac{3}{24} \times 360° = 45°$.

Social Studies: $\dfrac{1}{24} \times 360° = 15°$.

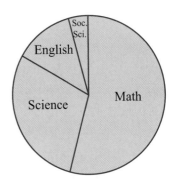

Data-gathering Activities

Elementary students learn that statistical data can be gathered in several ways:

- observations
- experiments
- surveys.

Elementary textbooks and teacher manuals suggest many such data-gathering activities. Teachers must decide which ones to use.

EXERCISE 1.2. *Which of the following data-gathering activities would make a valuable fifth-grade lesson?*

a) *Students compare how many licks it takes to consume red, green and orange lollipops.*

b) *Water is heated on a stove and its temperature is measured every minute for 10 minutes.*

c) *Each student polls 20 family members and neighbors to determine their favorite animals.*

d) *Students use the internet to list (estimated) world population in 100-year increments beginning at 1000 A.D.*

Decisions about which activities are worthwhile are easily made if one keeps three principles in mind:

- **Keep it short.** Gathering data can be very time-consuming, yet the accompanying mathematics lesson starts only *after* the data are gathered. Teachers can save everyone time and effort, with little loss of educational value, by simply providing students with data and having a brief discussion on how it might have been gathered.

- **Avoid drudgery.** Besides being time-consuming, data-gathering activities are usually repetitious and involve little thinking. They can quickly become tedious and stultifying. One technique to reduce drudgery is to have each student gather a small amount of data—enough to understand the process—and then combine everyone's results to create a data set.

- **Make it enlightening.** In the best data-gathering activities the information found, or the process used to find it, opens students' eyes to a fact or procedure that is valuable for their future understanding of some aspect of science or social science.

EXERCISE 1.3. *In Exercise 1.2, b) and d) are valuable activities. How might these activities be modified to make them less valuable?*

Homework Set 37

1. *(Study the textbook!)* Read pages 58–63 of Primary Math 3B and answer these questions:

   a) Second grade students work with pictograms. In third grade the transition is made to bar charts. Between which two pages does this transition take place?

   b) Write answers to the questions on page 60 in your textbook. How many different types of questions are asked here?

   c) Answer questions (a)–(f) on page 61 in your textbook. Which of these ask students to read the chart "backwards", using dollar amounts to find a month?

   d) Answer the questions on pages 63 in your textbook. Which of these require students to solve an arithmetic problem?

   e) Assuming that 1 – 2 pages can be covered in a day's lesson, estimate how many class days would be spent on data analysis in third grade.

2. *(Study the textbook!)* When answering questions about bar charts, students can determine the height or length of bars by either

   • counting squares

   • reading the scale, or

   • doing both.

   In Primary Math 3B, which of these methods can students use to answer the question on page 58? The questions on page 59? Questions (a) on pages 60, 61, 62, 63? What have students learned to do in these 6 pages?

3. *(Study the textbook!)* Read pages 70–72 of Primary Math 4A and write answers to the questions in your textbook. Then answer these questions:

   a) Do problem 4 on page 73.

   b) Do problem 5 on page 73.

   c) Assuming that 1 – 2 pages can be covered in a day's lesson, estimate how many class days would be spent on data analysis in fourth grade.

4. Line graphs are introduced on pages 51–53 of Primary Math 5B. Imagine that you are teaching these pages to a fifth grade class. Write down a 3-part question about the graph on page 53 that would help prepare your students to learn about the slope of lines.

5. Do Problems 1–6 on pages 39–41 of Primary Math 6B.

6. *(Study the textbook!)* Now reread pages 39–41 of Primary Math 6B and answer these questions:

   a) List the questions in Problems 1–6 that require students to calculate a fraction (your answer should start with "1c, 2a, ...")

   b) List the questions in Problems 1–6 that require students to calculate a percent.

   c) List the questions in Problems 1–6 that require students to do arithmetic.

   d) To answer question 2c) students use what they learned about the area of sectors on pages 31–37. Give a Teacher's Solution for this problem.

   e) For Problem 6b) on page 41, what geometric fact is used in determining the percentage of shirts? (See the list of facts at the beginning of Chapter 4 in this textbook.)

10.2 Center and Dispersion of Data Sets

A **statistical algorithm** is a procedure that associates a number to each numerical data set. The resulting number is called a **statistic**. School mathematics involves statistics of two types. Some (mean and median) are designed to indicate the "average" or "center" of the data set. Others (range, quartiles, variance and standard deviation) that are designed to indicate the dispersion of the data set, that is, the extent to which the data are concentrated or spread out. Again, the concepts are straightforward.

The Mean

For numerical data, the most commonly-used notion of "average" is the *mean* (or *arithmetic mean*). The idea can be explained using an area model as follows. Given a set of numbers, draw a bar chart with columns of equal width and height equal to the given numbers, as is done below for the data {6, 13, 9, 15, 5, 10}. Then "level off" the columns to form a rectangle. The height of this rectangle is the mean of the given set of numbers.

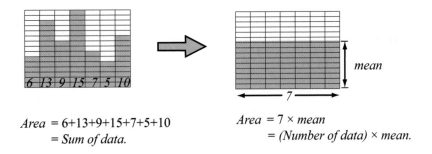

$$Area = 6+13+9+15+7+5+10$$
$$= Sum\ of\ data.$$

$$Area = 7 \times mean$$
$$= (Number\ of\ data) \times mean.$$

Now compare areas. Because the leveling process does not change area, we have

$$Sum\ of\ data\ =\ (Number\ of\ data) \times Mean.$$

Therefore

$$Mean\ =\ \frac{Sum\ of\ data}{Number\ of\ data}.$$

EXERCISE 2.1. *Study pages 38–40 of Primary Math 5B to see how elementary students can be taught to find means without formulas of any kind.*

EXAMPLE 2.2. *(Grade 4) 5 girls are 49, 50, 52, 53 and 54 inches tall. What is their mean height?*

Teacher's Solution:

$$\text{mean height} = \frac{\text{Sum of heights}}{\text{Number of girls}}$$
$$= \frac{(49 + 50 + 52 + 53 + 54) \text{ in}}{5}$$
$$= \frac{258}{5} \text{ in}$$
$$= 51.6 \text{ in.}$$

The mean is defined algebraically in middle school books. If the data set consists of n numbers called $x_1, x_2, x_3, \ldots, x_n$, then the mean is written as $\bar{x}$ and is

$$\bar{x} = \frac{x_1 + x_2 + \cdots + x_n}{n}.$$

Either way, the arithmetic mean is a statistical algorithm: it is a specific procedure that can be applied to any numerical data set to obtain a number.

EXAMPLE 2.3. *(Grade 6) The mean weight of 5 boys is 46 kg. When another boy joins the group, the mean weight of the 6 boys becomes 48 kg. How much does the 6th boy weigh?*

Teacher's Solution. For the first 5 boys:

$$46 \; kg = \text{mean wt.} = \frac{\text{Sum of weights}}{5}$$

∴ Total weight of first 5 boys: $46 \times 5 \; kg = 230 \; kg$.

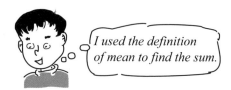

I used the definition of mean to find the sum.

For all 6 boys:

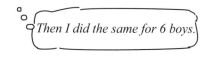

Then I did the same for 6 boys.

$$48 \; kg = \text{mean wt.} = \frac{\text{Sum of weights}}{6}$$

∴ Total weight of all 6 boys: $48 \times 6 \; kg = 288 \; kg$.

The 6th boy weighs $288 - 230 \; kg = 58 \; kg$.

It is often helpful to think of the mean as the "balance point" (mark the data as points on a number line and imagine each as a small unit weight).

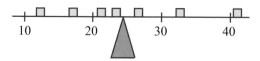

The mean is the "balance point".

Median

It is sometimes misleading to report the mean as the "center" of a set of data because the mean is sensitive to extreme data points. Here is an example illustrating the effect of extreme values:

EXAMPLE 2.4. *The summer earnings of five 6th graders were* $80, $100, $120, $140, *and* $900. *What was their mean earnings?*

$$\textbf{Solution:} \qquad \text{mean earnings} \ = \ \frac{\text{Sum of earnings}}{\text{Number of 6th graders}}$$

$$= \ \frac{80 + 100 + 120 + 140 + 900}{5} \ \text{dollars}$$

$$= \ \$268.$$

All but one of the students had below-average earnings! In this example the mean earnings are not typical, so one might want to use a different notion of the "center" of the data. A common alternative is the value that is literally in the middle of the data set:

The **median** of a list of n numbers is found by arranging the numbers in order from smallest to largest and taking either

(i) the middle number (if n is odd), or

$$8 \quad 9 \quad \boxed{12} \quad 13 \quad 16$$

median: 12

(ii) the mean of the middle two numbers (if n is even).

$$14 \quad 17 \quad \boxed{23 \quad 26} \quad 31 \quad 38$$

median: (23+26)/2 = 24.5

EXERCISE 2.5. *In the picture below, each small square represents a data point. Which arrow points to the mean? Which points to the median?*

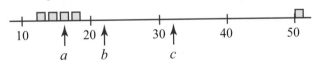

Most elementary curricula also discuss a third notion of the "center": the **mode** of a list of numbers is the most frequently occurring value. The mode has limited use and has multiple shortcomings. It is not a statistical algorithm because it is not defined for all data sets.

1, 2, 3	*1, 2, 2, 3, 4, 4*	*0, 0, 97, 98, 99, 100, 101*
mode not defined	*two modes*	*mode doesn't indicate "center"*

Measures of Dispersion

The term *dispersion* refers to the extent to which numerical data are concentrated or spread out along the number line. Statistics (as defined in the first sentence of this section) that indicate dispersion are called **measures of dispersion**. Here are some examples:

- The smallest number in a data set is called the **lower extreme**; the largest is the **upper extreme**.

- The **range** is the difference of the extremes.

- The **lower quartile value** (Q_1) is the median of the lower half of the data and the **upper quartile value** (Q_3) is the median of the upper half of the data (when the median is one of the data points, it is included in both halves).

Given a data set, one finds the quartiles by (i) listing the data in order from smallest to largest, (ii) finding the median Q_2, (iii) separating the data into upper and lower halves, and (iv) finding the medians Q_1 and Q_3 of the halves.

The quartiles Q_1 and Q_3 are statistics: the definition gives a specific algorithm for calculating them. Actually, we have chosen one of several, slightly different, algorithms commonly used by calculators and textbooks. As a result, students may notice discrepancies in their calculations of Q_1 and Q_3 (see Homework Problems 10 and 11).

Information about dispersion can be displayed in a **box plot** (also called a **box-and-whisker plot**) The box extends from Q_1 to Q_3 with a vertical line indicating the median Q_2.

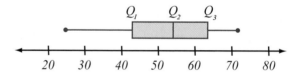

To draw the whiskers, one first identifies the outliers. An **outlier** is a data point whose distance from the ends of the box is more than 1.5 times the length of the box. Outliers are considered unusual data points. Therefore the whiskers on each side are drawn out only to the farthest data point that is not an outlier. Of course, the definition of outlier is a matter of convention and may vary from book to book.

A single box plot is usually less informative than the corresponding bar chart. But box plots are very useful for displaying multiple subgroups or samples on a single chart.

The chart on the right clearly shows how both the median height (drawn as a line graph) and *the dispersion in heights* increase with age. Charts like this one are common in science, social science and medicine.

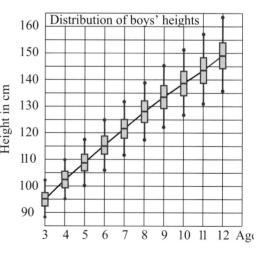

Standard Deviation

In statistics, dispersion is almost always expressed in terms of "standard deviation". Students usually first encounter standard deviation in a high school statistics or precalculus course. We include it here for completeness.

Any numerical data set can be visualized as points on a number line "balanced" at the mean $\bar{x}$. For each data point the distance to the mean is the absolute value of the difference:

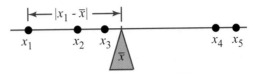

The average of these distances is called the **mean deviation** and written MD. If the data points (which are numbers) are $x_1, x_2, \ldots, x_n$, then the mean deviation is given by the formula

$$\text{MD} = \frac{|x_1 - \bar{x}| + |x_2 - \bar{x}| + \cdots + |x_n - \bar{x}|}{n}$$

For technical reasons, statisticians prefer to average the *square* of the distances-to-the-mean. The resulting measure of dispersion is called the *variance*. It is given by the similar formula

$$\text{Var} = \frac{(x_1 - \bar{x})^2 + (x_2 - \bar{x})^2 + \cdots + (x_n - \bar{x})^2}{n}.$$

The variance is not quite what we want because by squaring *we have changed the units*. When the data are measurements in pounds, for example, the variance is expressed in square pounds (lbs)^2 — very peculiar! We can return to the original units by taking the square root. The square root of the variance is called the standard deviation and is denoted by the Greek letter σ ("sigma").

The **variance** of a set of numbers is the average squared distance to the mean. If the numbers are written $x_1, x_2, \ldots, x_n$ with mean $\bar{x}$ then the variance is the number Var given by

$$\text{Var} = \frac{(x_1 - \bar{x})^2 + (x_2 - \bar{x})^2 + \cdots + (x_n - \bar{x})^2}{n}.$$

The **standard deviation** is the square root of the variance: $\sigma = \sqrt{\text{Var}}$.

Students can find the standard deviation of a list of numbers by (i) subtracting the mean from each, (ii) then squaring each, (iii) finding the mean of this new list, and (iv) taking the square root.

EXAMPLE 2.6. *For the data set $\{6, 7, 9, 13, 14, 17\}$ find the mean deviation MD, the variance V and the standard deviation σ.*

Solution:

$$
\begin{aligned}
\text{list of data} &= 6, 7, 9, 13, 14, 17 \\
\text{mean } \bar{x} &= (6 + 7 + 9 + 13 + 14 + 17)/6 = 11 \\
\text{distance to mean} &= 5, 4, 2, 2, 3, 6 \\
\text{square of distance to mean} &= 25, 16, 4, 4, 9, 36
\end{aligned}
$$

Therefore

$$MD = \frac{5 + 4 + 2 + 2 + 3 + 6}{6} \approx 4.67$$

$$Var = \frac{25 + 16 + 4 + 4 + 9 + 36}{6} \approx 15.67$$

$$\sigma = \sqrt{15.67} \approx 3.96.$$

Of course, many calculators will compute standard deviations with a single keystroke. The ability to instantly calculate standard deviations is great for high school students writing up the results of a chemistry experiment. But when students are initially introduced to standard deviations the emphasis is on the concepts and on learning to interpret algebraic formulas like the ones above. Students need to construct this understanding by doing calculations by hand or with a four-function calculator.

Homework Set 38

1. *(Study the textbook!)* In Primary Math 5B, read page 38 and do Problems 1 and 2 on page 39.

   a) Is the picture in Problem 1 essentially the same as the area model at the beginning of this section?

   b) Give a short explanation on how to use the pictogram in Problem 2 to *quickly* find the average.

2. Do parts (a), (f), and (g) of Problem 1 on page 43 of Primary Math 5B.

3. Find the mean, median, and mode of the following sets below:

   a) 1, 2, 2, 3, 4, 5.

   b) -20, 2, 3, 2, -1, 2, -1, 4, -1.

   c) 15 cm, 3 dm, 1 dm, 20 cm, 1 dm.

   d) 4 quarts, 3 pints, 6 cups, 2 quarts, 1 gallon, 4 pints.

4. Give Teacher's Solutions to Problems 2–8 on page 43 of Primary Math 5B.

5. Do Problem 2 on page 51 of Primary Mathematics 5B.

6. Mr. Smith's daily expenses for the 7 days in one week were $120, $72, $58, $233, $82, $91 and $108. What was his mean daily expense? What was his median of his daily expenses?

7. Give a Teacher's Solution to this problem: The mean of 5 numbers is 12 and the mean of 9 other numbers is 22.8. What is the mean of all 14 numbers?

8. Give a Teacher's Solution to this problem: Katie's mean score on 4 hourly exams was 88%. Course grades are computed from the 4 hourly exams and the Final Exam, which counts as 2 hourly exams. What score must Katie get on the Final Exam to achieve a course grade of 90% ?

9. Imagine that you are teaching from a textbook that gives this algorithm for finding the first quartile: Q_1 *is the median of the data points that are less than, but not equal to, the median Q_2.*

   a) Use this algorithm to find Q_1 for the following two data sets:

   Group A: 102, 107, 110, 111, 112, 112, 123, 136.

   Group B: 98, 100, 102, 105, 112, 113, 114, 119, 128.

   b) Find Q_1 for both groups again, now using the algorithm you described in Problem 9.

   c) For Group B, are your two values for Q_1 the same?

10. Another textbook says: Q_1 *is the median of the lower half of the data (do not include the median in the lower half).* Two students disagree about how this applies to the data:

    Group C: 50, 62, 70, 73, 77, 77, 80, 81, 85, 90, 94.

    a) Annie drops both 77s and gets $Q_1 =$ ____.

    b) Jorge drops only one 77 and gets $Q_1 =$ ____.

    c) Is the textbook's definition ambiguous?

    d) How might you, as a teacher, resolve it?

11. Draw box plots for the Group A and Group B data given in Problem 10 above.

12. Six children ran a 50 meter dash. Their times were 9, 10, 10, 11, 12 and 14 seconds. Find the mean deviation MD, the variance Var and the standard deviation σ. Express your answers in the appropriate units.

10.3 Probability

If you flip a coin 6 times, what is the chance of it landing heads-up exactly 4 times? Probability is the branch of mathematics that seeks to answer such questions by creating a certain type of mathematical model called a "probability model". Probability models provide a systematic method for answering questions about situations whose outcomes are not precisely predictable.

This section describes how to use area models to teach probability to elementary and middle school students. The comments about textbook language at the end of the section are absolutely crucial for teachers.

Mathematical probability applies to situations, called **experiments**, where different outcomes are possible and that can be repeated many times, always with the same set of possible outcomes. The set of all possible outcomes of an experiment is called the **sample space**.

To solve a K-8 probability problem, one draws a model — every problem requires a model. A *probability model* is a region S composed of rectangles, one rectangle for each possible outcome. The probability of an outcome is proportional to its area. Often, probability models can be drawn as bar diagrams or rectangular arrays.

EXAMPLE 3.1. *Here are some examples of probability models.*

a) In the experiment of flipping a fair coin, there are two equally-likely outcomes, heads (H) and tails (T). The probability model can be drawn as two rectangles of equal area:

H	T

b) In the experiment of rolling a fair die, there are 6 possible outcomes (the numbers 1–6). The probability model can be drawn like this:

1	2	3	4	5	6

c) In the experiment of simultaneously flipping a fair coin and rolling a fair die, there are $2 \times 6 = 12$ possible outcomes, which we label $H1, H2, \ldots, T5, T6$. The probability model can be drawn as a rectangular array:

H1	H2	H3	H4	H5	H6
T1	T2	T3	T4	T5	T6

In these pictures, each outcome or set of outcomes corresponds to a collection of small rectangles. In probability, any such a collection is called an **event**. Thus an event is a subset of the sample space.

EXAMPLE 3.2. *a) In the probability model of Example 3.1a, the outcome "heads" is an event.*

H	T

Event A: coin shows heads.

b) *In the probability model of Example 3.1b, getting a "2" is one event, getting "a 2 or a 5" is another event, and getting "an even number" is a third event.*

1	2	3	4	5	6

Event B: roll a 2.

1	2	3	4	5	6

Event C: roll a 2 or 5.

1	2	3	4	5	6

Event D: an even number.

c) *Here are 3 events in the probability model of Example 3.1c.*

H1	H2	H3	H4	H5	H6
T1	T2	T3	T4	T5	T6

Event A: coin shows heads.

H1	H2	H3	H4	H5	H6
T1	T2	T3	T4	T5	T6

Event B: die shows 5.

H1	H2	H3	H4	H5	H6
T1	T2	T3	T4	T5	T6

Event C: die shows an odd number.

EXAMPLE 3.3. *Next consider the experiment of rolling two fair dice, one red and one white, and recording each roll as a pair of numbers putting the red die's result first. The probability model has 36 equally-likely outcomes, so it can be drawn as a rectangular array. The picture shows the event "the sum is 6".*

Event A:
The dice sum to 6.

(1,1)	(1,2)	(1,3)	(1,4)	(1,5)	(1,6)
(2,1)	(2,2)	(2,3)	(2,4)	(2,5)	(2,6)
(3,1)	(3,2)	(3,3)	(3,4)	(3,5)	(3,6)
(4,1)	(4,2)	(4,3)	(4,4)	(4,5)	(4,6)
(5,1)	(5,2)	(5,3)	(5,4)	(5,5)	(5,6)
(6,1)	(6,2)	(6,3)	(6,4)	(6,5)	(6,6)

Now comes the intuition and the key definition. When rolling two die one supposes that all 36 outcomes are equally likely, and our model is built so that each outcome has the same area. Thus the chances of getting one of the 5 (shaded) outcomes in Event A should be

$$\frac{\text{Area of } A}{\text{Area of entire square}} = \frac{5}{36}.$$

In general,

DEFINITION 3.4. *In a probability model with region S, the **probability of an event** A is the number*

$$P(A) = \frac{\text{Area of } A}{\text{Area of } S}.$$

Here are the probabilities of some other events for Example 3.3:

Event B: roll two 1's $\qquad P(B) \;=\; \dfrac{1}{36},$

Event C: dice sum to 3 $\qquad P(C) \;=\; \dfrac{2}{36} = \dfrac{1}{18},$

Event D: dice sum to 3 or 6 $\qquad P(D) \;=\; \dfrac{7}{36},$

Event E: dice in any combination $\qquad P(E) \;=\; \dfrac{36}{36} = 1.$

The same pictorial approach can be used to solve many elementary probability problems. Before giving examples, we clarify exactly what we mean by a probability model:

DEFINITION 3.5. *A probability model consists of:*

- *A region S with finite area called the sample space.*

- *A decomposition of S into subregions (e.g., rectangles), one for each possible outcome.*

With this setup,

- *An event A is a collection of subregions in S.*

- *To each event A we assign the number* $P(A) = \dfrac{Area\ of\ A}{Area\ of\ S}.$

P(A) is interpreted as the probability that event A will occur, i.e. that one of the outcomes that belong to A will be observed.

While $P(A)$ is defined as a ratio, it can also be thought of directly as an area: $P(A)$ *is the area of A measured in units for which the total area of S is 1.* Either way, since $P(A)$ is proportional to the area of A, it satisfies the properties of area listed in Section 5.2. In particular,

- $0 \le P(A) \le 1$ for all subsets A,

- $P(A \cup B) = P(A) + P(B)$ whenever A and B do not intersect, and

- $P(S) = 1.$

Teacher's Solutions to Probability Problems

In the homework problems you will be asked to give "Teacher's Solutions". Your Teacher's Solutions should include a probability model with labels and should be organized in a way that makes the reasoning clear to students. Here are some examples.

EXAMPLE 3.6. *A letter is chosen at random from the word "MATHEMATICS". What is the probability that the letter is: a) a 'T'? b) a 'C'? c) a vowel?*

Teacher's Solution:

a). Event A: a 'T' is picked.

$$P(A) = \frac{2}{11}.$$

b). Event B: a 'C' is picked.

M	A	T	H	E	M	A	T	I	C	S

$$P(B) = \frac{1}{11}.$$

c). Event C: a vowel is picked.

M	A	T	H	E	M	A	T	I	C	S

$$P(C) = \frac{4}{11}.$$

EXAMPLE 3.7. *Two letters are drawn at random from the word MIAMI. If they are drawn one-at-a-time with replacement, what is the probability that they are the same letter?*

"With replacement" means that one letter is chosen, then replaced, and then the second letter (perhaps identical to the first) is chosen.

Teacher's Solution:

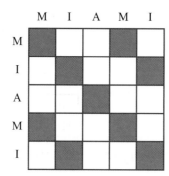

$$P(\text{Same Letter}) = \frac{9}{25}.$$

Notice the labeling in this solution: each square is associated to a pair of letters according to its row and column. To draw the figure, one goes through the array row by row, shading in the squares whose row and column letters are the same.

EXAMPLE 3.8. *Two letters are drawn at random from the word SEVEN. If they are drawn one-by-one without replacement, what is the probability that they are both consonants?*

In this problem the phrase "without replacement" means that one letter is chosen, and then a second is chosen *from the remaining letters.* For example, if the first letter is "V" then the second cannot also be "V". As a result, there are fewer possible outcomes than in the previous example. When we draw the sample space we must omit the squares corresponding to drawing the same letter twice.

Teacher's Solution:

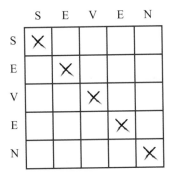

$$P(A) = \frac{6}{20} = \frac{3}{10}.$$

Sample Space:
The 20 squares without x's.

Event *A*: Two consonants are picked.
The 6 shaded squares out of 20.

Comparing Examples 3.6 and 3.7, one sees that the words "with replacement" or "without replacement" cannot be ignored. They are crucial instructions telling students which sample space to use. Probability problems cannot be solved unless the question includes words or clues that specify the model. Students need explicit instruction on recognizing and using these clues.

One can also use a **tree diagram** to help create a probability model.

EXAMPLE 3.9. *A fair coin is tossed 3 times. What is the probability of getting a head and two tails?*

Teacher's Solution:

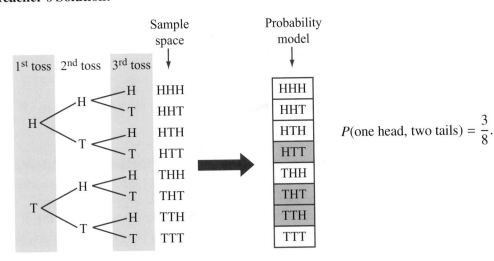

$$P(\text{one head, two tails}) = \frac{3}{8}.$$

Each of the above examples used a model in which all outcomes have equal probability. Here is an example with unequal probabilities.

EXAMPLE 3.10. *A spinner has a 36° red sector and a 45° blue sector; the rest of the spinner is green. What is the probability of obtaining each color? Express your answers in percent.*

Teacher's Solution:

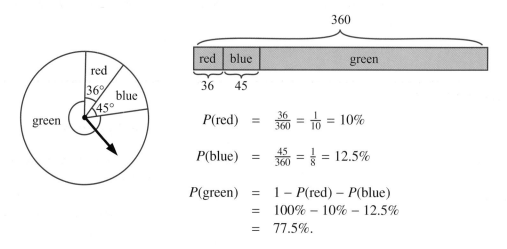

$$P(\text{red}) \;=\; \tfrac{36}{360} = \tfrac{1}{10} = 10\%$$

$$P(\text{blue}) \;=\; \tfrac{45}{360} = \tfrac{1}{8} = 12.5\%$$

$$\begin{aligned}
P(\text{green}) \;&=\; 1 - P(\text{red}) - P(\text{blue}) \\
&=\; 100\% - 10\% - 12.5\% \\
&=\; 77.5\%.
\end{aligned}$$

Deciphering the Language of Probability

The terminology of probability can be diabolically confusing. Problems and discussions are routinely phrased using words with double meanings. Teachers and students are expected to sort out the ambiguities, usually without any help from the textbook. As a result, it is essential for teachers to repeatedly explain and clarify the vocabulary and the underlying concepts.

Misleading terms are a hazard. Probability, like many subjects, has its own vocabulary — words that have special precise meaning within the subject. For historical reasons, probability has adopted common English words and given them new, genuinely different technical meanings. Confusion occurs because *students are familiar with the common meanings, but not the technical ones*. Here are some examples.

- A *sample space* is a set of possible outcomes of an experiment. It needn't have anything to do with a survey or samples of anything.

- In common English, an "event" is a notable occurrence. But in probability any collection of outcomes is called an *event*. The collection can be totally unremarkable.

- Students are familiar with scientific experiments, but in probability an *experiment* need not have any purpose or goal and need not "test" anything.

An even bigger hazard is confusion between the physical objects and mathematical models. Very often, textbook language creates the impression that probabilities are properties of a physical object, such as a coin or a die. They are not; *probabilities are properties of the mathematical model used to make predictions about the object, and nothing more.* Whenever we discuss probabilities, all we are doing is constructing a model and hoping that it works. Students cannot be expected to figure this out on their own; in fact, mathematicians were confused by this very point for over a century. It is up to teachers to explain this most basic fact about probability.

Similarly, the phrases "fair coin", "unloaded dice", "equally likely" and "chosen without replacement" do not describe physical properties or processes. Rather, they are *instructions to the student about which model to use*. If a problem begins "3 fair coins are tossed...", it is expected that students will answer using a model in which all 8 outcomes are equally likely. Students who have been taught to spot and use these coded instructions find probability problems are easier because they immediately start thinking in terms of a model and do not get bogged down visualizing flipping coins and rolling dice — such visualizations are actually impediments to solving the problem!

Homework Set 39

Give Teacher's Solutions to all problems by drawing a probability model for each.

1. In a class with 18 girls and 12 boys, what is the probability that a student chosen at random will be a girl?

2. A ball is drawn at random from a bag containing 6 red, 8 blue and 4 green balls. What is the probability of drawing a) a blue ball? b) a green ball? c) a ball that is not red?

3. There are 24 eggs in a basket and 3 are bad. If an egg is chosen at random, what is the probability that it is a good one?

4. If a whole number from 1 to 20 (inclusive) is picked at random, what is the probability that the number is a) even? b) a multiple of 5? c) not a multiple of 2 or 3?

5. The figure shows three semi-circles whose bases lie on the line AD and partition it into thirds ($AB = BC = CD$).

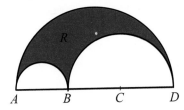

a) What is the ratio of the areas of the 3 semi-circles?

b) If a dart lands randomly at some point in the figure, what is the probability that it lies in region R?

6. There are 14 girls in a class. If a student is selected at random, the probability of choosing a girl is $\frac{2}{3}$. How many boys are there in the class?

7. Two letters are drawn at random without replacement from the word EXPERIMENT. What is the probability that these letters are a) the same, b) vowels, c) consonants?

8. Two letters are selected from the word BANANA. What is the probability that the letters are the same if the selection is made at random a) with replacement and b) without replacement.

9. If you pick a telephone number at random from a directory, what is the probability that the last two digits are 76?

Hint: choose your sample space so that the initial digits do not matter.

10. Kira's class has 6 more girls than boys. Kira determines that the probability that a student selected at random from her class is a boy is $\frac{5}{12}$. How many boys are in her class?

11. Two fair coins are tossed. What is the probability that at least one coin will land heads up?

12. Two fair dice are thrown. Find the probability that

   a) Both dice are 6.

   b) At least one die is 6.

   c) The numbers on the dice are the same.

13. In the previous problem, what do the words "fair dice" mean? (Read this section carefully before answering!)

14. Two fair dice are thrown and the resulting numbers are multiplied. What is the probability that the product of the dice is greater than 10?

15. A fair coin is tossed 3 times. What is the probability that a) the first two outcomes are both heads? b) there is at least one tail?

16. The numbers are equally spaced on the spinners shown. Each spinner is spun once. Find the probability that the pointers will stop at

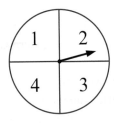 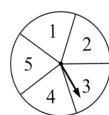

   a) the same number.

   b) two odd numbers.

   c) numbers having a total of 4.

   d) numbers whose product is even.

10.4 Inferential Statistics

Inferential statistics makes estimates and predictions about populations based on data from samples. It is a beautiful mathematical theory of enormous practical value; it is used routinely in science and social science and in formulating public policy. But the subject is built on top of calculus-based probability theory, and consequently is far more abstract and subtle than it appears. Even routine applications require judgements that are based on expert knowledge of mathematical statistics and of the population being studied. Because it requires such sophisticated mathematical background, many mathematicians believe that inferential statistics should not be taught below the college level.

Nevertheless, most school curricula try to teach something about inferential statistics. The examples in this section illustrate one approach at the middle school level that emphasizes the underlying concepts.

Statistical inferences are always made by a two-step process:

(1) the sample data are used to build a probability model, then

(2) the model is used to make inferences about the populations.

You are already adept at Step (2); you used models to make predictions in the homework problems for the previous section.

Students and teachers are often befuddled by texts that do not carefully distinguish between these two steps. Thus it is important that instruction be broken into distinct phases according to the mathematical structure. First, students learn what a probability model is and how to use models to make predictions (the material of the previous section). Then, secondly, they learn to use sample data to build probability models and learn to combine Steps (1) and (2) in the manner explained in this section.

Populations and Random Samples

The **population** of a statistical study is the entire group of people or things that the study is designed to investigate. Populations can be concrete (e.g., all polar bears) or abstract (for a study of weather in Seattle, the population consists of all days, past and future, in Seattle). Since it is usually impractical or impossible to study the population as a whole, we take a sample from the population. A **sample** is any subset of the population.

The central idea of statistics is that *random samples reflect populations*. For example, the opinions of a random sample of 1000 voters should give a good estimate about the outcome of an election. Statistics is the science of designing studies (how do you select a sample?) and analyzing information that comes from the sample in order to make inferences about the population.

The process of selecting a sample is called **sampling**. Samples can be taken from either an **observational study** or an **experiment**. An observational study records data without attempting to influence outcomes, while an experiment deliberately imposes conditions that may influence outcomes and observes the responses.

In any study, the sampling method should be set up in such a way that every possible sample has an equal chance of being chosen; when this is done, the resulting samples are called **random samples**. Random samples are important because of the two-step process described at the beginning of this section: data is analyzed using probability models that assume all samples have equal probability. When samples are not random, statistical analysis may produce unwarranted conclusions.

How much of this discussion is appropriate for K-8 mathematics? Not much, except for the key intuition that *random samples reflect populations*. Many curricula include activities that build this intuition without – appropriately – claiming that this is a mathematical fact.

Experimental Probability

The task of building a probability model from sample data is called *experimental probability*. Students are given the outcomes of an experiment (or they record their own data) and are asked to calculate the probabilities of various outcomes. These problems are actually about ratios. In each, students apply the idea that samples reflect populations.

EXAMPLE 4.1. *Julie has a spinner with two sectors, blue and white. She has spun it 90 times with the results shown. She challenges you to predict how many of the next 20 spinner outcomes will be blue. Without seeing the spinner, what is your prediction?*

Blue	63
White	27

Solution: In the sample, the outcomes occur in a ratio of $63 : 27$. It makes sense to assume that future spins will reflect the same ratio. Thus we build a probability model with this ratio:

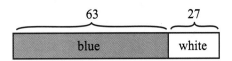

With this model, $P(\text{blue}) = \frac{63}{90} = \frac{7}{10}$.

Of the next 20 spins, we expect $20 \times \frac{7}{10} = 14$ to be blue.

EXERCISE 4.2. *One can build a spinner using the same ratio by taking the central angle of the white sector to be*

$$\frac{27}{90} \times 360° = 27 \times 4° = 108°.$$

Are the angles in this spinner identical to those in Julie's?

EXAMPLE 4.3. *At a lightbulb factory, a random sample of 100 lightbulbs was tested; 3 bulbs were defective. How many defective lightbulbs should one expect in a carton of 350 bulbs?*

Teacher's Solution: In the sample, 3 of 100 bulbs were defective.

Probability Model:

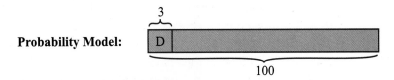

Expected number of defective bulbs in carton: $\dfrac{3}{100}$ of $350 = \dfrac{3 \times 350}{100} = 10.5$.

Obviously, no carton can have exactly 10.5 defective bulbs. But the phrase "expected number of defective bulbs" refers to an expected average in the long run: after selecting a large number of cartons and testing all bulbs in them, we expect that the mean number of defective bulbs per carton to be 10.5.

EXAMPLE 4.4. *Amanda counts the birds that visit her birdfeeder in one hour. Her record shows:*

Finches (F)	8	Grackles (G)	6
Chickadees (C)	16	Others (O)	6

Of the next 90 birds to arrive, how many should Amanda expect will be a) chickadees? b) not finches? c) neither finches nor grackles?

Teacher's Solution: The ratio of sample outcomes is $8:16:6:6$ or more simply $4:8:3:3$.

Probability Model:

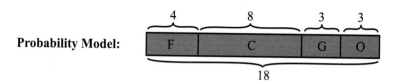

$$P(C) = \frac{8}{18} = \frac{4}{9} \qquad P(\text{not } F) = \frac{8+3+3}{18} = \frac{7}{9} \qquad P(\text{not } F \text{ or } G) = \frac{8+3}{18} = \frac{11}{18}.$$

Of the next 90 birds, Amanda should expect a) $\frac{4}{9} \times 90 = 40$ chickadees, b) $\frac{7}{9} \times 90 = 70$ birds that are not finches, and c) $\frac{11}{18} \times 90 = 55$ birds that are neither finches nor grackles.

Notice the order and the logic of the Teacher's Solution: the sample data told us how to build the model and then the model determined the probabilities. The concluding sentence makes predictions about future arrivals by assuming that the probabilities for the sample reflect those for the general population of all birds arriving at the feeder.

Bell Curve Probability Models

By far the most useful of all probability models is the one defined by the **normal distribution curve** or **bell curve**. The standard bell curve is one particular curve in the plane. It has several notable characteristics:

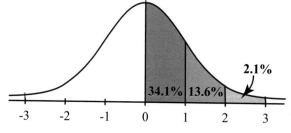

- It is symmetric about $x = 0$.
- It is bell-shaped. Both ends approach the x-axis but never touch it.
- The region under the curve and above the x-axis has total area 1.
- The area is distributed as shown in the figure.

We can transform this one curve to make other bell curves, one for each choice of a mean $\bar{x}$ and a standard deviation σ. The pictures below show how to construct bell curves with a mean of 6 and any σ. The first step translates the center to 6. In the second, the curve is simultaneously stretched horizontally by a factor of σ and vertically by a factor of $1/\sigma$ (the figure includes dotted rectangles to help you visualize this transformation). By the Scaling Principle of Section 9.4, this stretching does not change areas because $\sigma \cdot \frac{1}{\sigma} = 1$.

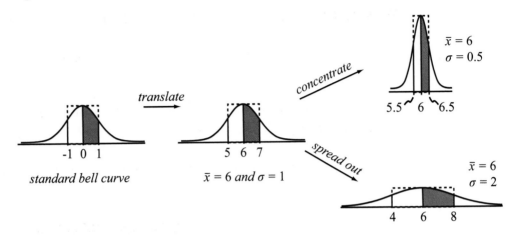

The resulting curves are tall and concentrated near the mean when σ is small, and are spread out along the x-axis when σ is large. Each is transformed from the original bell curve in a way that *corresponding regions have equal area*. In particular, for every choice of $\bar{x}$ and σ, the total area under the curve is 1 and 34% of the area lies above the interval from $\bar{x}$ to $\bar{x} + \sigma$.

Each bell curve determines a probability model. In the model, outcomes are finite or infinite intervals in the real line. For an interval A, the probability $P(A)$ is the area of the region directly above A and under the bell curve.

EXAMPLE 4.5. *The IQ of children is normally distributed with a mean of 100 and a standard deviation of 15. What percent of children have IQs a) between 85 and 115? b) between 85 and 130? c) above 115?*

Solution: The phrase "is normally distributed" means that the IQ distribution of children is well-predicted by the Bell Curve Probability Model with $\bar{x} = 100$ and $\sigma = 15$. Therefore:

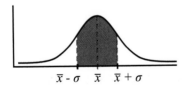 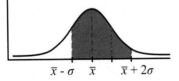 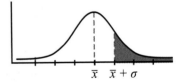

a) Percent between 85 & 115
= Percent between $\bar{x}-\sigma$ & $\bar{x}+\sigma$
= $(34.1 + 34.1)\%$
= 68.2%.

b) Percent between 85 & 130
= Percent between $\bar{x}-\sigma$ & $\bar{x}+2\sigma$
= $(68.2 + 13.6)\%$
= 81.8%.

c) Percent above 115
= Percent above $\bar{x}+\sigma$
= $50\% - 34.1\%$
= 15.9%.

Homework Set 40

Answer problems 1-3 by describing a sample space and probability of the various outcomes.

1. The side of a cereal box states that the contents weigh at least 1 pound. 200 boxes were weighed to the nearest tenth of an ounce with the following results:

Weight (oz.)	No. of boxes
under 15	16
15-15.9	42
16-16.9	72
17-17.9	41
18-18.9	29

Based on this data, what is the probability that a randomly-chosen cereal box is under-filled?

2. 30 students in a class were weighed to the nearest pound. The results are tabulated below.

Weight (lbs)	0
50-59	2
60-69	5
70-79	12
80-89	8
90-99	3

If a student is chosen at random, what is the probability that the student's weight is

a) between 70 and 79 pounds?

b) more than 70 pounds?

c) between 60 and 89 pounds?

3. Three coins are tossed simultaneously and the number of "heads" obtained is recorded. This is repeated 100 times, with the following results.

No. of heads	0	1	2	3
Frequency	11	39	38	12

a) Based on this data, what is the probability of getting two heads?

b) Based on the "fair coin" model, what is the probability of getting two heads?

c) How might you respond when a student asks "Which is the right answer: a) or b)?".

4. A certain department store is open 365 days a year. Its daily sales total is normally distributed with a mean of $200,000$ and a standard deviation of $20,000$. What is the expected number of days per year with sales below $180,000$?

5. The lifetime of one brand of 100-watt bulbs is normally distributed with a mean life of 2000 hours and a standard deviation of 250 hours. In a carton of 200 lightbulbs, find the expected number of bulbs with a life

a) between 1750 and 2500 hours,

b) more than 2250 hours.

6. The students in Mrs. Santos' 6th grade class measured their heights in centimeters. The results were:

132, 152, 145, 154, 160, 148, 151, 150, 146, 152, 154, 144.

a) Using a four-function calculator, find the mean and the standard deviation.

b) Assuming that the heights of 6th graders are normally distributed with the same mean and the standard deviation as Mrs. Santos' class, how many of the 400 sixth graders in the school district do you expect are under 142 cm tall?

10.5 Appendix: Other Ways to Display Data

Some K-8 mathematics curricula cover types of data display beyond those mentioned in Section 10.1 This appendix briefly describes one common type (histograms) and one useful only in special situations (stem-and-leaf plots).

Histograms. A histogram displays numerical data in the form of a bar chart by separating the data into classes. The classes are intervals of equal width. In the histogram, the height of each bar is proportional to the frequency of the corresponding class. Constructing a histogram therefore involves three steps:

(i) Choose consecutive intervals along a number line with equal width (taking enough intervals to include all the data). These intervals are the classes.

(ii) Make a frequency table showing how many data points are in each interval.

(iii) Use the frequency table to make a bar chart.

Steps (i) and (ii) describe a general method for turning numerical data into categorical data. In step (ii) one must settle on a convention for handling any data points that lie on the boundary between two intervals: consistently include them in either the lower interval or the upper interval.

EXAMPLE 5.1. *The following histogram shows the heights of a grove of 50 pine trees.*

Interval	Tally	Frequency
0 - 5	‖	2
5 - 10	ℋ ‖	7
10 - 15	ℋ ℋ ℋ ‖	16
15 - 20	ℋ ℋ ‖	12
20 - 25	ℋ ‖‖	9
25 - 30	‖‖‖	4

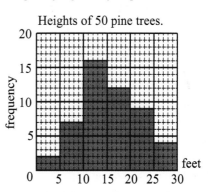

Heights of 50 pine trees.

Stem-and-Leaf Plots. Stem-and-leaf plots are a method for quickly creating rough pictograms by using the numbers themselves as pictures. They have limited utility, but are mentioned in many state standards.

EXAMPLE 5.2. *Ms. Ramirez recorded her class' exam scores in no particular order. She then used the leading digits to group the scores into categories (7 in this case). She made a stem-and-leaf plot by drawing a vertical line, placing the leading digits to the left and, for each datum, recording its last digit (a "leaf") in the appropriate row. Finally, she put the leaf digits in ascending order and included a key.*

Exam scores

92, 79, 59, 88, 68, 87,
82, 75, 89, 76, 56, 94,
85, 67, 76, 102, 87,
73, 45, 68, 95

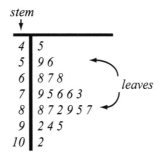

stem

4	5
5	9 6
6	8 7 8
7	9 5 6 6 3
8	8 7 2 9 5 7
9	2 4 5
10	2

leaves

Exam scores

4	5
5	6 9
6	7 8 8
7	3 5 6 6 9
8	2 5 7 7 8 9
9	2 4 5
10	2

key: 82% = 8 | 2

The stem-and-leaf plot makes it easy to spot, for example, the preponderance of scores in the 70s and 80s.

Index